Applications of
information technology in
construction

A CIP catalogue record of this book is available from the British Library

ISBN 0-7277-1653-0

First published 1991

Published for the Institution of Civil Engineers by Thomas Telford Ltd, Thomas
Telford House, 1 Heron Quay, London E14 4JD.

Printed in England by Redwood Press Limited, Melksham, Wiltshire.

624.02854
APP

Contents

Project management and construction

Ports and water

Coasts and geographical information systems

Public utilities

Roads and buildings

The BBEST approach to computer aided design

R. J. STEEL, Management Services Manager, Balfour Beatty Construction Northern Ltd

SYNOPSIS. Computer aided systems were developed by Balfour Beatty through a Teaching Company in conjunction with Loughborough University to increase efficiency in estimating and site measurement. The systems were designed by the estimators and quantity surveyors themselves at regular meetings with the software programmers, and include features unique to their requirements. Implementation of the systems into the Company was achieved by training local experts, and further enhancement was undertaken to suit detailed experience in use. Substantial improvements in efficiency have been achieved in the throughput and production of tenders, and in the setting up and operation of contract measurement.

PURPOSE AND OBJECTIVES

1. In the early 1980's preliminary investigations into the use of computers in estimating showed that there was considerable potential to improve the computation and data handling of the process, but that the state of the art in commercial software had not reached the level suitable for the wide range of tender types and sizes required in a large construction company. In addition it was recognised that the specific requirements of the Company would necessarily involve changes to any commercially available software, and that there would be benefits in developing our own software specifically written to match and improve on the existing manual system.

Purpose of the development

2. The purpose of the development can therefore be summarised into several headings:

(a) to improve the efficiency of the estimating process, by increased accuracy of calculation and increased throughput of tenders in a department

(b) to provide at least the same facilities as the existing manual system, and to provide better information at all stages of the estimating process

(c) to use electronic methods to set up measurement systems as early as possible on a contract

(d) to update the existing measurement and cost allowance system

(e) to improve our competitiveness in the handling of tenders and contract measurement in all sizes of contract for building and civil engineering

3. With these purposes in mind, it was necessary to find a cost effective method of development, and initial studies showed that traditional means of software development using either a commercial software house or our own computer staff were unlikely to offer satisfactory returns. The use of a teaching company was proposed and found to offer a likely recovery of cost within 3 to 4 years, based on improved throughput of tenders rising to 30% after 3 years in use.

Objectives of the development

4. A teaching company was set up in conjunction with Loughborough University Department of Civil Engineering, with the following objectives:

(a) the development of an advanced data management system for the storing of estimators data

(b) the production of an estimating system utilising data held within the database

(c) the implementation of the system into Balfour Beatty and the training of Company personnel

(d) the development of a measurement system and the consolidation of estimate data into this system

5. All of these objectives were achieved by the Teaching Company, and have been extended by Balfour Beatty staff after the initial implementation.

THE TEACHING COMPANY

6. It is relevant to outline the method of operation of the Teaching Company, since it contributed substantially to the success of the project. As well as providing some external funding, the scheme offered access to the extensive research already done on the subject of computer aided estimating. Benefits accrue to the Company from the opportunity to develop the system, and to the University from contact with industry and the opportunity to further and apply research.

7. Due to contacts made during the early research into the use of computers in estimating, an agreement was made with the Department of Civil Engineering at Loughborough University to seek approval from the Science and Engineering Research Council for a Teaching Company with the above objectives, to run over a 3 year period with 4 Associates to be employed each for 2 years. Acceptance was given by the Research Council in October 1984, and with the employment of

2

the first Associate, the Project Leader, in April 1985, the Teaching Company (TC) operated for 3 years from that date.

8.   A Management Committee, which met quarterly, was set up with representatives from Balfour Beatty (BB), Loughborough University (LUT) and the Science and Engineering Research Council (SERC), to provide general direction and monitoring of progress, while detailed supervision of the Associates was provided by LUT.

9.   It is a requirement of the TC scheme that the Associates are recruited to the Company under the age of 27 and with a First or Upper Second Class Honours Degree. Our Associates included 3 with computing degrees, and the fourth with a civil engineering degree. In addition LUT offered to provide the close supervision necessary by allocating their funding for an Assistant to the secondment of one of their staff into the TC. She had substantial experience of development work done to date in the University, which was of enormous benefit to the project. The TC staff were employed solely on this project, with no distractions from other operational concerns usually found within internal development staff.

10. Funding provided by SERC covered 80% of the staff costs and expenses, with BB paying 20% and additional costs to offer commercial salaries to the Associates otherwise being paid at University rates. Hardware costs were paid at 50% by SERC and 50% by BB, with final ownership given to LUT. The Management Committee regularly monitored both physical and financial progress, and the project was completed to time and budget.

METHOD OF DEVELOPMENT
Functional Specification
11. The first stage of the development was the production of a functional specification for the estimating system, based on extensive discussion with BB estimators in five Building and Civil Engineering departments covering work in the United Kingdom and internationally. Although this provided a valuable focus on the system requirements, the final system varied substantially from this specification as a consequence of the detailed development method.

System Design Reviews
12. At monthly intervals System Design Review (SDR) meetings were held in the TC office, attended by representatives of the five estimating departments and the Associates. At each meeting the next stage of programming was considered, allowing the estimators to detail their requirements before programming commenced. This often entailed vigorous discussion on the existing system and its operation, and frequently resulted in compromise to provide a single system to suit all needs, including the major differences between the single currency used in the UK and

dual currency requirements for international tenders. The other part of the meeting considered the work done during the previous month which was demonstrated to the estimators, who commented on screen and report layouts, calculation requirements, etc. so that every detail of the system met their requirements, and was accepted by them.

13. Development of the measurement system and the transfer software from estimating was carried out in the same way, but with groups of Quantity Surveyors from the various Divisions of the Company.

14. This prototyping approach occasionally led to abortive work, or at least to the redesign or reprogramming of sections of the system, but resulted in a system which was agreed by the estimators, and recognised by them as their own. This made a substantial contribution in the subsequent implementation into their departments.

CHOICE OF HARDWARE
Estimating System
15. The Estimating System software was commenced in late 1985, and the choice of hardware was carefully considered at that time. The Company were currently operating ICL ME29 machines, but it was decided that the system should utilise as much as possible of machine facilities and operating systems to reduce programming effort. The capacity of micro computers was insufficient at that time. Choice was made of IBM System/36 machines, which had a number of features in the Control language which were used in the software, were available in a range of capacities, and also were suitable for communications within the Group. Programs were written in COBOL in line with Company standards.

16. In 1990 the system has been transferred to IBM AS/400 machines running in S/36 mode, and progressive rewriting of the software has been undertaken to transfer to native mode to take advantage of the relational database and other facilities.

Measurement system
17. The Measurement system software was commenced in early 1987, by which time the machines for contract use had been selected as IBM micros, or compatible. The system was therefore written for IBM micros under DOS.

MAIN FEATURES OF SYSTEMS
18. Most estimating and measurement systems share the common features of a database allowing allocation of resources to Bill items through a coding structure, and the manipulation of data after the initial input. The BB Computer Aided estimating system (BBEST) and Quantity Surveying system (CQS) follow this general pattern.

Trade Analysis

19. The existing manual system required a detailed
analytical approach to the pricing of each item, and the
ability to view the data in several ways. BBEST has unique
features within it to allow these facilities, but to provide
improved editing and update facilities at the same time. For
example, items of a similar trade, eg formwork, are extracted
from the Bills, and displayed in spreadsheet format. It is
therefore possible to review these similar items as
comparisons with each other, and to edit directly into each
item as required. With the advent of readily available
relational databases this is a relatively simple technique,
but at the time when the software was written, the coding had
to be developed to allow this facility.

Libraries

20. Because of the differing requirements of each
department due to work type, geography, values, etc, BBEST
allows the creation of multiple libraries of estimating and
resource data, and the allocation of particular libraries to
each tender as deemed appropriate.

Data Input

21. Electronic transfer of data into BBEST from clients is
encouraged where possible, since this reduces the set up time
of a tender and improves the accuracy of the input
information. The use of scanners has been investigated, but
not so far implemented, partly due to the level of accuracy
offered and partly since the system does not hold more than a
single line Item description.

22. After long discussion it was agreed by the SDR that
full item descriptions were unnecessary for the estimating
system, since its use would be in conjunction with a printed
Bill on which the estimators notes would be added. This
substantially reduces the storage requirements for item
descriptions and notes, with particular consideration to the
fact that the majority of tenders will ultimately be
unsuccessful. The measurement system, on the other hand, is
for awarded contracts, and almost always requires full item
descriptions.

Transfer from BBEST to CQS

23. The electronic transfer from BBEST to CQS is carried
out in two stages by specially written software, BBLINK, with
the addition of full item descriptions as a third stage. In
the first stage the Bill item number, quantity, unit, gross
rate and one-line description are transferred, while the
second stage, after input of details on the coding
requirements for contract costing, transfers the details of
the resources in each item.

Features of CQS

24. In addition to the usual facilities for progress measurement and calculation of allowances for contract costing, CQS offers additional facilities to assist in more efficient commercial functions on the contract. Resources may be allocated to Bill items to allow the consolidation of quantities of the resource to match current progress, and hence speed up reconciliations of resources, particularly bulk materials and labour.

25. Items may be split into component parts to facilitate accurate costing as work proceeds, eg in manholes, cofferdams, and similar items. Facilities also exist for dealing with items that are in dispute either in rate or quantity, and to ensure that costing accuracy is maintained for consistent contract and financial management.

IMPLEMENTATION

26. The introduction of any new major system, whether computer or otherwise, requires careful planning and staff training. If the implementation includes the use of new technology, the preparation and requirements are increased.

The "Local Expert"

27. The approach taken on the BBEST estimating system was to train a "local expert", who was relieved of other duties while the techniques of using the computer and the software were learnt and practised. Training was given by the TC Associates and by BB computer support staff, allowing transfer of the technology from the TC into the Company. The system was then used in parallel with manual tenders, both for tenders done by the "expert", and for tenders done by others in the department. Once full confidence was established in the system, live tenders were carried out.

Staff training

28. Other estimators in the department were then trained on a one-to-one basis by the local expert, who was also immediately available to deal with difficulties in understanding or implementation. Disruption of the work of the department must be kept to a minimum during implementation, and this approach was successful. The choice of using the system was then left mainly to the individual, since it was felt that some types of tender, eg refurbishment work with many unique items not held in libraries, would be done manually in preference. In fact this has not happened, and the system is used for all tenders as a preference.

29. The time required to learn the system initially is about one week, but it is necessary to have a further three weeks of practice and familiarisation to develop sufficient speed and proficiency to allow the estimator to progress to pricing a tender within the time scales normally available. At least one more month is required in parallel pricing, and generally a total of three months training and practice is required before live pricing is achieved.

30. Initial fears among staff of possible redundancy were reduced by regular briefing on progress of implementation, and on the requirement to retrain some members of staff. Those who had carried out the computational work in the manual system were retrained to handle data input and tender setup on the system, and no redundancies were required.

CQS training

31. A more traditional approach has been taken for the implementation of CQS to contract measurement staff. The software runs on local micro computers, and operates like many other software packages, with access from a top-level menu. The software itself is menu driven, and is relatively simple to understand and operate. Training of staff can therefore be undertaken in small groups, with only 1 day required to become sufficiently proficient to use the system without close support.

32. In practice it has been found effective to carry out the set up of the contract on CQS, whether by transfer from BBEST or by direct input, using data preparation staff, working in conjunction with the surveyor responsible for the contract. Once the decisions have been made by the surveyor on specific requirements, the contract is set up on the system, including full descriptions, contract cost coding, etc, without the further detailed involvement of the surveyor. Only when the contract has been balanced against the tender is the data released to the contract, and training is given to new users of the system on handover. Unless the Bills are abnormally large, the system and data are on site ready for use on the first valuation.

PROBLEMS DURING DEVELOPMENT AND IMPLEMENTATION

33. As with all large computer system developments, a number of problems had to be overcome during the project, although the use of the SDR reduced many of the more traditional problems caused by lack of communication or understanding of the process, the programming restrictions, etc.

Development

34. It was, and still is, a primary requirement that there should be a single system for estimating for the construction Divisions of BB, to simplify staff training and system support and upgrade. In addition to the problems of geography with offices spread from Edinburgh to Croydon, there were the additional problems of the detailed application of the manual analytical system, and the detailed requirements of each local management from the estimating department. This problem was resolved by the SDR, despite the amount of travel required to meet at the TC office at Derby, but often required long, often heated discussion and

compromise to achieve the single system. However, the discussions also brought immediate benefit in the sharing of techniques and methods, which improved the operation in local offices.

35. Further problems were found in the need to create understanding of the estimating system by the TC Associates, and of the complexities and possible limitations of the programming by the estimators. The former problem was demonstrated by difficulties in understanding the intricacies of the calculation process, particularly in sections like allocation of on-cost, and was substantially overcome by the Associates spending reasonable periods of time in an estimating department. The latter problem was more apparent, in that occasions arose when the requirement from the estimator could not be provided without great programming difficulties, and was overcome to a great extent by the forward looking part of the SDR.

36. The problem of providing relational database techniques before these were available has already been mentioned, and was overcome by extensive, and often complex, programming. The principal example of this problem was the trade analysis sheets, both in screen handling and in data editing.

37. It is undoubtedly the case that many more problems would have occurred during development, had it not been for the available experience of the LUT staff, and in particular the Assistant seconded into the team. This highlights one of the benefits of the Teaching Company approach.

Implementation

38. The principal problem in implementation is an organisational one, namely of making staff time available to allow training and practice on the system. The actual training and use of the system has been taken up with relative ease, but the constraints of maintaining an operational estimating department with a constantly varying workload are difficult to overcome. Once staff are conversant with the system, benefits in improved speed are available, but this is often hard to achieve.

39. The problem anticipated beforehand that there would be staff resistance to the new system did not in fact materialise to any great extent. This was avoided in part by the early introduction of micros for part of the manual computation process, thus giving familiarity with keyboards and computer procedures, and in part by the use of the local expert, who created interest in those around him, and a desire to get the visible benefits that he was enjoying.

40. During testing and the early months of use, a system of Problem Logs was set up to record faults and difficulties found. These were discussed at the SDR, and action agreed to

resolve the problem. Enhancements to the system were also identified at this stage, and in subsequent operation, and are dealt with in the same way for resolution at the SDR, or, as is now the case, at system User Group meetings.

STRUCTURE OF LIBRARIES AND CODING
Libraries
41. There are two approaches to the size and contents of the estimating library, and both are in use in different departments of the Company. Each has merits and disadvantages, but the system has the flexibility to allow either to be used. The choice of method is left to the Chief Estimator concerned, but the first option suits Building and small Civil Engineering Bills, while the second option has advantages in large Civil Engineering Bills.

42. The size of the library can be kept small and compact, by using variables to which values are attributed when the item is used in the project. Prices in the library are approximate, and more editing of items is required at tender stage to ensure completeness.

43. At the other end of the scale the library is very detailed and precise, allowing coding to be allocated exactly and reducing subsequent editing at tender stage. The disadvantage is the data storage and access times, and the complexity of the coding required.

Coding
44. Great care is required in the development of the coding structure, both for resources of labour, plant, materials, sub-contractors, etc, and for the combinations of resources that are used to price items or operations, called in BBEST a "make-up".

45. Unless the libraries are small, a mnemonic structure is difficult to achieve, and we have found combinations of letters and numbers to be the most effective. The code list is tabular, with the first character a significant letter, eg for resources, L, P, M, S, etc, and for make-ups, relevant tc the trade, C for concrete, etc. Subsequent characters alternate as numbers or letters for clarity, and are selected in succession across the page in ever-increasing detail as required. It is therefore possible to code to varying methods of measurement, and to classify the work by suitable levels of selection of the codes.

46. The coding structure used in estimating has of necessity to be very detailed to recognise individual resources, whereas the costing system requires codes that are more inclusive to cover particular operations or other aspects of the contract. The BBLINK software has the facility to convert the codes in the transfer of data from BBEST to CQS, and is flexible enough to deal with a variety of coding structures in both systems.

BENEFITS FROM THE SYSTEMS
BBEST system

47. The introduction of the BBEST system has brought benefits to the individual estimator, to the workload of the department and to the efficiency of the Company.

48. To the individual estimator, much of the boring routine has been removed without in any way reducing the expertise which the estimator offers. Allocation of codes for pricing from the library is done by the estimator, and subsequent review and edit of items remains his responsibility. Items are priced immediately, allowing a better feel for the value of each item and its completeness. Items of the greatest financial significance are quickly identified to allow effort to be concentrated on those, and amendment of resource rates and usage is easily done to give "what-if?" investigation of alternatives.

49. With no reduction in staff numbers, improvements in efficiency are necessary to offer benefits to the department. The original cost benefit analysis assumed that a 30% improvement in throughput would be achieved in three years, and in fact 50% has been attained in less than two years. It is also possible to deal with larger tenders in less time, reflecting requirements in a tighter market. Other benefits include schedules of materials and sub-contracts produced immediately after input of coded items, and the rapid production of a reasonably accurate estimate. Arithmetic errors have been eliminated.

50. For the Company greater efficiency has been offered by better information being available for scrutiny at appraisal of the tender, and for the improved facility to allocate late adjustments to the tender to the correct places in the Bills. Final decisions can be left until closer to the submission date, due to rapid calculation of final changes in rates and the spread of on-cost to produce gross rates for the submission of Bill rates.

CQS System

51. Considering the CQS measurement system, the benefits can again be taken at the three levels. To the contract surveyor, the system offers rapid data entry and processing to produce monthly requirements for valuations and costing allowances in a fraction of the time required in a manual system. The system is available for the first valuation, and offers greater accuracy in calculation.

52. To the contract, benefit is derived from improved financial information both in speed of production and in accuracy of costing allocations. More time can therefore be spent in other aspects of the commercial function.

53. Among other benefits for the Company, the earlier submission of valuations leads in turn to earlier payment by the client, and hence to an improvement in cash flow.

CONCLUSION

54. The project has been judged to be successful in its method of approach and its completion of its objectives to time and to budget, and has provided Balfour Beatty with software that has become essential to the business. As with all systems, it is under continuous review, and further additions and enhancements to the software, both BBEST and CQS, are under development.

The Travers Morgan management information system

R.W. REDGATE, Managing Director, Savoy Computing Ltd

SYNOPSIS. There is a basic application common to all consultants. This is the collection of consultants' time and disbursements against a particular job plus the associated calculation of fees. In addition there is a management requirement to control the financial aspects of all work done on that job. When the Travers Morgan Group decided to replace the existing computer system which ran this application, it chose to do so in a way which both complemented its corporate strategy and gave a greater return on the investment it had already made in over 300 microcomputers used within the Travers Morgan Group of Companies.

THE COMPANY
1.   The principal activity of the Travers Morgan Group of Companies is the provision of multi-disciplinary professional services in engineering, management, transport and the environment, to clients concerned with the built and rural environment worldwide. The group has grown very rapidly since 1986, with turnover increasing fourfold and staff levels doubling. Including site staff, the group currently has over 1000 employees working in the United Kingdom based in 22 offices in 14 different cities and towns.
2.   Managerially the group comprises six operating companies with five of those companies divided into business units (known internally as divisions) each of which has responsibilities in a particular discipline or geographic territory. In effect this gives a total of 56 individual business units within the group. Savoy Computing Limited is an operating company within the group providing a complete service to the rest of the organisation with regard to its information system requirements. Savoy also has a rapidly expanding business providing software, consultancy and computer services to organisations outside the group.

THE APPLICATION
3.   A very simple application in concept. It was to collect all the information necessary to enable Travers Morgan to accurately calculate fees and invoice its clients. In addition, the application required that the costs associated with those invoices should be monitored, hence providing an ability to control profitability. Within the Travers Morgan environment complexities arose when considering the information to be collected, the group structure (both geographically and managerially), the actual fee calculations, the number of staff and the number of jobs undertaken for clients.

Applications of information technology in construction. Thomas Telford, London, 1991   13

4.   The main information to be collected related to the
time spent by staff during a month working on one or a number
of client jobs plus the disbursements associated with any work
done on those particular jobs. The time spent, measured to
the nearest 6 minutes, could be during normal working hours or
as overtime during the week, at weekends or on bank holidays.
The disbursements could be anything from car mileage to
printing charges depending upon the particular contract agreed
with the client.

5.   Geographically, information had to be collected from
22 offices from Colwyn Bay in North Wales to Lewes in East
Sussex, from Newcastle to Bristol. The application did not
require the collection of information from any of Travers
Morgan's overseas subsidiaries or associates, but did require
the collection of time information from all of the company's
site staff on a consolidated basis from one office.

6.   Managerially, staff usually worked solely for clients
who had placed a contract with that member of staff's
division. However, many jobs required the skill of staff from
more than one division and in general, any of the individual
divisions could work on jobs for any of the other divisions as
well as on jobs for its own clients. The application had to
provide the vehicle for all inter-operating company and inter-
divisional cross charging as part of the process of
calculating client fees.

7.   The calculation of a client's fee was, in itself, a
very complex task. The group used 15 defined ways of
calculating the individual member of staff's fee which could
be applied to a client's job. Only one of those was a fixed
rate per hour, all of the others were calculated from
differing aspects of a staff member's cost to the group. In
addition, the application required that any member of staff
working on a client's job could be charged using any of the 15
different fee rates.

8.   In volume terms, the time information had to be
collected from 1000 staff, over 800 of whom worked on an
average of 6 client jobs during the course of a month. In
addition, those 6 jobs could be any of over 10,000 jobs
potentially active at any one time.

9.   Add to the above that the whole process of information
collection, fee calculation and invoice and report production
was required to take place in the shortest time possible and
the application takes on an interesting level of complexity.

THE EXISTING SYSTEM

10. The computer system which ran the application before
the recent developments was known as the MIS (management
information system) and had evolved over a number of years.
The very first implementation went live in 1970 using an IBM
360 on a bureau basis. In 1971 the application was brought
in-house when Travers Morgan updated its central IBM 1130
mainframe to have 32 Kilo bytes of memory and 3 Mega bytes of
on-line disk storage. Computer technology has progressed
somewhat since that time, but although the software had been
developed significantly and the hardware platform used by
early 1989 was a Prime 9955 super mini, it is believed that
certain small parts of the original coding logic had actually
survived during the 19 year life of the system.

11. By this time the Prime was accessed via 78 terminals
using slow 9600 baud serial communication lines. Despite
providing access from all offices within Travers Morgan, the
system only used the local terminals for collecting time
information. There was little ability to produce reports

under local control and no facility to add or modify any information which was not time related. All control of the information relating to a client or a client's job resided within the group's finance division, as did the ability to instigate the production of all reports produced about the information which had been collected.

12. To add a new client or client's job to the system or to modify existing client or job information, a project manager had to fill out the appropriate form and send it to the finance division where the information was input onto the system. All disbursement information was also input onto the system via the same route. All reports were produced centrally and distributed to offices using the serial communication lines at fixed times during the month. Interim reports could be produced between these fixed times by special request to the finance staff.

13. The above comments could imply that the system did not successfully perform the required application. This is not the case, it performed the task very well within the constraints of the technology used, and hence the decision to develop a new system was made that much harder to take. However, there were a number of disadvantages associated with continuing with the existing system. These were

(a) A system which was centralised in nature conflicted with the business strategy adopted by Travers Morgan when it incorporated in 1988. This strategy required that control of the day to day business of the group should reside with a number of relatively autonomous operating companies and divisional business units.

(b) The MIS ran on a centralised Prime computer, the operational life of which was considered to be strictly limited. This restricted life was being forced essentially by the future plans of the software authors of the major technical systems being run on the Prime. McDonnell Douglas with GDS and MOSS Systems with IMOSS both had strategic development plans centred on technical workstations, very powerful microcomputers and mini manufacturers other than Prime. Another factor weighing heavily against the Prime central system was the strategy being adopted by Travers Morgan with regard to its general computing capability. This strategy was very clearly directed towards the use of microcomputers installed in local offices thereby placing computing power under the control of local staff rather than generating that power from a central facility. This strategy is described later in detail.

(c) As MIS ran on the Prime, it had to share available processor power and disk access channels with technical software such as GDS and IMOSS, the use of which within the group was growing significantly. This, combined with the relatively slow serial communication lines, meant that the response time during normal working hours for staff inputting time information was to say the least unsatisfactory. As GDS and IMOSS migrated to other computing platforms the response would have improved significantly. However, the cost of running a 5 year old super mini computer designed for technical application efficiency and occupying 600 square feet of air conditioned computer room precluded this option.

(d)   The existing MIS was a database structured suite of programs written in Fortran which over the years had been substantially expanded and amended by a number of staff, many of whom no longer worked for Savoy Computing or Travers Morgan. Even though the system's technical documentation was excellent, it was becoming increasingly difficult to maintain. This was particularly the case given the group's very fast expansion. The original system was simply not designed to cope with a company employing over 1000 staff and running 10,000 jobs at any one time.

14. All of these disadvantages pointed towards a requirement for change.

TRAVERS MORGAN'S COMPUTING STRATEGY
15. Before discussing the basis on which the decision was made to proceed with a new system, it is worth noting the strategy which was being adopted at the time with regard to Travers Morgan's computing capability. In early 1989 the strategy was very firmly set towards the use of microcomputers in local offices. The strategy had effectively started in 1985 when a number of Wang word processors were purchased. In 1986, 1987 and early 1988 the move towards microcomputer technology continued with the installation of some 60 Olivetti 8086 and 80286 processor based units.

16. Even at this early stage the potential benefits of using a local area network (LAN) had been recognised, with the group's first LAN being installed in late 1986 in the personnel department and its second being installed in early 1987 in the accounts department.

17. In April 1988 a decision was made to move to Compaq as the group's standard microcomputer supplier, a policy which remains to this day. By early 1989 approximately 130 microcomputers were in use within the group and the rate at which individual operating companies and divisions were investing in such technology was accelerating rapidly. At the time it was forecast that saturation point would be reached in early 1992 with an installed base of some 400 microcomputers. This forecast would still appear to be realistic in that by January 1991 the installed base was 330 units.

18. By early 1989 the use of LAN's within the group was not, to say the least, widespread. In addition to the two already mentioned only three further LAN's were operational in early 1989 and two of those were within Savoy Computing in its offices in London and East Grinstead. Despite this, the required information system strategy which would provide the key to enhancing the long term group strategy became crystal clear. This was the combination of local computing power with fast electronic communications capabilities both within an office location and between office locations.

19. Such an information system strategy, as opposed to a simple computing strategy, would enhance the overall group strategy in a number of ways as well as providing a demonstrable contribution towards the group's longer term financial success.

20. The strategy required the achievement of three objectives. These were

(a)   all of the microcomputers within each Travers Morgan office would be connected onto an office based LAN

(b)   all of the LAN's installed in local offices would be connected together providing a wide area network (WAN)

(c)   all centralised computing facilities, such as the Prime, would be connected as nodes on the WAN.

21. The strategy was elegant, commercially beneficial and technically feasible, and the investment and work required to fully implement such a network system has been in progress since mid-1989.

POTENTIAL BENEFITS OF A NEW SYSTEM

22. Although the disadvantages associated with the existing MIS were very real, so was the fact that the overall system worked and worked very well. As such there needed to be some very significant commercial benefits associated with the development of a new system and that system itself had to make a positive contribution towards the overall commercial strategy of Travers Morgan.

23. The direct commercial benefits identified for the new system were broadly as follows:

(a)   A new system would help significantly in the efforts being made to produce client invoices as quickly as possible, thereby reducing the elapsed time between cash outlay on staff and overhead costs and cash receipt from the collection of debts. Given the size of Travers Morgan the potential increase in cash balances was significant.

(b)   The new system would help in the ever present efforts to increase the productive, fee earning time spent by staff. Every one percent improvement in productive time spent by staff represented a significant increase in productivity and profitability.

(c)   Reductions in longer term costs would result from fewer staff being involved in system maintenance, system operation and system development.

24. The benefits which were far more difficult to quantify in commercial terms were those which enhanced the group's longer term business strategy. These were

(a)   the system could provide the information needed by divisional managers to better control their day to day business and it could provide that information locally whenever they wanted it

(b)   increased local control would lead to increased productivity and profitability and an improvement in the quality of service provided to clients

(c)   increase local control would lead to a higher level of job satisfaction for all staff.

25.   The potential benefits described so far refer only to the new version of the existing MIS. If the new system was capable of being integrated into the overall information system strategy, then there would be further commercial and strategic benefits. The most significant of these benefits would be provided in the case where the new MIS could be installed with the system's database available via a node on the WAN. In this case the majority of the computing power and all of the input/output terminals required by the system could be provided by the installed base of microcomputers increasingly available throughout the group structure. The resultant reduction in new hardware and software costs plus the greatly increased return on the investment already made in local microcomputer hardware would be appreciable.

THE SOLUTION CHOSEN

26.   The solution chosen for technical feasibility checks and overall costing was quite naturally the one providing the greatest commercial and strategic benefits. That was to establish the new MIS database on a file server in its own LAN linked to the WAN and to use the access capability and computing power of installed microcomputers to provide all other system resources. Savoy's systems development department declared the required implementation to be technically viable and provided recommendations and alternatives with regard to hardware and software products. In particular they provided information on the known future developments of a number of vendors.

27.   Then came a number of far more subjective decisions. The new MIS had a projected life of at minimum 7 years, probably 10 years. Such a period is a long time in any business sector and in the computer business many large companies had arrived and disappeared in shorter time spans. As such it was decided that the implementation chosen already carried a relatively high burden of innovation and that the prudent decision was to use established, commercially sound vendors with good reputations in customer service to balance out the equation. As such the following were chosen:

(a)   The core database system was to be Oracle based.

(b)   The hardware platform for the file server would be from Compaq. Development would start on a Compaq 386/33 and switch, as soon as the unit was available, to a Compaq SystemPro configured with a single 80386/33 processor, 840 Mega bytes of file storage and 16 Mega bytes of memory.

(c)   The LAN system software would be Novell Netware with communications hardware from Racal and Case. The WAN would use Ethernet protocol.

(d)   The required operating system would be UNIX based. However, until such time as compatibility between Oracle, Novell and a UNIX based operating system could be established, then IBM OS2 would be used.

(e)   Some defined parts of the system would be written in the computer language "C", which would generate SQL requests into the Oracle database.

28. The eventual choice also provided some commercial benefits which supported those previously defined. They were

(a)   The choice of the specialised Compaq SystemPro fileserver provided a very cost effective solution. This was particularly the case given Savoy's established discount structure with its Compaq distributor and Oracle's pricing structure for microcomputer based software compared with mini or main frame based software. The savings were such that it was cost beneficial to acquire a second SystemPro for further development and system backup in case of hardware failure.

(b)   The Compaq SystemPro also provided a very cost effective hardware expansion route, with the "live" system being easily expanded from its initial configuration to one with two 80486/33 processors, 1.3 Giga bytes of file storage and 256 Mega bytes of memory.

29. The resulting "best solution" then required outline costing. This required a relatively high level of subjective judgement based on previous experience, caused mainly by the fact that the final specification had, at the time, to be ratified by the users within the divisional management of Travers Morgan. In addition, the practical implementation of certain aspects of the proposed system used techniques which were unfamiliar to the existing Savoy staff.

30. However, the forecast "worst case" position with regard to system implementation costs would still enable the commercial benefits to be fully enjoyed and the decision was made to go ahead.

THE SYSTEM IMPLEMENTATION

31. In computing theory and in terms of the specifications of hardware and software products chosen, all of the building blocks necessary to construct the system were or would be available when required and were all fully compatible with each other. Savoy's previous experience indicated that in practice this would definitely not be the case, but there was a high level of confidence that all foreseen problem areas could be resolved successfully. This forecast turned out to be realistic, however it became increasingly obvious that very few organisations had previously constructed a system of such a size and complexity using a client/server architecture. Even the computer jargon "client/server architecture" was new in the first half of 1989.

32. Despite not wishing to be a pioneer, Savoy pressed ahead with the production of the new system which is known as MITRE. The implementation was started in April 1989 with a target date for going live of 1st May 1990. It was roughly divided into the following areas:

(a)   The specification for the MITRE system was produced by Travers Morgan's finance division in conjunction with Savoy staff well versed in the functionality of the existing MIS.

(b)   Once the specification had been written, it was distributed to all operating company and divisional management for assessment and comment. Once the specification had been distributed, senior Savoy and finance staff conducted a series of seminars in all office locations at which questions about and comments on the specification could be put forward. The seminars, plus the formal responses, resulted in a number of changes being made to the specification.

(c)   Separate from, but an essential vehicle for the MITRE system, was the installation of office LAN's and the associated WAN. It became increasingly apparent as the implementation progressed that all Travers Morgan staff would not be covered by LAN's and the WAN by 1st May 1990 and so developments took place to enable access to the central fileserver using the existing low speed serial lines and also via dial-up access through modems.

(d)   Savoy was very fortunate in having a number of staff who were experts in LAN and WAN hardware/software and also in microcomputer operating systems/low level programming. However, Savoy lacked Oracle experience and so a senior development manager, well versed in Oracle implementations, was employed to lead the development team. Other development staff attended a series of courses run by Oracle to get them up to the required level of expertise.

(e)   The main part of the development was associated with the construction of the Oracle database, the definition and production of over 100 input/output screens and 50 reports, the routines handling disbursements, staff data, client and job information and finally the fee calculations. In addition, a sophisticated system of access control was built into the database structure to put into effect the data security requirements defined by senior Travers Morgan management.

As required by the system architecture, all access was designed to be via a microcomputer with the central fileserver containing the database only being used for data acquisition, input data verification and data updating.

(f)   A relatively small part of the development effort was the production of the program which was to be used by all staff to input time information. (All client information and job information was to be restricted to and maintained by project managers and senior divisional managers.) Although only a small part of the system it was the critical part so far as user friendliness and user acceptance was concerned. Also, with staff inputting time information on average every week, the fact that the program would be run over 40,000 times during a year meant that it also had to be fast and robust. The program was written in "C" and used sophisticated screen handling to duplicate, in effect, the functional characteristics of a simple spreadsheet package. Quite naturally many "user aids" were built in and accessed via function keys.

All access to the MITRE database was by internally generated SQL requests which were batched before transmission to minimise the user response time and WAN traffic.

(g)   A major effort was required to ensure that the
        communications systems being used for access not
        only worked but were robust under as many
        conditions as could be generated under testing.
        This was particularly the case given that in the
        first year of operation access would be split
        between fast Ethernet lines, slow serial DCX lines
        and a small number of connections via dial-up
        modems.
        Equally much effort was expended to ensure that
        the software would actually run on the wide
        variety of microcomputers used within the group.
        These varied between older Olivetti M24's with
        8086 processors at one end to Compaq 386/33's at
        the other.

(h)   Documentation and training were key areas. User
        and technical manuals were written for both the
        time input and main part of the system and pocket
        sized quick reference cards were produced for
        both. A keyboard template was also produced to
        act as a quick reference guide with regard to
        function key meanings. All user documentation
        replicated the functionality of the context
        related "help" screens available at any stage
        during system use.
        To keep the system fresh in the minds of staff,
        the majority of the training took place in the 6
        weeks before the system went live, with some
        further training taking place previously in the
        divisions chosen for pilot usage. With over 900
        staff left to train in 6 weeks, Savoy's trainers
        were kept busy. Subsequently, training courses
        for all parts of the MITRE system were added to
        the standard course schedule offered by Savoy to
        Travers Morgan staff.

(i)   Well before the system was scheduled to go live it
        was installed on a pilot basis in 3 areas within
        the group. In February 1990 Savoy switched from
        the existing to the new system in both London and
        East Grinstead offices with strict instructions to
        all staff to try and "break" the system. Using
        Savoy staff as the first pilot group enabled the
        testing procedure to be enhanced and gave an
        opportunity to continue the testing of the
        communications facilities under live conditions.
        In March 1990 two divisions within Travers Morgan
        moved to the MITRE system after receiving the
        newly developed training courses. During the
        months of March and April 1990 comments and
        recommendations came back from those divisions and
        changes reflecting their comments were built into
        the system.

(j)   The MITRE system went live, on schedule, on 1st
        May 1990. The existing Prime based system
        continued running in parallel with the new system,
        but was not used for the input of information
        apart from disbursement data. Computerised
        procedures were set up to transfer the information
        collected by the MITRE system onto the Prime over
        the WAN. This enabled the fee calculation and
        report generating parts of both systems to run
        simultaneously.

Parallel running of the two systems was essential.
It provided a "disaster backup" facility for use
in extreme conditions, but more importantly, it
provided an ideal environment in which to
supplement the months of testing and quality
assurance that had already taken place. The MITRE
system had already been tested using many months
of live data transferred from the existing system
as well as data generated by internal testing
procedures. However, the complexity and size of
the system defined that the increased combinations
of data and conditions provided by more live data
could only increase the level of confidence
already present in the quality of the system.

THE PROBLEMS
    33. There were relatively few problems encountered with
the actual programs written with regard to programming errors.
Those there were related mainly to misinterpretations of the
specification and were quickly cleared. There were, however,
some severe operational problems with the interface between
the Oracle database software and Novell software in the first
few weeks of live running when the system came under high user
loads. In a relatively short space of time Oracle software
specialists, working with Savoy technical staff had identified
the problem areas and subsequent versions of various Oracle
products removed the vast majority of the problems
encountered. In fact over the months a very good relationship
grew between Oracle and Savoy, as Oracle began to understand
the advanced way in which the MITRE system utilised their
database software. Now, Savoy are an advanced test site for
Oracle, utilising software releases before they become
commercially available.
    34. The main problem areas were encountered with those
connections which used the low speed serial lines rather than
the high speed Ethernet WAN links. Access was through a
microcomputer, and staff were used to the excellent response
normally provided by such a system. Some of the larger input
screens within MITRE had to interrogate the database
frequently to perform data verification checks and over the
slow lines the response time was, to say the least,
inadequate. The problem is still outstanding, but as the WAN
grows larger, the inconvenience is being gradually minimised.
Equally, the Oracle product FORMS, which was used for input
screen generation, is an old product and does not have many of
the advanced characteristics users currently expect in
microcomputer software. This problem will be alleviated with
the forthcoming release of this product.

THE RECENT DEVELOPMENTS
    35. Shortly after the release of MITRE a user liaison
committee was formed comprising representatives from each of
Travers Morgan's operating companies. It was chaired by the
managing director of one of the company's divisions. As with
any new non-technical computer system it is very difficult, if
not impossible, for a user to accurately define what he or she
wants by looking at a system specification. In essence a user
typically needs to see and use a new system for a period of
time before coming to proper conclusions about the exact
requirements. The purpose of the liaison committee was to put

forward staff opinions of the MITRE system with particular reference being made to the system's suitability for their day to day business requirements and the system's "ease of use" characteristics for the typical user.

36. The system was taken apart piece by piece, screen by screen and report by report, and required changes to the original specification were noted. By April 1991 MITRE will have been modified to reflect the experienced view of its users as well as continuing to provide the central finance department requirements for the group as a whole. As part of these modifications it is also under consideration that the new version of the Oracle FORMS product will be incorporated, which it is expected will provide a far more user acceptable feel to the microcomputer based software.

37. The installation of LAN's continues and by May 1991, when all Travers Morgan staff based in London will be located in a single, purpose built office building, nearly 95% of all group staff will be connected to a LAN and hence the WAN. At this time all offices will be connected via, at minimum, 64 Kilobit per second communication lines with the main centres (London and East Grinstead) connected by a 2 Megabit per second facility. This line will also carry 12 voice channels effectively joining together the two locations as one internal telephone network. In the London building all 300 staff will use a single LAN based on dual Compaq SystemPro file servers, whilst in East Grinstead the 5 separate buildings are already linked by 2 Megabit per second lines or fibre optic cables.

38. It is envisaged that MITRE will be the first of a number of Oracle database systems attached to the WAN. Savoy have recently completed a system known internally as MARKIT providing all contact and internal marketing information relating to the group's clients and the prospective clients. This system is currently undergoing user acceptance tests and will be released in the near future.

THE FUTURE

39. The recent installation of MITRE is only the start of the longer term development of such systems. Plans are currently being developed to extend MITRE further into the areas of financial and project management while other work is being conducted in the requirements of an Executive Information System combining both internally and externally sourced information. In the shorter term, it is the applications possible on the LAN's and WAN which are the most interesting in terms of commercial benefit and support for corporate strategy.

40. Group wide electronic mail is already under development and electronic file transfer between LAN's and local electronic mail are already widely used. Plans for group wide electronic diary facilities, bulletin boards, computerised facsimile and video conferencing are being compiled and as each application is implemented it will have an increasingly beneficial effect upon the commercial activities of the Travers Morgan Group.

CONCLUSION

41. In a commercial environment, a new computer application should not be judged by its speed or by its high quality graphics or by the fact that it uses the latest technology. Given the achievement of appropriate levels of system suitability, robustness and user acceptance there is only one question which needs to be asked to determine the success or failure of any new application. Does the new

system make a positive contribution to the financial success of a company through the enhancement of corporate strategy? If the answer is not a very definite "yes" then the company concerned needs to look very closely at the reasons for implementing the system concerned. Also, for the answer to be "yes" then both criteria used in the question need to be fulfilled. It is of little use to a company if a financially successful application does not complement longer term strategic aims. The expense involved would be far better utilised in funding a different initiative which did help achieve those strategic objectives.

42. Could the answer "yes" be given if the question was posed about MITRE? The system required some 6 person years of effort to specify, write and implement, with hardware and software licence capital expense amounting to some £58,000. These figures do not include the time or capital expense associated with the construction of the LAN's and WAN as they were implemented to derive commercial and strategic benefits complementary to those generated by MITRE.

43. The potential commercial benefits envisaged for the system have been and will be increasingly enjoyed by Travers Morgan and the implementation used, by definition, supports group strategy with regard to local management control of day to day business.

44. For MITRE, the answer to the question must be a definite "yes".

The strategic use of information technology in the construction sector

M. BETTS, Lecturer, K. MATHUR, Senior Lecturer, G. OFORI, Senior Lecturer, and C. LIM, Researcher, University of Singapore

SYNOPSIS. Plans for the use of IT in construction are extending beyond the immature stage of improving the efficiency of discrete operations by individual organisations. This is necessary for all sectors as IT use progresses to a mature stage. This paper charts the background to this progression by examining proposals by Earl of nine prerequisites to the IT era which make a strategic approach timely. The extent to which these prerequisites apply in construction, is examined. It is argued that organisations involved in construction will ultimately have to think strategically about their use of IT and the extent to which some are already doing so is described.

INTRODUCTION

1. Earl (ref 1) describes ours as an information society where the key resource is knowledge and where IT is the enabling mechanism. He supports his observation by pointing out that information workers form the largest category of employees in some more advanced economies and that technology accounts for a majority of capital formation in some sectors. The conditions precedent to this dawning are described as three areas of dynamic change in technology advancement, commercial globalisation and social advancement.

2. The dawning of the IT era in turn marks the demise of the Data Processing (DP) era and Earl suggests that the distinction between these two is based on the much greater need for IT and its implementation to be planned, managed and used strategically by organisations.

3. The potential of IT in organisations, according to Eason (ref 2) is immense. He stresses the importance of the involvement of the senior management in the planning of an organisation's IT applications strategies and policies for the reasons outlined below.

- Strategic application of IT depends on conceiving ways in which technology can be harnessed to serve the organisational objectives which are set by the senior management.

- Application of IT can be used to strengthen the power of some sections of the organisation against others. Therefore, the involvement of the senior management will prevent the development of sectional interests.
- IT involves data processing, text processing and telecommunications. This could involve three different departments in an organisation. It is then the responsibility of the senior management to make the decision regarding the control of an integrated system.
- Implementation of IT must be carefully monitored as it should take place simultaneously with major organisational changes, and the establishment of future forms of organisational structure and the management of the change process are under the jurisdiction of the senior management.

4. Eason also gave the following propositions which in his opinion will ensure the successful creation of IT systems.

5. First, it will have to be known that IT technical design alone is not enough. Compatible social and technical systems should be created so that the systems can be effectively harnessed and exploited by the users and serve some important organisational purposes.

6. The design process to achieve this will require a planned change which creates the appropriate systems and creates in the users the willingness to exploit the technical capabilities. This will involve the participation of the stakeholders in the design process and individual collective learning process. Both organisational and human change will have to go through evolutionary development so that decisions are made on the basis of mature reflection.

7. Lastly, the concepts of the systems must compliment the existing design procedures and organisation change practices.

8. These alternative views of how IT can be strategically used would all form a useful basis for examining the construction sector.

9. As an example of how strategic views of IT can change our thinking, we have applied Earl's nine propositions to our knowledge of the construction sector situation. The other approach of Eason could equally have been used for this purpose.

WHAT MAKES AN IT ERA ?

10. Earl refers to nine propositions that he believes distinguish the IT era and by examining these in turn we can comment on the extent to which they have been reached in construction.

IT: a high expenditure activity

11.   The proportion of revenue spent on IT can be used as a guide to the extent to which a sector is participating in the IT era.   There are average levels for a sector or industry as a whole but Earl observes how enterprises that are industry leaders have a proportion of IT expenditure from revenue higher than the average.   The figures he quotes for different industries are shown in Table 1.

Table 1.   Levels of expenditure in various sectors in the UK, 1988.

Table 1. Levels of expenditure in various sectors in the UK, 1988		
Industry	Expenditure on IT as a proportion of revenue %	
	industry average	industry leader
High tech manufacturing	2.0	7.0
Aerospace	3.5	6.0
Equipment manufacturing	1.0	2.0
Financial brokerage	5.0	7.0

Source: Earl (1989)

12.   In Singapore more than 75% of construction firms spend less than 2% with the mean being less than 1%. There is a large range between firms with the less than 10% of the industry leaders in this regard spending more than 5% (Cheah, ref 3).

13.   On the basis of this analysis it must be concluded that construction is required to invest more heavily in IT resources if it is to be considered to have reached the IT era.

IT: critical to many organisations

14.   Some sectors such as financial services, particularly personal banking, are fast approaching the stage where IT is critical to the success of entire operations. Others have IT playing a much more supportive role to their activities. McFarlan and McKenny (ref 4) suggest a strategic grid of four types of IT activity; from support to strategic.   IT is a support activity if it is not critical to either the current operations of an organisation nor to the strategic plans for development of that organisation.   At the other extreme an organisation could be said to be using IT strategically if it is critical to both its current operations but also to its

future plans for strategic development. The authors also give examples of some different types of enterprises that may be currently placed in different segments of this grid.

15. In thinking about where construction organisations fit onto such a grid we must distinguish between different types. The construction sector within an economy is made up of a number of different overlapping industries which comprise a large number of different enterprises. Some enterprises are large but most are small or medium sized enterprises (SME). Some enterprises have loose or formal associations between them and form working relationships between each other when they combine on projects. Individuals working for enterprises may be grouped into professions which can be very strong in their influence over current and future procedures and activities.

16. For the vast majority of construction enterprises one can only conclude that IT is a support activity. The impact of IT has been shown to be low to existing organisations by different studies (Chow, ref 5) and (Peat Marwick McLintock, ref 6).

17. However, there are isolated examples of some construction sector organisations making IT a critical part of their strategic development plans if not of their current operations. Koskela (ref 7) describes the detailed plans of a number of Japanese contracting firms who are clearly planning to exploit the full range of IT including data processing, telecommunications and automation technologies.

18. It could also be argued that the professional institution representing surveyors in the UK, the Royal Institution of Chartered Surveyors (RICS), are aiming to exploit IT strategically albeit in a less extensive way. Their initiative in participating in the Alvey research programme (Brandon et al, ref 8) to create new strategic opportunities for their members suggests that they may be making IT critical to their future plans even though it may only be of low impact to their current operations.

19. From both of these examples it could therefore be argued that some construction organisations have reached the turnaround stage in their progression through the strategic grid and that as time passes these and other construction organisations may find themselves firmly in the strategic quadrant of IT use.

20. However, for the construction sector generally, it must be concluded that IT is still being used mainly in a supportive capacity and that it is far from being critical to the operations of the majority of its organisations.

IT: a strategic weapon

21. It can be argued that IT offers new opportunities as a strategic weapon to: gain competitive advantage; improve productivity and performance; enable new ways of managing and organising; and develop new businesses.

22. The way in which strategy can be implemented can also be achieved in different ways according to the combination of business strategy and application orientation. Lim, (ref 9) suggests how this combination can lead to IT being used strategically to improve: internal productivity; external productivity; internal competitiveness; and external competitiveness. The following are examples from Lim of how each of these strategies have been followed in other sectors.

23. As an example of internal productivity, Lim quotes the Ford motor company and its process of supplying parts to dealers and wholesalers. An IT based distribution, storage and stock management system has been implemented which has led to major increases in the productivity of the organisation itself.

24. The Society for Worldwide Interbank Financial Telecommunication (SWIFT) is an international financial network for the exchange of financial messages between different organisations throughout North America, Japan, Southeast Asia, Latin America and Western Europe. It is an inter-organisational system which has become the industry norm and which all new enterprises must participate in if they wish to survive. It improves the productivity of all organisations externally.

25. OTIS is a major enterprise in lift and escalator installation and operation. In such a business much competition between enterprises is based on the speed and efficiency with which maintenance can be performed. OTISLINE is an example of how an enterprise has strategically used IT to create an internal competitiveness advantage over other enterprises. The system helps in allowing a highly efficient maintenance service with faster and better performance than competitors.

26. Lim's example of strategic use of IT for external competitiveness is of great relevance to us because it comes from what is considered to be a low technology industry. Selling used car parts would seem to offer fewer opportunities for strategic IT use. However, a group of geographically dispersed non-competing suppliers in the US have combined to use an IT network to enable each of their stocks of parts to be considered as a larger pool from which orders and distribution to customers are possible. Each individual supplier is, as a result, able to offer better customer services and re-define the boundaries of their company.

27. An organisation looking to use IT as a strategic weapon can therefore look to improving its internal or external productivity or competitiveness to create new opportunities for itself. Most construction enterprises seem only to be examining IT as a means of improving internal productivity. Governments, professional institutions and groups of enterprises may have more opportunities to examine external productivity. The RICS in the UK provides a further

example of how this can be done in the form of the Building Cost Information Service. This system is a central database of price information supplied by subscribing members who are all able to exploit the shared data to improve their individual productivity. The external productivity of all surveying enterprises is thereby improved and it could be argued that the better quality of data also improves their competitiveness.

28. The Royal Institution of British Architects (RIBA) is offering a similar form of use of IT through the RIBACAD system (Ray-Jones, ref 10). This has obvious benefits to external productivity but not really to external competitiveness.

29. There are many isolated and individual examples of enterprises and projects where IT is being used for small improvements in internal productivity. The area where construction organisations appear to be failing to exploit IT strategically is for their internal or external competitiveness. Few appear to be able to offer a new or improved service by virtue of their IT use and even fewer to consider new ways of managing and organising themselves or to develop new businesses. From this it can be concluded that on the basis of IT being a strategic weapon, the construction sector falls short of having fully arrived in the IT era.

IT: needed in our economic context

30. The sectors where IT appears to have made most dramatic impact are where other major forces for change also exist. Some examples of these are quoted (Earl, ref 1) at both the macro and the micro level. At the macro level: deregulation of airline and financial services; the need for global survival in automobile manufacture and textiles; and the structural changes that are effecting retailing are all quoted as forces which are leading some organisations in some sectors in some countries to use IT as a strategic response.

31. In construction, the emerging economic context is also dynamic such that the strategic exploitation of IT may be appropriate. This current lack of stability is evident at organisational, national and international levels. Organisationally, there have been sufficient criticisms of industry practice (Construction Industry Development Board, ref 11) and responses suggested to it (British Property Federation, ref 12) to suggest that structural change within industries of a fundamental nature may be imminent. The possibility of this happening has been discussed by many commentators and by the industry itself. IT may be an important strategic tool by which organisations can respond to such changes.

32. Nationally, the construction industries of different countries are constantly moving through different stages of development and maturity that reflect the economies of which

they are a part. In Singapore the domestic industry has proved very successful in rapidly providing mass public housing for a large proportion of its population, infrastructural works, and a modern business city. Having done so the excess capacity that now exists is having to be rapidly re-orientated to the maintenance and retrofitting sectors and to construction exports.

33. The economic context at the international level is similarly dynamic particularly with the coming of the common western european market and the general internationalisation of construction.

34. The economic context of construction is thus highly volatile and this is an attractive situation for potential strategic use of IT. Many procedural changes are likely that will be able to be designed with IT in mind, new markets and business opportunities are going to be encouraged and IT could play an important part in the securing of these. On the basis of this proposition then, construction appears well placed to enter the IT era.

IT: affects all functions and levels of management

35. A further symptom of an organisation having entered the IT era is stated as the technology having permeated all functions and levels within an organisation. Early uses of DP were restricted to distinct DP departments and for specific number-crunching applications. Organisations that have more fully embraced IT are now in a situation of having a range of hardware and software technologies being used by a diverse range of groups of people and for a variety of different tasks and activities.

36. In construction this is far from the case. The majority of construction organisations still appear to have IT being used by IT specialists or for discrete applications and it would seem only by staff at the technical levels. This situation has been borne out by the different studies referred to earlier (Chow ref 5) and (Peat Marwick McLintock, ref 6). Both identified that IT is still restricted to administrative functions of an accounting nature or for highly specific and technical functions within the construction disciplines.

37. On this basis we must conclude that the construction sector is a long way from having reached the IT era and that a significant change is needed in the variety of levels of management that are using the technology and the diversity of functions to which it is being applied. For this to be necessary will require all construction organisations to reconsider their size, organisation structure, recruitment policy and their education and training activities in the light of their requirements in the IT era.

IT: a revolution in management information systems

38. IT is embracing a range of technologies that are being

applied to a range of existing and new techniques and processes. A sector could be described as more fully being in the IT era if it is exploiting a range of technologies for a range of existing and new applications. Examples that are quoted by Earl of soft technologies include expert systems and decision support systems and of hard technologies, teleconferencing and executive management information systems.

39. In this regard there appears to be an implementation gap. There are many new initiatives and completed research projects that have led to the development of expert systems and other information systems tools for construction which have not been applied or incorporated into industry practice. Part of the reason for this must be the inability of construction organisations to be sufficiently flexible and far-sighted in their willingness to embrace technological improvement. A change of attitude by construction organisations would appear to be necessary.

IT: involves many stakeholders

40. Earl refers to seven different categories of stakeholders in IT. These are: government through regulations and policies, business users through their information needs and standards they demand, IT manufacturers through their technology and standards they set, customers and suppliers through networking and integrating arrangements, consumers through their expectations and behaviour, competitors through their use of new products in new markets and new businesses, and employees through any union agreements and their job satisfaction.

41. Construction organisations are in many ways more diverse and complex in their range and inter-relationship. A picture of the relationship between IT stakeholders for the construction sector may look more like that in Figure 1.

42. Consideration of IT stakeholders is important for two reasons. The diversity of stakeholders that are involved with IT in a sector may indicate how well the IT era has been embraced but could equally be seen as an obstacle for more extensive IT use not having been achieved.

43. Stakeholders are also important to IT government planning. A sector may enter the IT era either through its own commercial pressures, because of the planning and direction of the industry itself or through direction of economic policy makers and implementers. Central planning and direction may sometimes be necessary as an extra push to support the movements taking place in an industry or could be used to speed up the process. This is particularly important in construction where the diversity and complexity of stakeholders is such that this may in itself restrict the extent to which strategic use is made of IT. If central planning and direction is to be followed, it is important that all stakeholders are considered by implementation plans

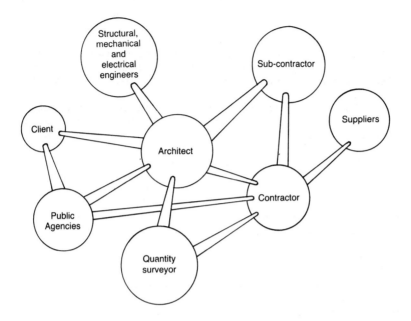

Fig. 1. Construction IT stakeholders

and even that they are involved and consulted during the process of plans being drawn up.

IT: technology matters do matter

44. It is easy to get carried away with technological developments and always assume that the next stage of technological improvement will remove all of the inadequacies of the current stage. It is also tempting to currently assume that incompatibility problems between parts of an industry will be able to be overcome as technology improves although in construction the extent of this problem could be very significant (Peat Marwick McLintock, ref 6). The other factor with regard to technology is that ultimately, for a sector to enter the IT era, the right sort of technology must be owned by a sufficiently large number of the organisations that participate in it. There are signs that in construction this is beginning to happen (Chow, ref 5).

IT: management makes the difference

45. The final proposition for the IT era is perhaps the most important of all and also the most likely reason for us concluding that construction has not yet fully embraced it. IT continues to be thought of as a technological issue to be handled by technologists. One of the most important ways in which IT differs from DP is in its need to be managed.

46. A report by Kearney (ref 13), a firm of management consultants, identified important management factors as top management support, degree of IT awareness by management, level of IT investment, degree of Board level IT direction. It concluded that it was factors such as these that distinguished the leaders in successful strategic IT exploitation from the rest.

47. In construction organisations, because of the predominance of SME's, because of the poor management skills found generally in the industry, and because IT continues to be treated as a technological issue, the strategic exploitation of IT has been much less successful. The remedy may lie more in improvements in the education of managers rather than the employment and training of technologists.

DEVELOPING THE CONSTRUCTION SECTOR FURTHER

48. The propositions outlined above can be taken as the principal ways in which the IT era can be distinguished from the DP era.

49. When we look at the current situation of construction organisations, we need to consider where construction is placed between these two states of development and, secondly to identify what is necessary for further movement from one to the other. Before doing this we must look at the current problem of IT implementation in construction caused by the particular nature of the design and production processes.

Problems of IT implementation

50. The most important issue in the implementation of IT, which distinguishes construction from other sectors, will be the integration problem: that is, how to exchange information among different designers and also between designers, clients and contractors. This problem has been the subject of study of national level projects in Finland (Bjork ref 14) and other Nordic countries, but is far from being resolved. A relatively easy approach to solving this problem would be for all participants to use the same information systems and share their central database. It is also now becoming technically feasible to exchange data between dissimilar systems and therefore the use of the same information system is not imperative, though it is desirable.

51. Many of the available IT tools have been developed without due regard to the total construction process, i.e. how a specific program would fit into the total process and be compatible with other software. In particular, considering the mixed results of attempts to introduce prefabrication and industrialised building in many countries, systems which are based on this or any other form of construction, would be inappropriate as nuclei for IT development in places such as Singapore where the long-term future of the method of construction is uncertain. Information technology which suits the general construction

process can be used for prefabricated construction or any other form of building but not the other way round. Finally, it is significant to note that most of the IT tools have been developed as commercial ventures. It is difficult to say to what extent each software developer would have had the real needs and interests of the users at heart.

IT at a strategic level

52. Considering the difficulties discussed above and the fact that each construction project is unique, IT, in the near future, is likely to remain a supportive (and not critical) technology; will be used for small productivity gains (and not for strategic advantage over competitors); will be used for low level activities (and not by higher management); and will not be used by all participants and stakeholders in the construction process. To move well beyond the DP era and harness the critical and strategic advantages of IT would require us to overcome a tremendous amount of inertia because all participants work inter-dependently and many inter-actively and recursively.

53. For example, during pre-tender stage the architect, engineers, client and cost advisers share and exchange information and data which evolves as design progresses. Unless the IT tools used by these participants can communicate and interact with each other, one cannot expect any single party to independently invest in IT which cannot provide benefits beyond small productivity gains, unless other parties do likewise. There are other problems to be resolved apart from the compatibility and communication among dissimilar systems. The current tools and procedures were developed to exchange "data" among the participants and not necessarily "useful information".

54. To obtain strategic advantage of IT, one must reconsider traditional roles and hierarchy in the decision-making process. The construction industry operates such that each person has domains of expertise and these boundaries are rarely trespassed. The decisions are rigidly taken as relating to aspects such as architectural, mechanical, electrical, cost, and so on. The decisions regarding the space, structure, services, cost, etc. are highly interactive; the change of one affects many others. One possible response to this may be that multi-disciplinary enterprises or design and build contractors, who are able to internalise the integration problem, may be in a better position to exploit IT for strategic purposes.

55. The professional bodies and government agencies may have important roles to play in different environments; from coordination to developing and maintaining data and information bases for their members. This would avoid a lot of duplication of work and also help small to medium enterprises who cannot see justification in spending money on large data bases.

56. Organisations need to also see IT become critical to
their current and future activities. This can be enforced
by a central agency making IT necessary to certain key
activities where construction organisations interface with
them. In the UK, in order to ensure that co-ordinated
project information is adopted by the industry, all
organisations working on projects commissioned by the
Property Services Agency, which is a major and critical
source of public projects, are required to follow the
procedures and documentation recommended by the Co-ordinating
Committee for Project Information (ref 15). In Singapore, the
Construction Industry Development Board envisages making the
submission of tenders for public sector projects by building
contractors, required to be made in magnetic form as one of
the means of making IT critical. Such approaches by a
central agency may have a role in different economies
although the sort of IT use they encourage may not always be
the best for the longer term.

57. It seems, on all these counts, that in order to
harness the strategic advantage that IT use would provide,
efforts at the enterprise, industry and governmental levels,
will be necessary, appropriate to the circumstances in the
country concerned. A major study has been undertaken for
Singapore and many of the recommendation in this report
(Betts et al, ref 16) may apply to other developed economies
and newly industrialised countries.

CONCLUSION

58. It cannot be argued that the construction sector has
entered the IT era. However, it is possible to see that by
a number of criteria, this may change in the future. It is
also possible to identify what change is necessary to bring
the IT era closer. This may happen through commercial
pressures or through the industry itself recognising the need
for change. In some economies it may be necessary or
desirable for this process to be helped or speeded up by some
form of central direction or control. The form that such
direction should take can be concluded from the analysis that
has been made.

59. For IT to become a strategic weapon for construction
organisations requires that they do more than only consider
its contribution to internal productivity. Internal and
external competitiveness will be important strategies and the
role of research and development by the enterprises
themselves or through their trade associations or
professional institutions is important. Central agencies may
choose to offer financial or other incentives to such
research or may even initiate pump-priming projects of their
own.

60. The need for all levels and functions of management
to embrace IT is very important and a role can be played here
by many groups. The professional institutions may influence

this issue by identifying IT awareness and management skills as an important component of continuing professional development programmes. Educational institutions must ensure that such courses are able to be provided for both professional updating and for initial graduate education. Central agencies can again offer support to these activities.

61. The great diversity of stakeholders in construction, many of whom do not see beyond short-term gains, is such that advancing the strategic use of IT is a difficult management problem. The co-ordination and coercing of such a range of organisations will require strategic frameworks and detailed tactical planning of a central agency. Such an agency will also need to consider the problems of technological matters.

REFERENCES
1.   EARL M.J.   Management Strategies for Information Technology, 1989, Prentice-Hall, UK.
2.   EASON K.   Information Technology and Organisational Change, 1988, Taylor and Francis, London.
3.   CHEAH K.H. and TIAN S.   A Study of the State of Computerization in the Construction Industry in Singapore, 1989, Jointly prepared by International Data Corporation and Construction Industry Development Board, Singapore.
4.   McFARLAN F.W. and McKENNY J.L.   Corporate Information Systems Management: The Issues Facing Senior Executives, 1983, Dow Jones Irwin.
5.   CHOW K.F.   The Impact of Information Technology on the Construction Industry, 1989, Proceedings of the First IES Information Technology Conference, 25-27 May, Singapore.
6.   PEAT, MARWICK and McLINTOCK and THE CONSTRUCTION INDUSTRY COMPUTING ASSOCIATION.   Building on IT: A Survey of the Information Technology Trends and Needs in the Construction Industry, 1987, Peat Marwick and McLintock, London.
7.   KOSKELA L.   Construction Industry: Towards the Information Society; The Japanese Example, 1985, FACE (International Federation of Associations of Computer Users in Engineering, Architecture and Related Fields), Report No. 7, November, Finland.
8.   BRANDON P.S., BASDEN A., HAMILTON I. and STOCKLEY J.   Expert Systems: The Strategic Planning of Construction Projects, 1989, Quantity Surveyors Division of the Royal Institution of Chartered Surveyors, London.
9.   LIM S.S.   Singapore's Opportunities for Competitive Advantage, 1990, Keynote Address to Opening Session of the National IT Application Conference, 1-7 March 1990, Singapore.
10.   RAY-JONES, A.   The Why, What and How of a Graphics Library, 1990, in Proceedings of the National IT Application Conference, Construction Sector Programme, 1-7 March 1990, Singapore.

11.   CONSTRUCTION INDUSTRY DEVELOPMENT BOARD.   Report on the Cost Competitiveness of the Construction Industry in Singapore, 1988, CIDB, Singapore.
12.   BRITISH PROPERTY FEDERATION. Manual of the BPF System, 1983, The British Property Federation System for Building Design and Construction. BPF. London.
13.   KEARNEY A.T.   The Barriers and the Opportunities of Information Technology - A Management Perspective, 1984, a management consultant report prepared for the Department of Trade and Industry, London.
14.   BJORK B.   Computers in Construction; Research, Development and Standardisation Work in the Nordic Countries, 1985, Technical Research Centre of Finland.
15.   COORDINATING   COMMITTEE   FOR   PROJECT   INFORMATION. Coordinated Project Information for Building Works, a guide with examples, 1987, CCPI, Royal Institution of Chartered Surveyors, London.
16.   BETTS M., MATHUR K. and OFORI G.   Information Technology and the Construction Industry of Singapore: A Framework for A Communications Network, 1989, School of Building and Estate Management, National University of Singapore, 80 pages.

Artificial intelligence technology implementation strategy in project management

Z. DORDEVIC and N. IVANISEVIC, Assistants, Faculty of
Engineering, University of Belgrade

SYNOPSIS. There is lack of software based on AI technology, for
analyzing data, for advising senior managers and for proposing solutions
in project management. This fact is not in accordance to AI technology
state-of-the-art, and to amount of money invested in project
management research last years. Lack of adequate textbooks in project
management is not sufficient to explain that.This paper analyze causes
of this discrepancy. Present AI technology implementation strategy is
analyzed. Paper propose adequate strategies for companies of different
sizes and project management experience. Methods for obtain
cooperative experts in project management are discussed.

INTRODUCTION
1.   In the last few years artificial intelligence technology has been
commercially used in various fields. It is used for decision making based
on uncompleted and uncertain data. Also, artificial intelligence
technologies are successfully used as an aid for decision making in real
time. This is especially so for decisions and judgments which can have
great financial effects and where there is a shortage of qualified experts.
2.   Decisions in Project Management are also made on the basis of
uncompleted and uncertain data, and the time used for decision making
has a great influence on the final effect. These decisions directly
influence results of a Project worth many millions of dollars. Employing
experts in project management is not always effective due to uncertain
results and high cost.
3.   At the moment there is a shortage of software for project
management, based on artificial intelligence technologies. This paper is
an effort to shed some light on this case and to suggest solutions which
would increase the efficiency of artificial intelligence technologies in this
field.

STATE OF THE ART

4.   On the basis of existing surveys and reports on AI software for project management (refs 4-5, ref 7) it is noticeable that there is only a small number of programs in this field. At the moment (ref 4) there are 7 operating expert systems, 14 operating prototypes and 16 expert systems in development, intended for project management. Some other programs which have not been taken into account (ref 5 and 7) together with some special technologies of artificial intelligence (neuron networks, intelligent data bases etc.) may be added. The final estimation of programs based on AI technology, intended for project management would be: 10 operating expert systems, 20 operating prototypes and 30 expert systems in development.

COMPARISON WITH THE STATE OF AI SOFTWARE IN OTHER FIELDS

5.   A survey on the usage of AI software in various organization shows that 37% of organizations use one or more expert systems in their work, 23% develop an expert system but do not use one, 24% are seriously considering the use of ES and 16% are not considering the possibility of using ES.

6.   In the organizations that apply or seriously work on applying ES of the organizations interviewed) around 44% apply ES in production and 29% in management. In all the remaining fields (bookkeeping, finance, marketing, education, distribution of goods, etc.) ES are applied in less than 20% of organizations. In interviewed organizations there are 180 ES in operation, 532 are being developed and 735 ES are being discussed.

7.   Results of the investigation can not be directly compared due to different composition of the sample and the different methods of grouping the results. However, the following conclusions can be drawn:

- at the moment one of the leading fields in which AI software is in use is management
- the participation of the existing software for project management is very small in comparison with AI software which is used in management. On the basis of the above data the participation is less than 20%

THE SPECIFIC PROBLEMS IN DESIGNING AI SOFTWARE FOR PROJECT MANAGEMENT

Defining the goals

8.   The goals of management for certain projects depend on the firm's business strategy. The project manager may be requested to complete the project without taking into account the costs if the contract

is of a "cost plus" type. The goal may be to complete the project with maximum claims and in this way gain much higher profits than the profit calculated at the time of signing the contract. Sometimes the goal is to complete the project with minimum costs without taking into much account the quality of the work. Sometimes the strategy can be to prolong the time of completion if gains are greater than losses. The choice of the strategy is left to the small group of top managers and must be kept as a secret. The revelation of the strategy could cause many problems which could seriously damage the firm's reputation.

9. A certain number of project goals may be made public. Such goals are ending the project in the shortest possible time, maximal possible profit, etc.

<u>Knowledge acquisition</u>

10. The thing that makes most businessmen working on project management so special is their knowledge of the market, contacts and procedures which they use in their work. This knowledge is usually not shared. Knowledge is gained through experience and through exchange and buying.

11. The other kind of knowledge used in project management includes the knowledge of the standard methods of data acquisition, for making contact with other people, for organizing teams and team leadership, for assessment and prediction. It is based on research and many years of experience. This kind of knowledge may be gained from educational courses and books.

<u>Data acquisition</u>

12. Estimations on other participants in the project (personal and business characteristics) are a part of the data used by project managers in everyday decision making . Estimations on the financial situation of other participants also come into this category. Much of this data is confidential.

13. A part of the data needed for project management can be acquired from public information systems. Such information consists of stock exchange reports, data on new technologies, estimates made by special consultants etc.

PROBLEMS IN DESIGNING AND THE USE OF AI SOFTWARE FOR PROJECT MANAGEMENT

14. Usage of AI software consists of knowledge acquisition, data acquisition, estimating the effects of certain decisions, defining goals and suggesting methods for achieving these goals. As we said earlier, there are certain goals, knowledge and data which are not commonly known and are not available to the public. Very often the above

mentioned information has a market price. Project managers or firms very rarely allow the existence of such data in an electronic form.

15. There are two reasons for this. The first is that many people are involved in writing software and data processing. Owing to the speed and low cost of electronic copying and storage, the reliability of the system for maintaining secrecy is low. A little carelessness could cause great damage to the project and to the firm.

16. The second reason lies in the managers personal feeling of uncertainty when using technology not familiar to him. A large majority feel that computers and computer technology are beyond their control. Publicity on computer crime increases this fear. This problem exists with a large number of managers, especially those without computer education.

CHOICE OF STRATEGY IN IMPLEMENTING AI TECHNOLOGY FOR PROJECT MANAGEMENT

17. Managers of firms and projects often have goals, knowledge and data which they do not want to share with others. The main problem in applying software for aid in decision making is their unwilling to share information. Every strategy in implementing AI technology in project management must solve this problem.

Methods of implementing ai systems

18. Method I.The first method is the use of existing software and data (knowledge) bases which can be easily bought. In such program packages knowledge can be partly modified to suit the needs of the user. Systems formed in this way are most efficient in solving widely spread problems or problems which do not depend on types of company or market. OCR software, software for assistance in exchange transactions etc. are models of such software.

19. Method II. A professional software firm with experience in this field can be hired to form the system. In this method the orderer has to define the goal of the system and to provide experts in the requested fields. The software firm has to design the requested programs and knowledge base as well as to carry out the training of the orderer's personnel.

20. Method III.The third method of introducing AI systems is the development of software and knowledge base in R&D departments of the companies in question. An adequate program language (lisp, prolog) or tool (NEXPERT, LEVEL5, VP Expert etc.) is used. Company experts are used as a source of expert knowledge and the role of knowledge engineer is given to the members of the R&D department. This method is suitable for solving specific problems in a company or market. This method is also used when necessary to achieve

considerable technological improvement in comparison with the competition. In this way business secrets are kept within the company. However, this method is often the most expensive.

Classification of companies based on the strategy of accepting new technologies

21. Companies type A. Companies of this type use the strategy of technological leadership. Profit is achieved by using technological innovations before other firms. To achieve this objective companies have large and successful R&D departments, finance research by independent institutions and have good reputation as technological leaders.

22. Companies type B. Companies of this type use the strategy of technological follow up. Technological innovations are applied when their feasibility is certain. Innovations are introduced by means of buying licenses, know-how and reverse engineering. Expenses and quality of R&D departments are proportionally lower then in A type companies. They usually build their image on design, quality, etc.

23. Companies type C. Companies of this type use the strategy of technological copying. Technological innovations are accepted when their value is already tested on the market. New technologies are introduced by means of copying or buying licenses. The expenses and quality of R&D departments are low. These firms build their reputation on qualities such as low prices, good purchasing conditions etc.

The goals of implementing ai technologies for project management

24. Improvement in the preparation of reports which have so far been carried out by teams of experts - goal X. The basic goal of introducing AI technologies for project management is increased accuracy and speed in preparing data and analysis used for decision making and which has, so far been carried out by teams of experts.The main problem is the transfer of knowledge from the team of experts to an AI system.

25. Improvement in report preparation which has so far been carried out by a team of managers - goal Y. The next goal in the implementation of AI technologies is the increase in speed and accuracy in preparing analysis which have, so far been carried out by the members of a management team. To achieve this objective it is necessary to transfer knowledge which is personal property of the members of the management team. The transfer of knowledge is made more difficult by the fact that the experts are not usually willing to transfer their knowledge. Also, management is usually afraid that the use of such systems can make the leakage of information easier.

43

26. Advisory help to the project manager in operational decision making- goal Z. The final goal in implementing AI technologies is to form a system which will advise the project manager in everyday operational tasks. Special problems in designing and usage of AI software for project management must be solved.

27. Knowledge which is managers private property , data and goals which may not be publicly displayed have so far prevented the formation of such systems, or at any rate stopped the publication of reports on their existence.

Optimal strategy on introducing ai technology for project management

28. Method of introducing ai technology. The method of implementing the AI system depends on the goals of implementing AI technology and the strategy of accepting new technologies in an organization. In deciding on the strategy of implementing the AI system the organization's experience in management is more essential then the existence of a complete team for the development of AI systems. On the fig. 1 methods of implementation of AI technologies for various types of organizations and the various goals of implementing AI technologies are suggested.

29. The first step. The first step in introducing the AI systems is intended for improving preparation of some reports which have, so far been prepared by expert teams. Eg. a system for estimating the costs of an project, analysis of site conditions, estimates on the validity of claims etc. Examples of such systems are given in (ref. 4)

30. It is necessary to engage a member of the top management staff to become the head of the project for implementing the system into the organization. His function is to obtain the necessary back feed between the management team and the team in charge of the development of an AI system. In this way the system prepares analysis and data in line with the management's needs. The second task of the head of the project is to learn to use the system himself. The term "use" means: input of data, input and changes in knowledge, defining the relevant questions and the formation of reports. The head of the project must be able to finally present the whole system to the management team.

31. In this step the basic goal of introducing AI technology, goal X is partly or completely achieved. If the goal is only partly achieved, further work can take place simultaneously with the realization of further steps.

Companies
type A

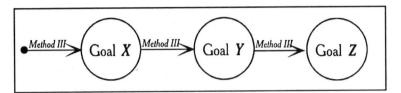

Acceptable area

Companies
type B

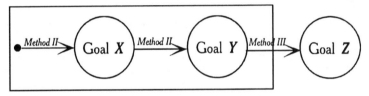

Acceptable area

Companies
type C

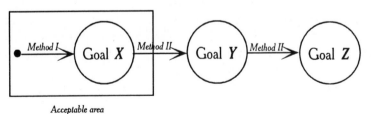

Acceptable area

Figure 1

<u>32. Second step</u>. The second step is an introduction to the improved preparation of reports which have so far been made by members of the management team - goal Y.

33. It is necessary for the head of the project, who was in charge of the first step, to form a specification for the special tool intended for forming an AI system. Taking over data from the existing systems (formed during the realization of goal X) should be simple and automatic, using programing and typing over as little as possible. The exchange of knowledge and data and forming reports should be simple and easy even for users that have no knowledge of AI technology and computers.

34. At the same time as specifying the tool training of the management staff for using the system developed in the first step takes place. The acceptable level of knowledge is the ability to perform a presentation and to answer ordinary user's questions.

35. On the basis of the defined specification a tool is developed. During the development it is possible to change the specifications with the approval of the head of project.

36. Whilst testing the tool it is necessary for the head of project to personally form prototypes of AI systems. His ability to do so is a measure of the tool's success. Testing of the tool is successfully accomplished when the head of the project is able to perform training of the management team to use the tool.

<u>37. Third step</u>. The third step is improvement in preparation of reports which have up to now been carried out by the members of the management staff - goal Y.

38. It is necessary for the head of the project to, alone or with a little help from a small number of associates, form an AI system which will be his advisor in preparing reports . The assisting team should not be larger than the standard team which helped in preparing reports: secretary, one or two trustworthy advisors.

39. At the same time management training for using the tool takes place.

40. The system is considered complete primary when the head of the project can prepare reports using only the system and secondly when the head of project knows he can train the management team to prepare the system in their own field.

<u>41. Fourth step</u>. In the fourth step advisory support in operational management is given to the project manager - goal Z.

42. Training of the management team in forming AI systems takes place. It is competed when members of the management team form a system for their own needs.

43. New members of the management team must go through training which will enable them to form AI systems for their own needs.

CONCLUSION

44. On the basis of the considerations in this paper the following conclusions can be made:

- AI technology is applied in decision making in project management much less frequently then in other fields of management
- The main reason for this is the knowledge which is manager's personal property as well as the data and goals which may not be publicized. Many managers also think that the use of computer systems in project management is a great threat both for the firms they work for and them personally.
- A classification of firms, goals and methods of implementing AI technology can be made and with its help an optimal strategy for implementing AI technology can be proposed.
- Optimal strategy, among other things, consists of a plan of management training which will enable the management team to form AI systems for their every day work.
- The creation of AI systems by the managers themselves provides an acceptable degree of security for the goals, knowledge and data required for project management.

REFERENCES

1. Ashley D.B. and Levitt R.E. Expert systems in construction : Work in progress. J. Comp. in Civ. Engrg., ASCE 1(4), 1987, 303-311.

2. Ćirović G. Procena uticaja internih i eksternih faktora na građenje (Estimation of external and internal influences in building construction). Zbornik radova Treći jugoslovenski simpozijum organizacija građenja, Građevinski institut Zagreb, Cavtat, Yugoslavia, 1987, 219-230.

3. Harmon P. and King D. Artificial intelligence in business systems : Expert systems. John Wiley and Sons, New York, N.Y. 1985

4. Mohan S. Expert Systems Applications in Construction Management and Engineering. Journal of Construction Engineering and Management, Vol. 116, No. 1, March, 1990, 87-99.

5. Moselhi O. and Nicholas M.J. Hybrid Expert System for Construction Planing and Scheduling. Journal of Construction Engineering and Management, Vol. 116, No. 2, June, 1990, 221-238.

6. Philip G.C. and Schultz H.K. What's Happening With Expert Systems? AI Expert, Vol. 5, No. 11, November, 1990, 57-59.

7. Russell J.S. et al. Qualifier-2: Knowledge-Based System for Contractor Prequalification. Journal of Construction Engineering and Management, Vol. 116, No. 1, March, 1990, 157-171.

8. Touran A. Integration of Simulation with Expert Systems. Journal of Construction Engineering and Management, Vol. 116, No. 3, September, 1990, 480-493.

9. Waterman D. A. A guide to expert systems. Addison Wesley Publishing Co., Reading, Mass., 1985.

Application of information technology in construction

F. J. HEMMETT, Chairman and Managing Director, CSSP pty Ltd, Adelaide

SYNOPSIS. The paper outlines one company's experiences in developing and implementing integrated information technology systems in the construction industry. It summarises the advantages and some of the problems, and proposes likely directions for the future, especially concerning redistribution of professional responsibilities and changing means of interaction between parties to a project.

INTRODUCTION

1.   The role of computers in construction project management is growing daily. From individual modules the software has moved into an integrated information system, laying the foundations for management of the total process and minimisation of input and re-entry of data.

2.   Based on the author's own experience, this paper and planned practical demonstrations deal with the linking of all parties on major construction projects through one computer network, to provide an integrated project management system.

3.   The problems encountered are discussed, the anticipated and actual benefits are identified, as are likely impacts on the professional activities of engineers, redistribution of professional responsibilities and changing means of interaction between parties to a project.

Concept

4.   The system runs through a multi-user machine with terminals in the client/project manager's office, linked to remote sites, each having one terminal and printer. These are located in the offices of the client, all consultants and contractors.

5.   These individual organisations involved in the project are required to use the terminals to execute all transactions and to supply and receive all information about the project from each other. Each organisation with a terminal represents a specialist information centre, decision-maker or technical contributor to the project.

6.   Every terminal has access to the central computer's programs through a predetermined controlled level of security. A user can access, make inputs or read data from only those parts of the central

software which are appropriate and permitted, and is barred from all other programs and information.

7.   The concept is one wholly integrated system in which all information flows back and forth between the users, being re-used in whatever form required throughout the ongoing processes of a project. It is re-used and maintained up-to-date by the latest input of data at any site or office involved in the project.

8.   It provides total management of all the information requirements of major projects from one centrally located processor. This ensures that the client/project manager is 'driving' the project.

9.   Whether the consultants keep their own computer systems running is their own decision, but under the conditions of their involvement in the contract, they must use the system terminals to fulfil their obligations.

10.   The system imposes a discipline on every member of the project team to ensure all records are current, that a database of integrity is provided, and that control mechanisms and standards are used leading to better co-ordination and eliminating risk.

System components

11.   The system revolves around Document Management and Action List modules. Document Management works over the whole network, and is responsible for issuing and updating all drawing transmittals and documents, managing program constraints, and producing a variety of reports.   Action List provides an audited centralised list of items requiring action.

12.   The other modules are Project Administration (which handles all contract administration), Room Data Sheets (interior design and FFE procurement) and Contract Financials (budget, actual cost and accounting functions).

Benefits recognised

13.   The benefits of integration are that all transactions under the contract in terms of document issues, instructions, project actions, variations or time extensions are recorded directly into the system.

14.   The computer reports the effect of those transactions. An audit trail is built in to provide status on each aspect of the project, reporting those parties who have not fulfilled their obligations.

15.   Developed over the past decade, the concept now is manifesting itself in the real world. To date the system has been selected for three major projects by commercial and governmental authorities, and it is being evaluated for further applications.

16.   This concept is being extended from a central processor-multi-terminal network to one which links processor to processor.

TOWARDS INTEGRATED NETWORKS

17.   Such a system has not been developed overnight; it is the result of a long term project in pursuit of a philosophy of total data integration and standardisation.

18.	In our organisation, CSSP, there have been three clear steps over the past decade in the development of construction industry software.

19.	The first step was as a technical organisation which solved its own computer and software problems by looking at the task from a construction industry user's viewpoint, not a programmers. The next step was providing similar computerised solutions to industry sectors such as engineers, architects and contractors inside their own technical requirements.

20.	The third was to computerise the complete information management through software which allows data to move throughout linked systems.

Why did this occur?

21.	Those with foresight have realised that mere computerisation of individual consultant tasks, eg estimating, job costing, project control, documentation, administration and accounting, was not enough to produce the efficiency and productivity required to take the industry into the next decade, let alone the next century.

22.	Information transfer is happening in the industry and it is recognised that total integration of information management across the industry is not only desirable but a practical possibility given the status of computer hardware and communications systems. Already demonstrable, such integration is being put into practice by progressive firms.

23.	Even more challenging was the realisation that integrated computer systems would be able to manage the total information and resources of a complete project. Indeed, for tomorrow's major projects, it is highly likely that only a computer network could satisfactorily cope with the massive amounts of information, the vast array of plans and the huge resources involved.

Integrated network reality

24.	CSSP can now talk with confidence about two major projects and our experiences in setting up those systems. Our system is called CLIENT (Construction Linked Information Exchange and Network Technology).

25.	CLIENT is designed to provide total management by the client or his project manager of all the information requirements of major projects through one central processor. It provides these facilities:

(a)	Action List
(b)	Contract Administration
(c)	Document Management
(d)	Standard Documents
(e)	Electronic Mail
(f)	Room Data Sheet

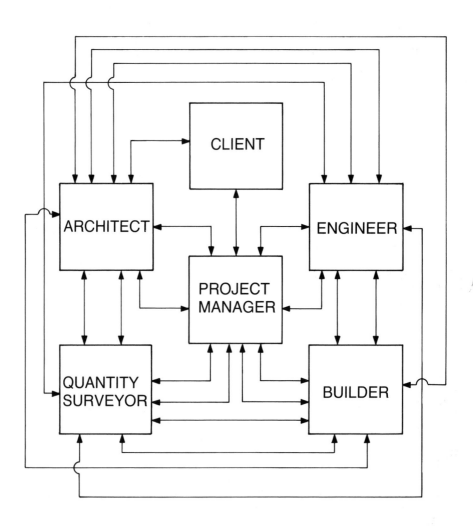

Figure 1

Advantages of integrated network

26. Among the advantages in an integrated, networked project management system are:

(a) Communication is faster and direct between the parties
(b) Large paper files are eliminated
(c) Errors of interpretation and transcription are eliminated
(d) Standard methodologies of input are enforced
(e) Reports are standardised and current as the last input
(f) Dated and registered documents, showing transmittals, recipients and action, minimise disputes and claims
(g) Direct access by authorised parties to status and information
(h) Information generated in one format reprocessed through the software facilities for other users and other requirements.

27. In terms of contract administration, it has a benefit in standardising the methodology of all parties.

28. The streamlined organisation of information flow is illustrated by comparing Figures 1 and 2.

29. Figure 1 shows the old way of doing things, with a project manager in the central control position with data flowing in a multitude of directions between various parties. The project manager only tells the client what he wants the client to know.

30. Figure 2 shows the 'CLIENT' system sitting in the middle, and the client has only one line of communication as has each of the parties - that is to the central system. However, the client has access to everything that goes in and out of the database.

APPLICATIONS

Elizabeth Street project

31. The first 'CLIENT' system was installed for a large property development, the £300 million project at 149 Elizabeth Street, Sydney. Commenced in January 1990, it involves a 20 storey office building and a 600 room 5-star hotel which are due for completion in 1992.

32. Because it is being built to a fast-track schedule, the danger of over-runs through poor management of information posed a real threat. To meet that threat the project has broken new ground in construction system integration, becoming the first Australian project in which all the parties are linked onto one computer network.

33. The system runs on an IBM RT multi-user machine with three terminals in the project management office. The RT was chosen because it offered the right balance between power, storage and back-up support from a known reliable supplier. This system is linked using DMS lines and multiplexers to six remote sites, each having one terminal and a printer on separate lines. These are in the offices of the project's structural engineer, services engineer, architect, interior designer, the contractor and the quantity surveyor.

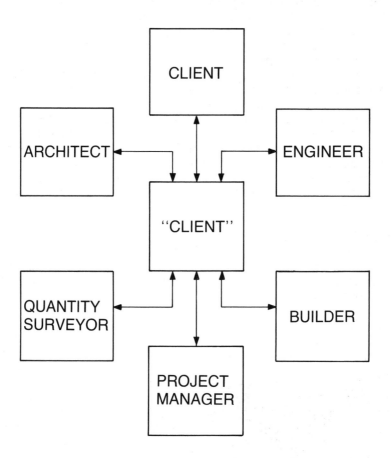

Figure 2

Telecom project

34. A similar integrated system has been chosen for the new £20 million high-tech telephone exchange in Adelaide, South Australia.

35. This project is expected to mark another step forward in the total integration of construction project management information with the first introduction of processor-to-processor links.

36. The system was chosen by the project manager at an early stage, and all consultants were obliged to use it as a prerequisite to their involvement in the project.

37. The system runs on a cost-effective 386 PC, linked by DMS to five remote sites. However, only a single communications channel is available to each remote site.

38. Because the operating system and applications software are perfectly transportable, it would be easy to upgrade to a more powerful computer if the network grows or system demands escalate beyond the practical capability of the PC. There was no advantage in buying a computer large enough to cope with growth three or five years hence; by that time computer development would have rendered the hardware outdated anyway.

IMPLEMENTATION LESSONS

39. There are both human difficulties and mechanical/technological difficulties in implementing new systems which cut across the boundaries of separate organisations, professional disciplines and personal empires.

Human reactions

40. The construction industry has had to face a philosophical change. It is not merely using the computer to automate an existing manual process, it is using it to do things it had never thought of before.

41. The initial negative reaction of participants is, firstly, as a fear of 'Big Brother', and a defending of tribal boundaries which are breached by this technology in which there are no real boundaries; everybody is a participant in one project. All users, particularly the client, know what everybody else is (or should be) doing, within the security restrictions imposed for reasons of confidentiality, ethics and legality. That is a new, unique situation in the construction industry and in the engineering profession.

42. It is a problem which looms larger every time we start. On the Elizabeth Street project, the concept of an integrated network was adopted in a low-key, step-by-step manner. One module or component was implemented, then another; enhancements, new facilities and links were added as experience was gained and improvements were sought. Individual users readily coped with that evolutionary growth. There were few objections to be countered and as the steps forward were relatively small, it was easy for the project manager to insist on their implementation.

43. The practical input enabled us to refine our own philosophical and technical approach as we progressed.

44.   On the Telecom project, the response was different. We started with a significant system structure already developed, but participants were completely uneducated in the concept, advantages and problems to be encountered in implementing such a system.

45.   The fear was greater because the unknown factors were greater. It was a quantum leap forward instead of knocking over one problem at a time. Consequently, a significant part of our commitment is outside of the software; it is education of the participants about:

(a)   why the system exists;
(b)   how it operates;
(c)   how to use it; and
(d)   what the benefits are to them.

46.   In view of such personnel concerns, it is important to have the right kind of skills managing the system.

47.   There must be strict adherence to recommended hardware/software configurations to eliminate unwarranted malfunction or unreliability which impinge on user confidence and attitudes.

48.   The consultants engaged on the Telecom job knew what the requirements would be. Nevertheless, some of the prospective users have been raising objections on some practical aspects and concepts.

49.   The project manager was trained before the hardware was installed. While he, theoretically, is responsible for managing and controlling the system, as system supplier, CSSP is heavily involved in the implementation and training stages and dealing with qualms as they arise. This is providing us with valuable experience with which to face future installations.

System configuration

50.   When we first considered setting up a networked project management system, where the control of consultants involved with the project was to be centralised in one place, it was unclear whether we should have a:

(a)   truly central system with one processor and multiple terminals; or
(b)   distributed system where every consultant ran their own copy of the software remotely, with information exchange between them.

51.   The latter seemed to be fraught with problems of security of information, making it much more difficult to exchange just the information required by a specific consultant in each location.

52.   If the client, who ultimately was paying for the service, had all the information on his system, and remote access was granted but controlled, security was more manageable. The client has the right to all the information and to control it.

53.   The central system was selected and experience has proven it a wise choice; data security is a very sensitive issue.

Communications options

54.   One of the early considerations was the means of linking remote sites to a central processor; today the choices are far greater. Available alternatives included (for local, not long distance communications):

(a)   Dial-up (telephone) lines - cheap but slow
(b)   Direct connect (dedicated) lines - expensive but fast
(c)   Digital network connection, usually involving packet switching.

55.   Considerations included: capital cost, ongoing costs, and level of performance - reliability, accuracy, speed and security.

56.   For remote sites, establishment costs can be high but long term costs assume greater importance. Generally, the higher the capital cost, the lower the ongoing usage charges.

57.   The equation between Volume of Data and Time of Access has to be balanced. For example, for short distance, low volume data transmission, a dial-up phone line with error correcting, high speed modems is a viable choice. Since early evaluation, dial-up line technology has improved in speed and reliability. However, the quality of transmission can degrade, seriously affecting speed and accuracy.

58.   For long access times and/or high volume, direct connect lines can be a problem in reliability and cost, especially when incurring toll fees. Digital networks are guaranteed and reliable, and for high volumes are cost-effective despite the high start-up costs. They excel in accuracy and speed.

59.   Both of our existing installations rely on direct connection and multiplexers, using the digital 'DMS' system   provided by Telecom Australia for metropolitan networks.

60.   For the Elizabeth Street project, another consideration was the number of lines/channels between the processor and consultants' offices. Because printers can tie up a line for a considerable time, it was decided to have two independent lines to each remote site - one for screen access and data entry, the other for printers.

61.   For the smaller Telecom project, one line was deemed sufficient.

System management skills

62.   Persons engaged to manage large computer systems must have demonstrable knowledge and experience with tele-communications installations involving remote sites. They should be flexible and have an understanding of hardware (not as a technician but in an operating role). It requires dealing with telephone authorities as well as hardware suppliers and knowing the relationships between hardware, software and communications equipment.

63.   In setting up remote networks there are two or three levels of technology and organisations to deal with This requires people with communications expertise, which is quite different than the experience gained in dealing only with computers. We know now that this is more critical than originally envisaged.

64. This industry is still learning what others have experienced. Knowing how to deal with all the suppliers and telephone authorities, and rationalising all the difficulties that may arise when you get disparate pieces of equipment communicating, requires experience, knowledge and patience as well as people-handling skills.

65. Each consultant must recognise that they are important links in a chain. It is the critical consultants who are connected to these systems - the contractor, the engineers, the architect - and if they are not on-line at the critical times, control of the project is jeopardised.

66. If the entire system is not tied together properly, the whole functionality of the concept is broken. When someone is inadvertently locked out of the system, he is isolated - he no longer receives the information he needs, he cannot respond to requirements or changes, and the project manager cannot gain the required knowledge of progress.

Hardware combinations

67. In implementing a system for a major project, there are enormous commutations and permutations of hardware, communications and peripherals to be considered.

68. The computer may range from a PC to a mainframe, from dozens of suppliers each with multiple choices of performance capability. As mentioned, there are many methods of communication, each with different capital and recurring costs and levels of reliability.

69. Each must be carefully evaluated to determine the most effective, cost-efficient solution through the life of the project. The cheapest up-front solution is often the most expensive in the long term.

70. Because integrated networked systems are reasonably complex in scope, a few technical difficulties must be expected. Among the problems experienced are:
(a) delays in installation of communications services
(b) hardware faults
(c) incorrect hardware supplied - eg printers would not work in the configuration requested
(d) operating system difficulties

71. Most problems have been resolved; however intermittent faults still occur with the operating system on one computer and the hardware supplier seems not to fully understand the operating system. We had to prove very carefully that the errors were not the result of the application software.

72. Lessons were learned in how to deal with the hardware suppliers; if you do not follow their methodologies and use the 'right' words you are not regarded as having a serious problem!

73. Compatibility of hardware must be stressed. Instances have occurred where consultants ignored recommendations on the types of peripherals to acquire. This introduces extra levels of difficulty in determining the cause of problems.

Paperless office

74.   There is some reluctance by users to adopt the 'paperless office' concept which the integrated network encourages. They ask how to get copies of documents transmitted to them, whereas there is no such entitlement or justification for paper transfer. If they want a copy, they should print it out themselves by accessing the database.

75.   Elimination of paper transfer saves the cost of postage, paper and packing as well as time, storage space and filing cabinets.

76.   Unless there is a legal requirement for a piece of paper to change hands, no paper should change hands. The information always exists in the processor and is accessible via the printer if there is a real need for it.

RECENT DEVELOPMENTS
Action list and audit trails

77.   A recent addition to the system is a built-in audit trail facility. We began to realise that the system must be audited to ensure that requests are actioned, that time deadlines are met, and that individuals are accountable for their actions - or lack of action.

78.   This option provides a centralised, consecutively numbered list of items requiring action. Any organisation connected to the system may generate items for the list. Each item is dated, showing date required, and identifies the organisation required to take action. An audit trail is generated and reports show the status of each action item.

79.   Right from Day One there is a trail of action between all parties, and.the system reports on those who have not fulfilled their obligations.

80.   The client, for the first time, is being given a big stick with which to force consultants to meet their obligations in accordance with a pre-agreed time schedule.

81.   As an example, nowadays nobody knows whether you really have done something. A week can go by and a critical drawing that you were supposed to supply may not have been supplied, yet nobody knows until the next site meeting. Then arguments arise about whether or not it has been sent, or if it was lost in transit. And if the intended recipient had not complained about not receiving the drawing, obviously it was not too critical.

82.   Smokescreens, ambiguity and collusion have, in the past, enabled obligations to be avoided. Now, all action and obligations will be codified - if you fail to meet them you forfeit certain rights or incur certain penalties. There is nothing unethical - we are all in business and have responsibilities to supply on time what we are paid for.

Financial reporting and correspondence

83.   A new development is the integration of the financial consequences of progress into the information management system; ie budgetted costs against actual costs.

84.   Future system agreements will stipulate that all correspondence by any respondent will be typed into and transmitted through the system. Thus the total correspondence for the project, apart from

letters originating outside the ambit of the system, will be in the system. There will be an audit trail of correspondence.

85.   As OCR scanning improves, letters from outside sources will be input to the database for instant circulation among project participants. Similarly, faxes could be delivered direct into the computer.

ENGINEERS ROLE
86.   Engineers have two roles in a construction project:

(a)   as prime consultant/supervising officer/project manager; or

(b)   as a consultant being part of a design team under the control of another authority such as a project manager or the client.

87.   It is in the latter role that the engineers on the Elizabeth Street and Telecom projects are working.   They are simply required to perform in accordance with the methodology set up by 'el supremo', using a terminal linked to the central processor.

88.   There is a third opportunity for engineers: there is no reason why the same integrated system and methodologies should not be applied internally if you are a consulting engineer with various divisions, such as bridges, electrical, mechanical, water and sewerage, which you bring together for a project.   The same Action List, correspondence by electronic mail and project management can operate within your organisation.

INTO THE FUTURE
Processor-to-processor links
89.   While existing systems use 'dumb' terminals in the consultants' offices linked to one central processor, the next step is the linking of processors.   For example, an existing processor in an engineer's office could be linked to the central processor in the project manager's or client's office.   The engineer's processor, used for the normal technical/professional work, would transmit through a security-authorised system in accordance with the necessary rights which the central processor has to access, control and record what the engineer has done.

90.   This processor-to-processor link was sought by the project manager on the Telecom project as well as one of the consultants.

91.   There may be some human barriers to this concept, despite the technical feasibility, logic and project management benefits.

Software house involvement
92.   An interesting recent development was the installation of a terminal in CSSP's head office, linked to the Telecom project system. Not only does this provide practical advantages in implementing and servicing the system, it represents a new, deeper involvement of a software house in the management of construction industry projects.

93.   The project manager was quick to grasp that the system developer should be part of the action list in his project.   If there are failures on our part, or actions required by us, then they should appear

on his action list. Previously such actions were 'off system', but there was no reason why we should not have the same level of obligations to the project as the other consultants.

94. From the software developer's point of view, I need to know:

(a) what we are supposed to be doing to maintain the project; and

(b) that we have actually done something about the users' requests.

95. If the system is a management device, then it cannot be allowed to be deficient, break down or interfere with construction processes. We need to have access for proper, instant support service. This is a different concept to the normal type of software support using a modem connection, as some of our customers do, so that when they have problems, we can access their system.

96. With the Telecom project, ours is an involvement in the project rather than in the software. We are a party to the efficiency of the project, to the benefit of the client, project manager and all consultants.

97. The software supplier is an integral part of the entire project. There may be no flaw in the software or its functioning, but if people don't understand how it is to be used or if there are difficulties, the project is slowed. By being tied in to the project system, our response is faster, more efficient and audited.

98. It is a reality that if there is a problem, the application software supplier gets involved first, whether or not the software is at fault. In that sense, the software supplier becomes a systems consultant, responsible for fault finding and directing the resolution of problems, whether they be software, processor, communications or peripherals.

Remote accessibility

99. The project manager for the Elizabeth Street construction recently presented a paper to a group of other project managers. He walked into the seminar with his portable computer and modem, plugged it into the telephone socket and called up information on his project from the central processor and projected it onto the wall. To their amazement they could immediately find out the answer to any questions on the status and action being taken on his project. A couple of years ago, this was in the sci-fi realm; today it is reality.

100. It is quite feasible for an engineer (or any other party to a project) to be in London, and plug into his database whether it be in the next town or in Far North Queensland. The potential flexibility and efficiencies in operation are enormous, especially in times of crisis when you are away from your office.

101. Instead of our present system of eight or so remote terminals connected to a central processor, there lies the probability of having as many people as are necessary connecting to the central processor by a phone line from wherever they happen to be. There would have to be appropriate security. They could manage a problem from wherever they were.

102. With the increasing interest being shown by transport operators in providing mobile telephone and fax facilities for their business

passengers, there lies the potential for controlling a project while you are mobile by using cellular telephone circuits and/or satellite communication links. It is a relatively short technology step from the ability of an engineer to phone his office from a commuter train, to dialling up his central processor from a portable terminal on an intercity plane or train.

Modification of roles

103. Beginning to emerge is the reallocation of some responsibilities for services provided by the consultants involved in a construction project. An example is the easing away from the cost engineer of the financial reporting function as this becomes an automatic consequence of transactions recorded in the computer system.

104. As this realignment of traditional practices and redistribution of responsibilities occur with the continued development of systems, engineers will be able to reap benefits in productivity, efficiency and profitability. But, you may need to take a flexible and realistic view of your role as part of the broader construction industry team.

105. There is an indication of a greater participation by the client in his own projects. While lacking the technical expertise, he can have the technical work expressed to him in a way that he can understand.

Future projects

106. Clearly, we are learning more as development and implementation of the early systems proceed. That these have created interest is undoubted, and prospects for new projects are promising. These include:

(a) A major design and build contractor has selected the system for national use.

(b) An Australian State Government construction authority proposes to link 40 major projects into its head office.

(c) Nomination of the system by client and project managers for new hospitals in Melbourne and Sydney, Australia. These will be the first applications where financial and information functions are merged.

CONCLUSION

107. Where is all this leading? In my view, the client will have a more active role in the administration of his project, not at a technical level but at an obligation level.

108. There will be greater emphasis on performance criteria or quality assurance.

109. Engineers and other professions are facing a realignment of traditional practices and redistribution of responsibilities with the continued development of systems; those who adapt have the potential for growth and greater productivity and hence greater competitiveness in the construction industry.

A structured analysis of data flow systems for client-based construction project management and for contracting companies

N. FISHER, Director of Postgraduate Studies, Department of Construction Management and Engineering, University of Reading

SYNOPSIS. If development progress is to continue in important areas of construction engineering and management that involve data, the identifying and recording of 'best current practice' and the consequential design of better more efficient data flows is vital. This paper describes a modified form of 'Structured Data Analysis' (SDA), a technique originally developed by computer systems analysts. The benefits and limitations of the modified technique are discussed. The conclusion is reached that SDA is an ideal tool for mapping and recording complex management data flows and in a manner that has major implications for robotics, expert systems and computer integrated construction.

INTRODUCTION

1. The flow of data is at the heart of the issues faced by construction project managers. Some progress has been made in this area by applying information technology, which has been increasingly used in the construction industries of the developed nations since the early 1980's. Gradually more difficult areas such as computer aided design (CAD), project simulation and project costing have been computerised (ref.1). Innovations in areas such as CAD and project simulation, have demonstrated in a limited way the benefits that can be derived from the technology, but not so far the much heralded 'holistic systems' and 'quantum jump' in design, management and construction methods. There are however promising projects at trial and development stages, in particular in the areas of expert systems, robotics and computer integrated construction. Kuhn suggests (ref.2), that in research and development terms progress is normally accelerated by new techniques or technological breakthroughs; in for example robotics possibly by better sensors, in expert systems perhaps by the availability of cheap larger faster processors or the development of self learning 'neuro-network' computer circuits, in computer integrated construction probably by the use of a systematic and structured method for dealing with and partitioning the complex data flows encountered; that allow major advances.

2. Major studies have suggested that the flow of data between the key members of a traditional construction project team is critically important. The results from these studies suggest that dealing with it occupies a very considerable amount of the time of those with key managerial responsibilities (ref. 3). To attempt to look in a holistic way for example, at the data aspects of a management system behind the procurement of a major

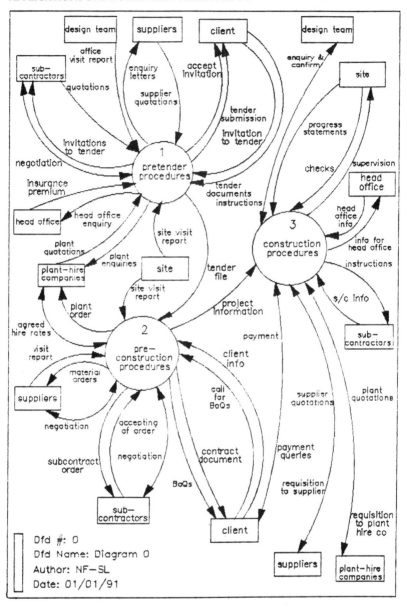

Fig 1   Data Flow Diagram 0

construction project, will require a rule driven research tool that is robust enough to cope with the partitioning, recording, mapping and analysis of very complex transmitted data. It will need to be in a form that allows repetition and challenge and important aspects of the 'data flow model' of the organisations to be compared. Extensive research at Reading involving a large number of separate studies at the various stages of the construction procurement process; stages such as feasibility study, evaluation of clients needs, selection of design consultants, preparation of design, selection of contractor, construction phase and post construction phase; suggests that a modified form of a systems analysis technique SDA meets the requirements outlined above for holistic computer integrated construction management systems. The early experimental work with SDA and the methodology used have all been fully described (refs 4-7). The technique involves developing in a rule driven manner a general 'data flow model' of the 'management system' data used by any organisation where there are flows of information, information processing and decisions taken. It is particularly of use when analysing design organisations such as consultant engineers and architects, project organisations, independent project managers, or any other socio-technical organisations that generate information. SDA consists of a number of related systems analysis tools. The first the Data Flow Diagram (DFD) is a technique to assist in the partitioning of the overall system; in a hierarchical grand-father, father, son way; and to document that partitioning clearly in a rule driven and therefore repeatable and refutable way. A DFD consists of a network of inter-related processes expressed graphically (see Fig. 1). Unlike the common 'flow chart' the DFD records the observed flows from the point of view of the data itself. When preparing a DFD, a systems analyst attaches himself to an individual piece of data, and follows it through the system, in a precise, logical, and rule driven manner.
This is clearly very different to other 'hard' and more traditional forms of systems analysis such as for example Jackson (ref.8), and the 'soft systems' methodologies of for example Checkland (ref.9).
A second set of tools is the ' data dictionary/mini specification' (see Fig. 6). A 'mini specification' is used to provide a clear and precise description of each DFD process; data flow (element), file, local file or terminator; which cannot be further partitioned. Such a data flow component, that is one that cannot be further sub-divided is called a 'functional primitive'. A data dictionary (DD) is used to show the hierarchy of descriptions of data flows, files, local files, terminators, and processes, building up from the functional primitive to higher more complex and less partitioned diagrams (ref.10).

AIMS OF THE STUDY
3. Behind this study there is an assumption that; despite the fact that the data flow systems of broadly similar companies in terms of work and performance, appear to have little commonality; a considerable level of commonality exists, and can be measured and recorded. It is evident when identical flows, processes, files and terminators are given 'common' names, and when the data flow systems are then compared. Rather than by a comparison of the way managerial tasks are organised in a particular company, what they are called, or who in the organisation performs it.

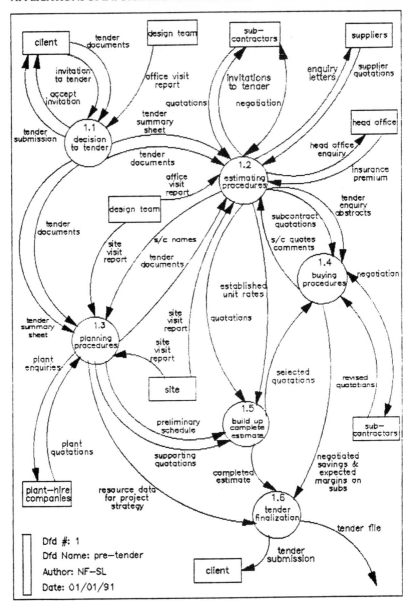

Fig 2   Data Flow Diagram 1   'pre-tender'

4. The aims of the studies described in this paper were:

(a) to adapt a systems analysis research tool; and use it in a new way of recording management systems so as; to allow the conducting of comparative management systems research.

(b) to undertake inter company information systems studies, with the purpose of developing a common system that incorporates the most sophisticated features of each system.

(c) to suggest as a result of the holistic perspective, improvement and simplification and allow relevant senior managers to develop an accurate picture of what is actually happening in an organisation rather than what they believe is happening in a given situation.

(d) to present a description/definition of a system that will allow operating managers to observe a similar but 'general system' (a GDFM) in a holistic way, and thus be able to compare it with their own system, or specific parts of it that are of interest to them.

(e) present a model (a GDFM) of the data flowing around a contractor's management system for a major construction project, that because of the rule driven research technique used would be in the 'public knowledge ' domain.

SDA AND THE SYSTEMS MOVEMENT
5. In his excellent book that describes the shape of the systems movement, Checkland (ref. 9) identifies just one area; he calls it 'problem solving development', a sub-set of systems thinking; that allows the recording and mapping of data. He classifies this as a hard system and argues that it has been influenced strongly by work in engineering, control theory and information theory. Checkland identifies two approaches within the hard system sub-set. They are:

(a) systems engineering - as typified by systems engineering and process engineering;

(b) computer systems engineering and systems analysis.
6. Of these the study described in this paper used a computer systems analysis approach, because as Checkland argues, a computer systems analyst attempts to use the methodology to build a model of an observed phenomenon and then from the model build a logical model of an improved system. The systems analysis approach is therefore the most suitable approach for building data flow models from fieldwork in a socio - technical organisation. Of the systems analysis techniques available that described by De Marco was used in the study described in this paper (Note 3).
7. As a result of initial fieldwork trials, modifications were made to the SDA technique as it is used by electronic data processing (EDP) system analysts, so as to make it more suitable for management system's research. A complete description of these modifications are described elsewhere (refs 6-7) .

CASE STUDY
8. Figs 1-5 show the DFD's of a small subsystem, which form part of a

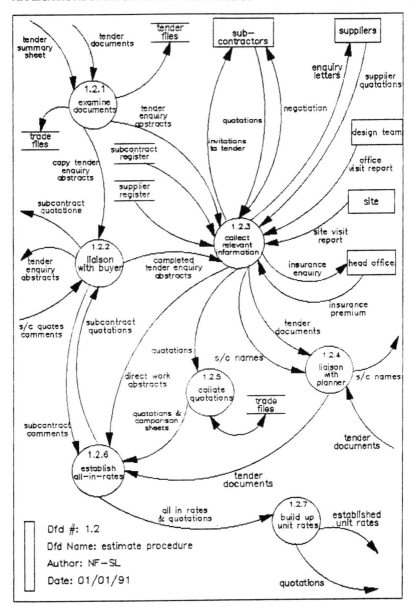

Fig 3   Data Flow Diagram 1.2 'estimate procedure'

large and complex GDFM. This example is a data flow 'map' of the important preconstruction subsystem 'pre-construction procedures' that will be found in a typical construction company.

Fig. 1 (DFD Name: Diagram 0) shows a complete subsystem that is found in a GDFM of a project management system for a construction company, together with data flows, terminators, files and processes. This is the highest level DFD in the GDFM. The three processes 'pretender procedures', 'pre-construction procedures' and 'construction procedures', are in turn broken down into their functional primitives. This partitioning activity is illustrated in Fig.4 (DFD Name: pre-con) where the process 'pre-construction procedures' is partitioned into eight sub-processes. Fig.5 (DFD Name: develop tender info) shows one of these eight sub-processes in turn being further partitioned into seven sub-sub-processes. Each of the flows and processes in Fig.5 are functional primitives. Every data element on a GDFM's set of DFD's is listed in the DD, but each functional primitive has a 'mini-specification', which is a statement of the policy governing the transformation of input data-flow(s) into output data-flow(s) at that functional primitive. Fig.6 shows an extract from the DD for the GDFM. Process 2.5.2 in Fig.5 is as has been already stated a functional primitive, it is a process called 'consider information required', and the relevant mini-specification is shown in Fig.6 (Note 4).

9. The DFD, DD and mini-specification together provide a precise rule driven description of the flow of data in an organisation that will allow examination and analysis.

RESULTS AND CONCLUSIONS
10. The results and conclusions drawn from this and related studies can best be examined in two parts. Firstly 'conclusions specific to the study', that is what can be learned about the systems analysed, and what can be learned about the SDA technique when used in the type of fieldwork described in this paper. Secondly, and perhaps of greater importance, conclusions that are 'general overall conclusions', that look at where this sort of research is leading; particularly at the implications for computer integrated construction, robotics, and expert systems; and where other benefits can be gained, and more general conclusions drawn, if this approach is applied.

Conclusions specific to the study
11. Clear evidence was found from the fieldwork data to suggest that all three companies had in system terms evolved in an 'ad hoc' incremental way. Further there was evidence to suggest that none of the three companies had looked at or attempted to improve their systems as a complete entity, despite considerable systems defect and redundancies. By way of illustration, in almost two thirds of the sample observed, cost engineers or quantity surveyors were found to be preparing masses of management information system (MIS) data, the vast majority of which was little used, even when preparing contractual claims. There was evidence that many parts of individual company systems, particularly cost related sub systems,

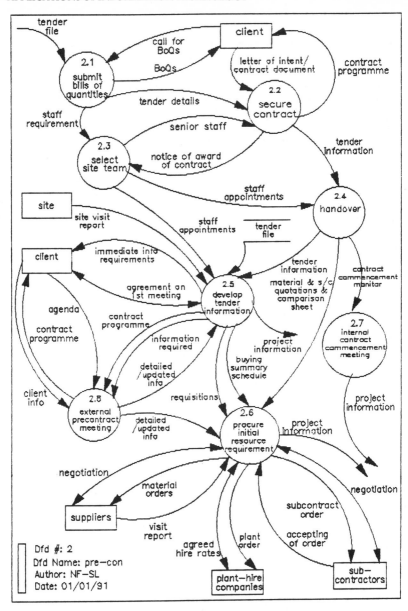

Fig 4   Data Flow Diagram 2 'pre-con'

had been repeatedly changed, amended or added to without any thought for the effect of the changes on the system as a whole.

12. The model developed provides a basis for comparison with other company systems. For senior managers it will allow comparison with their existing company system. For both practitioners and educators it will begin the process of demystifying the considerable managerial skill and complex systems necessary for successfully managing construction. It achieves this by specifying clearly and in a structured way the data system behind a contractor's management system for a major construction project. That is the backup that supports and prompts a successful manager. The model and the SDA technique together provide a piece of work and a research methodology in the public knowledge domain, that will allow national and international comparison of the GDFM's and the structured data systems maps (SDSM's) that will flow from similar studies conducted on a range of different contractors, consulting engineers and client's project managers in the UK and in a range of countries. A comprehensive description of the specific results and conclusions are given elsewhere (ref. 6).

General Overall Conclusions

13. The GDFM's that have been developed so far appear to have important implications for the systems design of 'integrated management EDP systems' for computer integrated construction, 'expert systems', robotics, and the design and construction process generally. The flow of data is at the very heart of the issues faced by construction project managers. It is a critical and time consuming activity. SDA has the promise of being a very effective tool, for ensuring the design of more efficient and effective flows of data between members of the construction project team.

14. Firstly for expert systems - attempts at linking together into one SDSM all DFD functional primitives of one sub-system of the construction process; for example the GDFM of the construction management system used by major UK contractors on large commercial building projects; with another GDFM such as 'the project design process', have proved to be successful. This is possibly because the SDA technique accurately identifies and specifies the interface points between the two sub-systems of the overall management system behind the procurement of a major construction project. By building up an SDSM of the total construction process in this manner; showing in a structured way the flows of data and the process points where data is manipulated or processed in some way; existing 'stand alone' expert systems can be plotted onto the SDSM and interfaces between them specified. This could have two very important consequences, on the one hand gaps where 'expert systems' do not currently exist or are inadequate, can be identified in a systematic and planned manner. Much of the initial work developing the algorithm for a new or improved 'expert system' will have been done as part of the SDA process. On the other hand the SDSM will demonstrate where interaction between the 'stand alone' systems might be fruitful.

15. Secondly for robotics - a truly 'smart' robot; as opposed to a

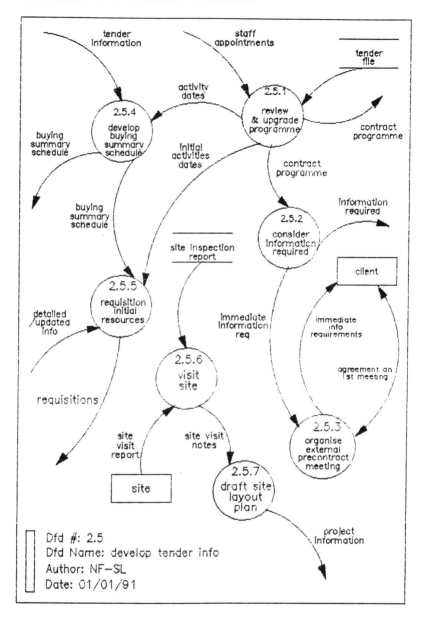

Fig 5   Data Flow Diagram 2.5 'develop tender info'

'quasi-robot' with umbilical cord to a remote control console; will need amongst other things to know its exact position (on a map) in the construction process, and use this position knowledge for the identification and a decision on the relevance, importance and priority afforded to other data, tasks and robots. Clearly if a truly 'smart' robots; or a robot management system for a gang of 'smart' robots; has access to a SDSM, one that has been personalised for a specific project, it will open up a number of exciting possible ways in which the robot could be used.
16. Thirdly for the building process and the systems design of 'integrated management EDP systems' for computer integrated construction - by using SDA to develop a full SDSM of the total construction process; showing best current practice; it will allow the systems engineer the unique opportunity to design holistically an efficient new total construction process that can utilise effectively the benefits of modern electronic technology. This step forward will enable the building process and the systems design of 'integrated management EDP systems' for computer integrated construction to be developed rapidly in a systematic and effective way.

GLOSSARY
BALANCING - The relationship that exists between parent and child diagrams in a properly levelled DFD set; specifically the equivalence of input and output data flows portrayed at a given process on the parent diagram and the net input and output data flows on the associated child diagrams.
CONTEXT DIAGRAM - Top level diagram of a levelled DFD set; a DFD that portrays all the net inputs and outputs of a system, but shows no partitioning.
DATA DICTIONARY (DD) - A set of definitions of data flows, files, information sources/sinks/terminators, and processes referred to in the levelled DFD set.
DATA FLOW - A pipeline along which information of known composition is passed.
DATA FLOW DIAGRAM (DFD) - A network of related functions showing all interfaces between components; a partitioning of a system and component parts.
DATA FLOW MODEL (DFM) - A representation of a specific company system using DFD's and a DD.
FILE - A data store, repository of data; a time delayed data flow.
FUNCTIONAL PRIMITIVE- Lowest level component of a data flow diagram, a process that cannot be further decomposed to a lower level.
GENERAL DATA FLOW MODEL (GDFM) - The combination of a number of DFM's drawn from fieldwork in several companies into one common system. A GDFM represents the best of current practice in the observed companies. The most complete or comprehensive of the observed systems within the individual DFM's are combined into one GDFM.
MINI-SPECIFICATION - A statement of the policy governing the transformation of input data-flow(s) into output data-flow(s) at a given functional primitive.

CONFIRMATION OF 'CALL OFF' FILES
Entry Type : Data Element

CONFIRMATION OF CALL OFF
Entry Type : Data Element/Local File

CONFIRMATION OF INSTRUCTION
Entry Type : Data Element

CONFIRMATION OF INSTRUCTIONS
Entry Type : Data Element

CONFIRMATION OF INSTRUCTIONS FILES
Entry Type : Data Element/Local File

CONSIDER INFORMATION REQUIRED
Entry Type : Process

Specification :

   This process deals with the following data : contract programme, information required, immediate information required.

   Having commenced the preparation of the contract programme the construction manager considers the project information required both immediately and in the short term. Using a standard 'initial information required summary sheet' the manager requests the information required immediately. The summary is dispatched to the architect with a letter as soon as the contract is awarded. The letter emphasised the need for detailed information without which the planning function and site set up cannot be effective.

   A further and more detailed examination of the information needed in the short term takes place with the manager and the site agent jointly reviewing the requirements. An 'information required schedule' is produced listing the bill of quantity reference numbers, descriptions of the items and the date required. In

addition a schedule of PC sums and provisional sums is completed listing the dates by which nominations and details should be received together with the associated value of each item. Therefore two schedules are presented to the architect at the external precontract meeting (see 2.8 in DFD No.2).

Fig 6   Data Dictionary   showing mini-specification

         'Consider information required'

PROCESS - The transformation of input data flow(s) into output data flow(s).
SINK - A net receiver of information outside of the subject system.
SOURCE - A data source outside of the subject system.
STRUCTURED DATA SYSTEMS MAP (SDSM) - The combination of two or more GDFM's to form a map of the data flows of part of a larger more complex system, or a whole system such as the construction procurement process.
TERMINATOR - A net receiver or supplier of information outside of the subject system (ie. a source or a sink).

NOTES

1. Fieldwork has up to now been undertaken in a number of broadly similar organisations. As the technique is rule driven and therefore consistent, it allows management systems researchers to describe data flows within an organisation in the form of a 'data flow model' (DFM), and compare specific systems or sub-systems within different organisations. It provides construction management researchers with a new and potentially beneficial avenue of research. For example it allows the construction of a GDFM; the combination of a number of DFM's; drawn from fieldwork in several companies that are perceived to represent the best of current practice. The most complete or comprehensive of the observed company systems are combined into one GDFM. DFD's and mini-specifications/DD's can be created either manually or by computer from fieldwork data. Creation by computer using commercially available system's analysis 'workbench' software, has clear benefits, not only in terms of speed and drafting, but because of the general checking, 'verification' and 'system balancing' sub-routines available. The GDFM's that have been developed so far appear to have important implications for the construction of SDSM's of parts or of the whole construction industry. SDSM's and GDFM's would appear to have important implications for the systems design of 'integrated management EDP systems' for computer integrated construction.

2. There is considerable evidence that the application of systems ideas within an existing discipline can bring about a considerable often dramatic developments in the level of understanding within that discipline. This is particularly so in the unrestricted sciences largely due to the complexity of the subject matter. Where the systems approach has been applied to unrestricted sciences such as biology or geography, the level of understanding has increased dramatically. Of particular relevance is the Cambridge geographers' rewriting of their subject (refs 11-15).

3. For a full description of the arguments behind the selection of the SDA technique see references (refs 6-7) below.

4. For the complete description of the GDFM briefly mentioned in this paper see reference (ref 6) below.

REFERENCES
1. Bennett J and Ormerod RN, Simulation applied to construction projects, Construction Management and Economics, Vol. 2, No. 3, pp 225-263.
2. Kuhn T, (1970), The Structure of Scientific Revolutions, 2nd Edition, Chicago University Press, Chicago.
3. Karlen I (1982), Information Methodology - Information Management, IN Information Study Group, CIB Publication 65, Stockholm, pp 134 -175.
4. Fisher GN, (1985), Project Monitoring and Control systems as Used by Broadly Similar and Successful Contractors, Science and Engineering Research Council Report.
5. Fisher Norman, (1989), Marketing for the Construction Industry - A Handbook for Consultants Contractors and Other Professionals, Longman, London, pp 55-67.
6. Fisher GN and Shen LY, (1991), General data flow model of a project management system for construction companies, Chartered Institute of Building, Ascot, UK. It is planned that this book will be published by the Chartered Institute of Building early in 1991.
7. Fisher Norman, (1990), The use of structured data analysis as a construction management research tool: 1 - The technique, Construction Management & Economics, Vol. 8, No. 4, pp 341-363.
8. Jackson MA, (1975), Principles of Programme Design, Academic Press, London.
9. Checkland PB, (1981), Systems Thinking - Systems Practice, Wiley, Chichester.
10. DeMarco T, (1979), Structured Analysis and Systems Specification, Yourdon Press, New York.
11. Chorley RJ and Kennedy BA, (1971), Physical Geography : A Systems Approach, Prentice Hall, London.
12. Chapman GP, (1977), Human and Environmental Systems, Academic Press, New York.
13. Bennett RJ and Chorley RJ, (1978), Environmental Systems, Methuen, London.
14. Bolton D, Mottershead P and Naughton J, (1977), Systems Behaviour - Modules, The Open University Press, pp 8 - 87.
15. Naughton J and Peters G, (1976), Systems and Failures, IN : Technology: A third level course, The Open University Press, pp 19 - 27.

Data coding and phraseology for production control

A. BAXENDALE, Principal Lecturer, Bristol Polytechnic

SYNOPSIS. Production control data are originated in transactions for labour, plant, materials and site management. Data coding is required to facilitate data allocation, processing, storage and retrieval for accounting purpose. This process also calls for a convention to be adopted by the organisation concerned which is readily understood by those who input, process and interpret the output of such systems. Coding systems that are being used by construction contractors are examined and the practical aspects of using such a system. The use of a standard phraseology, based on activity descriptions, is recommended as a means of classifying project information. Finally criteria for the evaluation of coding systems are given as a basis for investigating existing systems.

DATA CODING FOR PRODUCTION CONTROL

1. A construction operation can be characterised by its technology, resource use, breakdown into work tasks and sequences and the nature of its ultimate assembly and use. The best technology available has to be selected and the relevent construction method defined for each operation. The nature and working of the construction operation must be described in such a way that foremen and operatives may perform the site operation properly and efficiently. Finally progress and control have to be organised in relation to the changing conditions during the performance of the site opreation.

2. In establishing a system for analysis of construction operations a clear and readily understandable terminology must be defined (Ref.1). Construction operations may be grouped into different classifications, depending on which features are selected:

(i)   by finished product
(ii)   by material
(iii)   by function

The full description of construction operations requires the identification of the construction technologies involved, the sequencing of the various work tasks that make up the processes and the allocation of the required resources for the work tasks and processes of the operation.

3. Information is required for accounting, statutory and decision-making purposes as well as for routine project control. Performance data from one contract will have to be compared with that of other contracts and also used for control of the firm. If this situation exists a standard coding system for construction activities becomes desirable. Direct control of the performance variables of time, cost and content is not always possible. They are dependent on transactions involving labour, plant, materials and subcontractors. They reflect in cash flow, progress reports and site organisation services. A comprehensive system should encompass information involving all resources and at all levels from company director to site manager.

4. It is suggested (Ref.2) that a job costing system may be required to identify:
(i)   the business unit to which the account
         pertains - the division, region or
         subsidiary concerned;
(ii)   the site or contract;
(iii)   the job or cost centre for which specific
         resources are intended or to which they are
         to be allocated;
(iv)   the nature of the expense (labour,
         materials, etc.).

The point is made that a seven digit number is hard to memorise and that site staff would have to become familiar with as many code numbers as there are active cost centres associated with their work. The reliability of code allocation is fundamental to a systems effectiveness. An "add-on" system as shown in Figure 1, reduces the length of the code to be required on the stage at which it is applied. The relationship between site activities and cost codes must be readily seen and the use of the code as foolproof as possible.

5. Progress control based on a programme of activities will facilitate the allocation of cost centres to an operational coding system. It is clearly necessary for inter-project comparison for

broad activities, as used in the precedence diagram method of network analysis, to adopt the same codes. Detailed site subcodes need not be standardised, but be available for reference in explanation of significant differences.

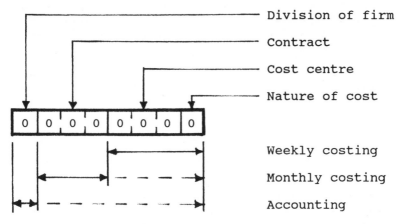

FIGURE 1   An "add-on" system of coding

COST ENGINEERING CODES

6. A review of cost codes in the USA (Ref.3) found two catergories being used. A "standard" cost code providing uniformity, transfer and comparison of information between projects and a "project" cost code acting as a framework for the control budget on specified contracts.   Both codes are often used to interface with the numbering of drawings and specifications, materials procurement and programme activity labelling. The codes therefore form the interface between all aspects of a project control system.   Where there is no standard method of measurement and contract documentation the process is not externalised and some of the problems of the UK approach are avoided.

Standard cost codes

7. A standard cost code classifies items of work or cost in relation to particular types of work. It is suggested that different codes are required for different types of work. For example, a code suitable for general building construction would fit uneasily in heavy engineering projects. A widely accepted industry standard code is the Cost Analysis Format in the Uniform Construction Index.

Project cost codes

8. A project cost code classifies work or cost pertainig to a particular project as a subset of the standard code. A different project code will be used for each project. They must be derived from the standard cost code if projects are to be compared on an historical basis. The project code will therefore be adapted to incorporate the particular features of a specific project while keeping it as concise and simple as possible. When developed the project code will incorporate a distribution code for documenting such items as: Labour
      Materials
      Plant
      Subcontractors
      Indirect costs

9. The derivation of project cost code is shown in Figure 2. The work-type code is taken from the standard cost code to which other codes are added: a project number, an area-facility code and distribution code. The project number will normally be used as a heading to each cost report and not included in each item reported. The area-facility code distinguishes between parts or sections of projects and can allocate cost to different managers responsible. The distribution code, like many standard codes, does not offer further breakdown of the resource components such as labour, plant and materials. An example of the use of the code is given in Figure 3. The resulting coding system is comprehensive and includes the requirements of a job costing system. The complexity of the system will not allow interpretation to be accurately made by trades foremen or subcontractors. Codes will have to be specified by site management, as with job cards.

Practical considerations

10. It is noted (Ref.3) that there are numerous practical aspects of a cost code and the cost engineering system that builds from it. To track bulk materials there is need of a holding account until they are incorporated into the project. Costs should be allocated and controlled where they occur. For example, formwork may be prefabricated and then fixed, stripped, cleaned and re-fixed, the number of uses being critical in assessing the economy of the process. Direct labour costs vary over time and if used for control purposes, it is recommended that targeting and control is carried out in terms of operative hours. Plant time may be difficult to

allocate, for example, a tower crane serving
different activities on a multi-storey building.
Such plant may then be allocated an overhead cost
centre and be treated as an indirect cost.
Imprecision and ambiguity in the written description
of the codes is the worst common source of error.
Also codes for miscellaneous and contingency items
should be avoided as site staff may take the easy
way and use them.

11. Experience in the USA has shown that project
cost codes should be simple, neat, concise and easy
to interpret. Exhaustive detail need not be
incorporated, with only essential and readily
identifiable activities used. It is clear then that
there is a conflict to be resolved by the system
designer between detailed cost modelling and
effective accounting. The answer is, as in so many
other aspects of management, a compromise.

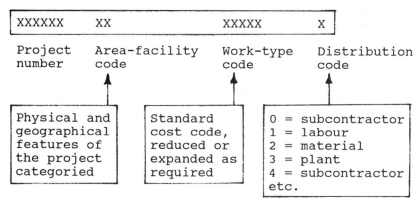

FIGURE 2   Developing the project code

Project	Area-facility	Work-type	Distribution code
88NB05	12	93210	2

	12th floor		Material
88 = year		Concrete,	cost
N = negotiated		fabric	
B = building		reinforcement	
05 = 5th this year			

FIGURE 3   Example of a project code

CODING SYSTEMS IN USE

12. A teaching company scheme to computerise site management procedures for civil engineering works is reported (Ref.4). The two year programme set out to improve by facilitating better use of largely existing systems, the analysis and forward planning of on-site operations, cost control, and evaluation of future contracts. It was hoped to develop an adequate data base.

13. A precedence diagram method of networking was applied to site programming. However it used a bar chart print-out in relation to a project calender. This planning system was installed by teaching company personnel. Site managers are starting to use the micro-computer package associated with it. A manual site cost control system existed. It is being replaced by a commercial data base package. It records labour, plant and materials and reports on both a weekly and monthly basis. Overheads are included as a weekly allowance to site. Cost control is head office based and is designed to exploit investment in a computer system that preceded the teaching company scheme.

14. There is no link between the planning and cost control systems. This is a matter for future refinements. Programme operations are classified by a code unique to each individual contract. There is no cross referencing between contracts. The cost coding system provides information for weekly and monthly control.

15. The composite code consists of a job number (4 digits), a section code (4 digits), and the cost type (3 or 4 digits). The section code is in two parts: the header code (2 digits) based on the Method of Measurement for Road and Bridge works, which will be common to all contracts; a sub-code (2 digits) used to suit individual contracts to locate the header section. The cost type is used to classify materials with all contracts using the same code and is taken from Table 1. An example code of 2999 0603 280 representing job number 2999, seeding to central reservation is built up by:
06, earthworks section
03, central reservation
280, top soil and planting.

16. Demarcation of tasks still exists within the company and is reflected by the computer system developed.

(i)   Weekly cost control on site for the site
        manager.
(ii)   Monthly cost control at head office by the
        accounts department (there are usually
        problems in reconciling weekly and monthly
        cost as head office have more complete
        data).
(iii)   Valuations on site by visiting quantity
        surveyor from the production department
        (valuations use information from the
        computer system).
(iv)   Planning of site work using the precedence
        diagram package by planning engineer from
        the production department.

17. It is recognised by the company that acceptance
of any new system will depend on the complexity of
the job (the more complex, the more help required)
and the attitude of managers on site. The system is
limited to minor civil engineering works and is
company specific. Improvements in performance have
been perceived from the improvement of data flow
from systems which themselves are not integrated or
initally designed for computerised processing.

TABLE 1. Cost type codes in use.

201	Aggregates
205	Brick and clay products
210	Cements
215	Cement precast products
220	Black top and bitumastic products
225	Cast iron products
230	Timber
235	Reinforcing steel
240	Fabricated steel
245	Structural steel products
250	Not allocated
280	Top soil and planting
285	Fitted extras (housing and small works)
290	Fuels
295	Tools

INFORMATION SYSTEM PHRASEOLOGY

Trade Measurement of Building Works

18. The preparation of a bill of quantities by the client's quantity surveyor to enable all contractors to price on the same information when tendering is a well established basis for project procurement. The practice has become so well established that contractor's estimators and surveyors will often prepare their own bill of quantities when, in other countries, a schedule of materials could be the likely choice. The bill is the basis for negotiations in contract administration between the contractor's quantity surveyor and client's quantity surveyor.

19. The bill of quantities sets down items of work in a logical seqeunce, in a recognised manner. Its units of measurement refer to quantities of finished work. The Standard Method of Measurement of Building Works (1988), or SMM7, covers most of the building items that are normally encountered. Each bill item is so worded that there should be no doubt in the mind of the contractor as to the nature and extent of the item being priced. The sectionalising of the bill into trades facilitates quotations from subcontractors. The sections of SMM7 are shown in Table 2.

20. The work sections are lettered and each clause numbered. For example, section E "In-situ concrete" has a numbered clause E10 for insitu concrete, E20 for formwork and E30 for reinforcement. Each clause is then further broken down in relation to information provided and a classification table for billing purposes. The SMM can therefore be used as a basis for classifying work section or trade or construction form or materials.

Classification of Project Information in the UK

21. The CI/SfB Project Manual (Ref.5) incorporates the authoritative UK version of the international SfB classification system as it applies to project information. The international SfB (Samarbetskomiten for Byggnadsfragor) classification system took its name from the Swedish committee that originally produced it, with CI standing for Construction Indexing, added to distinguish the new development. The system is recommended to architects for organising project drawings and other documents.

TABLE 2   Sections of the Standard Method of
           Measurement of Building Works (1988)

SECTION	SUBJECT	SECTION	SUBJECT
A	Preliminaries	N	Furniture/
B	Complete buildings		Equipment
C	Demolition/	P	Building
	Alterations		fabric sundries
D	Groundwork	Q	Paving/Planting
E	In situ concrete/		/Fencing
	Large precast	R	Disposal
F	Masonry		systems
G	Structural/	S	Piped supply
	Carcassing metal/		systems
	timber	T	Mechanical
H	Cladding/Covering		heating/cooling
J	Waterproofing		/refrigeration
K	Linings/Sheathing/	U	Ventilation/Air
	Dry partitoning		conditioning
L	Windows/Doors/	V	Electrical
	Stairs		power/lighting
M	Surface finishes	W	Communication/
			security
		X	Transport
			systems

22. CI/SfB contains five main tables or coded lists
of items. To illustrate how the system works Table
(1): Elements list building parts such as external
walls, internal finishes and gives each part a code,
e.g. (21) for external walls. All drawings,
specifications and measured information concerning
external walls will therefore be coded (21) or given
a related code. Tables (2) and (3): Building
products and materials are used together to code
building products by their form or shape, e.g.
bricks, tubes, sheets and finially their material,
e.g. wood, glass. Products are coded by capital
letter and the materials of which they are made by a
lower case letter usually followed by a number.
Sheet plywood would therefore be coded as Ri4. All
three tables of codes can be used together on
drawings. For example, (21) Fg2 represents external
walls: brick, clay, heavyburnt.

23. Architects, structural and mechanical and
electrical consultants and quantity surveyors can
use the standard lists of codes and headings to

organise their project documentation which will automatically cross reference all information dealing with the same subject, no matter who produced it. The short codes used in CI/SfB are not intended for use without written descriptions and it is not necessary to fully understand the meanings of the codes. For example, drawings coded (31) will give details of windows; (31) in the bill of quantities and cost plan will give the cost of windows; (31) in the client's brief will give the design requirements for windows. Some drawings may deal with more than one element, e.g. a drawing dealing with internal and external walls would be coded (2-). Other drawings covering all parts such as block plans and general sections would be coded (--).

24. The method of using item type coding as the link between drawings, specifications and bill of quantities can be summarised, in respect of each type of commodity, assembly and element there will be:
(i)   CI/SfB classification code with an identification code.
(ii)   Annotation.
(iii)   Specification description.
(iv)   Quantities.
Of these, (i) and (ii) will appear on drawings, (i) (ii) and (iii) in specification, and (i) (ii) and (iv) as measured items in bills of quantities. Bills of quantities using CI/SfB can provide cross reference to and from the drawings and specification will have a search pattern which will lead users quickly to the informantion they require. The rules of the SMM can be applied and the arrangement of measured work can then coincide with contractor's work packages.

25. CI/SfB work is further consolidated (Ref.6) in the Construction Indexing Manual which includes a Table (4) matrix of Activity and Requirement classification. Construction operations (D) are of particular interest dividing operations as follows:
(D1)   Protecting.
(D2)   Clearing, preparing.
(D3)   Transporting, lifting.
(D4)   Forming: cutting, shaping, fitting.
(D5)   Treatment: drilling, boring.
(D6)   Placing: laying, applying.
(D7)   Making good, repairing.
(D8)   Cleaning up.
(D9)   Other construction operations.

26. The Construction Indexing Manual is recognised (Ref.7) in the Manual of British Standards in Building Construction and Specification as being the definitive classification list as summarised below:

TABLE	0	PHYSICAL ENVIRONMENT
	1	ELEMENTS
	2	CONSTRUCTION, FORMS, MATERIALS
	3	MATERIALS
	4	ACTIVITIES, REQUIREMENTS.

CI/SfB therefore offers a link from design through to construction and accounting. It is possible that a menu driven computer program could permit network activities to be coded and that associated accounts could be then sorted for a variety of control purposes. The precision and predictability of coding is the essential feature.

CASE STUDY OF A CODING SYSTEM

27. A coding hierarchy is suggested in Table 3. The coding must provide uniformity for transfer and comparison of information between projects while including all items of building construction, although only a few items may be used on any one project. The code must also be capable of being applied in a consistent way from project to project. The structure of the coding system requires to be stratified for overall (e.g subcontractor) or detailed (e.g. material) control, with reporting taking place at weekly or monthly intervals. A molecular coding system that is capable of synthesis will reduce the number of items that have to be allocated codes on site. The coding hierarchy being a faceted structure should suit computer supported data files and their sortation.

28. Product determination may be defined as the process of acquiring information on production costs with the aim of estimating the final cost of new work with an acceptable accuracy, knowing the economic effect of choosing between alternatives. A data base of components and resources for standardised elements of construction may be derived from coded production costs to provide feedback. These costs may be changed as new materials and processes are applied to similar elements at different times.

TABLE 3   A coding hierarchy, in order of application

1.	Division of company		Printed head on control
2.	Project		records
3.	Work section	)	
		)	Taken from a
4.	Element	)	Cost Centre	schedule for comparison
		)	
5.	Location	)	between jobs
6.	Resource	(Labour	
		(Plant	
		(Materials	Allocated at
		(Subcontractors	site
		(Site overheads	
		((preliminaries)	
7.	Process	Not required with new work	Taken from a schedule

29. Master Lists of work section coding based on SMM7 (2 digits) and element codimg based on the CI/SfB Project Manual (2 digits) have been developed for cost centres. An aplication of the coding of programme activities is included in Table 4. The initial coding system proposed has been published as "Coding systems for new building work" (Ref.8).

30. During the course of a research programme a total of 2051 programme activities were coded for work section and element (4 digits) by a total of 77 practitioners and checked. 74.9 percent were found to be correct with conversely 25.1 percent of activities being incorrectly coded. In general work section coding was more accurate than element coding. These results do compare favourably with those reported (Ref.9) where it was suggested that recording cost data becomes highly erroneous when a large number of codes are available. The figures suggested are that with 30 cost headings about 2% of items are misallocated, with 200 cost headings 50% and with 2000 cost headings only 2% of items are correctly allocated. The implementation of any coding system will require a training programme and control with regular checks. The Master Lists can be considered as the basis of a coding system that has simplicity, yet contains sufficient data for use in a management information system.

TABLE 4   Coding of programme activity descriptions

ACTIVITY	CODE
Demolition	C111
Reduce level excavation	D211
Piling	D317
Insitu concrete foundations	E116
Drainage	R152
Hardcore	D213
Steelwork frame	G128
Metal sheeting to roof	H327
External brickwork	F121
Insitu concrete ground floor slab	E113

CRITERIA FOR CODING SYSTEMS

31. Activity codes should be simple, concise and easy to interpret, with only essential and readily identifiable activities used. The main critera for the analysis of coding systems are summarised as follows:

(i)   Provide feedback on production performances.

(ii)   Classify all essential production activities so that variation in performance can be correlated with their location and situation.

(iii)   Classify resources applied in performance (labour, materials, plant, subcontractors and overheads).

(iv)   Be consistent in application from activity to activity, job to job and contract to contract, over a period of time.

(v)   Give data base capability, through which to research values and particularly variations in value.

(vi)   Minimise coding discrimination at point of input.

(vii)   Be stratified in structure for reporting at various levels.

(viii) Be faceted in structure for transfer and comparison of information.

(ix)   Be related to existing, nationally recognised coding systems.

(x)   Provide a computerised data file.

32. A coding system must support output data from site, in the form of activity descriptions, that can integrate both time and cost for control.

REFERENCES
1. HALPIN D W and WOODHEAD R W, Design of construction and process operations, Wiley, 1972.
2. COOKE B and JEPSON W B, Cost and financial control for construction firms, Macmillan, 1979,
3. BARRIE D S and PAULSON B C Jnr, Professional construction management, McGraw-Hill, 2nd Ed., 1984.
4. JONES D P, Aston University with Kimbell Construction Ltd., SERC Bulletin, Vol.3, No.4, Spring 1986.
5. RAY-JONES A and McCANN W, CI/SfB project manual, Organising building project information, The Architectural Press, 1971.
6. RAY-JONES A and CLEGG D, CI/SfB Construction indexing manual, RIBA Publications Limited, 1976.
7. SMITH M, Ed., Manual of British Standards in building construction and specification, British Standards Institution and Hutchinson, 1985.
8. BAXENDALE A T, A coding system for new building work, Technical Information Service, CIOB, No.86, 1987.
9. HARRIS F and McCAFFER R, Modern Construction Management, 2nd Ed., Collins, 1983.

Role of database systems and historical databases in construction project management

B. IVKOVIC, Associate Professor, and Z. POPOVIC, Assistant,
Faculty of Engineering, University of Belgrade

SYNOPSIS.   The aspect of modelling a Project has been considered from the Contractor's point of view, and this aspect is, according to the authors, the initial step in creating the Information System at the level of a Project. The complete procedure of establishing Databases in construction project management, has been shown using the databases for individual Projects and starting from marketing through Databases for individual Projects up to the act of selecting and using the Historical Databases. At the end of paper, a practical example of a Database meant for handling of the technical documents has been given. The same was incorporated into the Information System of a Large Project performed at the Middle East.

INTRODUCTION

1. The implementation of Large Projects requires complemental functioning of various Production Systems in achieving the same goal. A "Production System" is defined as a complete technological process for which the individual operations, procedures and their mutual dependence as well as the resources required for an optimal functioning, have been determined. The number of Production Systems that are to be established at one and/or more locations within one Project, depends, of course, upon the type of a Project, namely upon the quantity and types of buildings under construction, the level of their equipping, conditions of relevant resources supply, any special requirements imposed by the Client, upon the valid contractual relationships, and so on. It is to be noted however that there are Production Systems characteristic for implementing of the majority of Projects such as, firstly, preparing of Design Documents in several phases, then, resolving of any supply issues, then, constituting the contractual relationships at the Project in question, establishing an information sub-system for the Project, carrying out of Earth Works and finally up to the Installation Works, Trial Runs and Quality Testing of Equipment installed. By applying the above definition of Production Systems as a starting point

and taking into consideration the mutual technological dependence of these Systems as well as a possible number of participants, it might be concluded that to manage a Large Project represents a considerably complex task.

2. It is outright clear that a successful management of Large Projects primarily requires the high-grade co-ordination of Production Systems functioning. Taking into consideration the disturbances within circumstances that influence the Production Systems as well as the mutual dependence of of individual Production Systems functioning, it is realistic to expect that a decision making is made under the conditions of uncertainty. Consequently, the co-ordination of functioning of several Production Systems is inevitably accomplished under the uncertain conditions both from the point of view of scheduled time periods and from the point of cost estimating and planned resources engaging.

3. In view of the conditions as described above, the justified efforts are made in developing the mathematical models that contemplate uncertainty in an appropriate manner and help estimating of risks taken in performing certain activities for the Project. All such attempts and provided methodical solutions are characterized by using certain possibilities that are to be accepted only upon analyzing the functioning of similar Production Systems at previously completed Projects. It is therefore the only regular course since it proves the appropriateness of applying a developed mathematical model.

4. Development and application of mathematical models are directly connected to the development of appropriate methodical approaches and Information System for collecting and using of quantitative and quality input data and information. In the context thereof it is possible to raise a question whether the endeavours to prepare and develop complex mathematical models in promoting decision making under uncertain conditions are more justified than the endeavours to establish a high-quality Databases thus to decrease uncertainty at the time of making decisions. Certainly, none of the foregoing activities could be eliminated and considered as excessive. Both are necessary although is worthwhile of mentioning that even the most excellent mathematical model with poor input data might provide the results that are non-applicable in practice. This paper therefore emphasizes the development of relevant Databases meant for promoting the Project management.

DEVELOPMENT OF INFORMATION SYSTEM AT THE LEVEL OF A PROJECT

5. Well-structured Information System is to provide duly, sufficient and understandable information as well as the possibility of their selecting and grouping both for the various levels of management and for organizational fields and/or levels. At the same time, the activities of Project management might be considered as an integral part of a continuous process of decision making that requires fast, precise and clearly-presented information relating to implementation of the Project in question. It is therefore obvious that an efficient Information System at the level of a Project, is to be established thus to decrease uncertainty while making decisions. In order to implement a high-quality management at the level of Company it is required that such an Information System has a clearly defined relation to the complete Information System at the level of Company. The fundamental components of the Information System are Databases that enable systematic collecting, storing and quick using of any data important for business activities of a Company and that may be expressed either in figures, text or as a drawing. It is to be pointed out that a systematic collecting of data is the most significant activity in up-dating the Databases. That activity is certainly preceded by an accurate defining of purpose of such data, namely, of methodical approach and procedures to be applied in that process. A well-established Database may become obsolete and unuseful after awhile if it is failed to be permanently supplemented with fresh data upon the current business activities. Establishing of a Database is therefore an initial step only to be followed by a constant care for development and expansion of a Database.

6. An approach to establishing of an Information System at the level of a Project is directly dependent upon understanding of Project modelling, namely, upon defining of the stages of Project implementation. The usual approach to Project modelling within the relevant literature (Refs. 3, 5, 9) indicates to defining of the following stages:- inception, feasibility, scheme design, detail design, contracting, construction, commissioning. It is obvious that these stages are to cover the overall life cycle of a Project: from articulating the Client's idea on a necessity to obtain a certain Building up to the stage of its using. These stages are, in a more or less different way, interpreted in the mentioned reference literature and it is to be concluded that these stages of a Project implementation, are in the Client's interest. It is the Client who, together with his Consultants, manages the implementation of these stages with a various approach in respect to the significance of the stages. It is to be understand that the Client and Consultants make the biggest efforts at the initial stages of Project implementation by the time of concluding the Contract, and especially at the stage of Designing. The obtained results of cost control for a few Projects indicate that 90%

(ninety per cent) of possible savings at a Project have been made by applying the proper controlling in these initial stages. At the stage of construction, the Client's activity is concentrated manly upon the control of costs, time and quality.

7. Taking into consideration the fact that in the course of construction also the Contractor is to have own interest both from financing and new references points of view, it is to be concluded that an approach to Project Modelling requires to be defined from the aspect of a Contractor - Contracting Company. By defining such an approach, the Contractor is enabled to develop his own methodical approach to Project Modelling and thus to create the conditions for achieving his goals at the Project. Also, it may be stated that these activities of a Contractor are in the interest of a Client, namely, that these activities decrease uncertainty in the course of carrying out the Works for the Project wherewith the realistic prospects of successful implementation of a Project are increased. Such a conclusion is in compliance with the experience of the Yugoslav construction companies being present on various worldwide markets for a long time as well as with the results obtained by authors having been engaged for a few Projects on the Arab and Soviet markets.

8. By considering the previous observations (Items 6, 7 above) the following stages of Project Management are to be defined from a Contractor's point of view:

I   Marketing
II   Preparing of an Offer
III   Contracting
IV   Preparing of the Design Documents and carrying out of the preliminary activities prior to implementation of a Project
V   Construction and Equipping a Large Project
VI   Payment of Works, and
VII Establishing of a Historical Database (Fig. 1).

This paper is not to deal with the listed stages in details. It is obvious that these stages have been made appropriate to the life cycle of a Company at a Project (Stages II thru VI), and that, at the same time, they take into consideration a continuity of knowledge within a Company (Stages I and VII). The success of a Company when it carries out the Works for a Large Project, directly depends upon the quality of Marketing and Historical Database stages. These stages (I and VII) also comprise the activities that should be of the Employer's interest, especially when Employers' groups are engaged at Large Projects for long terms or if are involved constantly in constructing Large Projects of the same type. In both cases, it might be stated that these two stages have the following characteristics:-

■   they go on constantly, and

- they represent the basic condition to perform the other stages successfully.

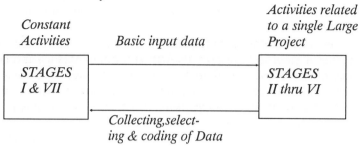

Fig. 1 - Relationships of stages in Proposed Project Modelling

9. From a Contractor's point of view, the proposed approach to Project Implementation defines the framework within which an Information System is to be developed at the level of a Project and built-into an Information System at the level of a Company. The basic elements required to create an Information System - a relevant Database, according to the author's opinion, and a suggestive example of a Database implemented in practice, are provided in the further text.

THE COMPONENTS REQUIRED FOR ESTABLISHING A DATABASE AT THE TIME OF MARKETING (STAGE I)

10. It has been already said that this Stage goes on constantly and it is being implemented within an Information System at the level of a Company. The Information Systems at the level of a Project excessively utilize the Company's Data, particularly at the Stages of Preparing an Offer and Contracting. In the course of implementing a specific Project, dating-up and supplementing of existing Database are constantly performed as following:

(a) Studying of possible sources of relevant resources of each market:
   - selling prices on the parity Ex Mill,
   - transport prices per measure units, and
   - analyzing of prospective suppliers;
(b) Recording of all the technical/technological data issued in specialist publications on the market in question and upon the company's field of activity;
(c) Recording of all the advertisements and competitions in respect of feasibility studies, design documents, and carrying out the investigation works on the market in question as well as all the information/data on the Government's and/or large economic systems measures. If the above information are obtained, then an immediate contact with a prospective Client may be made, and

even a free-of-charge service may be offered at the time when such a Client is preparing for Tender issuing;

(d) Analyzing and recording of all the basic elements of legal regulations that might be relevant to carrying out of a Large Project on the market in question;

(e) Analyzing and recording of valid expert regulations (such as codes of practice, standards, regulations and other codes);

(f) Analyzing and recording of possible traditional presence of a certain equipment manufacturer on the market in question in order to contact him and, eventually, to act jointly;

(g) Analyzing and recording of all the customs regulations due to possible effects upon the Works performance and financial results, and

(h) Collecting of the relevant data on individuals and companies significant for acting on a certain market.

This Stage comprises also making of contacts with certain Clients and collecting the information upon the activities and requirements on the market of construction industry services as well as upon the possibilities to present the capacities and successfully completed Projects.

ESTABLISHING A DATABASE AT THE TIME OF CONSTRUCTION (STAGES II thru VI)

11. An Information System for a specific Project might be obtained by making suitable and supplementing the solutions applied to the previous Projects, however, such an Information System is to be in compliance with the particular conditions under which the Works are carried out. Such particular conditions are determined by: size of a Project, applied organizational alternative of management, technological characteristics, specific customs and tax systems, the type of Contract, available hardware, the personnel training and so on.

12. The essential databases to promote management of a specific Large Project are as follows:

(a) **A Database containing the technical characteristics of a Project** (the size and type of rooms, floor areas, level of equipping, required working conditions, allowances). The sources of data are the Technical Specifications, contractual stipulations and Design Documents. The systematized technical data for all the field (electrical, HVAC, architectural, and so on) are the subject of constant interest and modifications in the course of Project duration, and any modifications thereof may have significant financial consequences.

(b) **A Database on the scope and value of Works** contains the quantities and unit rates of Works that are to be determined on the basis of the existing design solutions. When a Detail Design has been completed, it is possible to obtain a precise Bill of Quantities that represents the bases for preparing the final account together with modifications made in the course of project duration. The Unit Rate of each Work Item consists of the unit rates of materials to be built in, of labour, plant/equipment and transportation costs. The modifications to scope and/or Unit Rates of Work Items may be expected in the course of carrying out the Works for Project, this is therefore a manner to show the effects of such modifications. It is also required to have an up-dated scope of Works for any Sub-Contractor as well as for each Building within a Project.

(c) **A Database on import and storing of equipment and materials** is indispensable for Project of a greater complexity. A border crossing is recorded on appropriate customs documents and a list of imported goods, and by recording the time and place of storing at the Site, the documents on goods transported are made complete. It is of a special interest to have an efficient record on the goods imported on temporary basis since such goods are subject to more strict regulations and higher fines when the legally stipulated terms for extending such documents, are not met. The plans for creating such Databases solely depend upon the country where the Works are carried out.

(d) **A Database containing information on the payment of Works** is subject to the Contract stipulations that determine the preparation and verification of Payment Certificates. It is a common practice (both on the Eastern and Western markets) to get the payments for Work Items relating to labour separately from the payment for Items relating to materials. Therefore it is required to have not only the financial indices of the Works carried out, but also the actual quantities of the Works certified. Only such records could provide a clear final measurement and, also, high quality input data for the Historical Database.

(e) **A Database meant for Technical Audit** comprises computer records of all contractual and technical correspondence, protocols and Minutes of Meetings as well as other written documents relating to submission, revision and approval of Designs. Technically, it is provided to search and select quickly all the records taking into account several parameters such as dates, type of Works, participants of a Project as well as to store and display overall texts.

(f) **Databases meant for monitoring of efficiency at the Site, Work progress and consumption of resources** together with pertaining software for those purposes are available on the market. With certain knowledge and any possible modifications and/or additions they might be applied to various types of Projects.

97

13. The basic element that relates the said components of the Information System meant for implementation of a Project is the approved system of coding. For example, certain equipment may have a code applied to it within the Bill of Quantities, customs documents issued at the time of transport and also, at the time of payment for the Works. The success of functioning of established Databases primarily depends upon the available personnel and efficiency with which the organization has been resolved.

ESTABLISHING OF A HISTORICAL DATABASE (STAGE VII)

14. When a Contract has been awarded and upon several years' activity for the implementation of such a Project, produce fresh data and knowledge that overcome the interests of that specific Project. The Stage of establishing a Historical Database comprises selecting, coding and recording in a computer of all the data important for future Projects too. The basic source of the data required for establishing of a Historical Database of a Company, are the data obtained by analyzing and systematizing of Databases established in the course of carrying out the Works for a Large Project (Item Nos. 11, 12, 13 above). It is possible to use the software created for the Information System of a specific Project for these activities of a post-Project phase as numerous data are stored as per unaltered format for the future Projects. A Historical Database is established at the level of a Company and its data are particularly employed at the Stages of Preparing of an Offer and Contracting (8) as well as while planning and monitoring the implementation of specific Projects.

15. The Stage of establishing a Historical Database goes continuously on and comprises the following components:

(a) The Data on actually carried out quantities and unit rates of paid Works for a completed Project. These data de facto become a standard applicable to estimation of the scope and value of any future Project of similar type. Upon analyzing the final measurement, the library of actually carried out quantities and prices realized by a Company, is increased for several hundreds or thousands of Items representing a rich experience that shall repay the invested efforts through the future Projects.

(b) The data on consumption of labour, plant/equipment and materials and also on the financial effects and periods of time, are defined as per a unit of measure or other parameters. The financial effects are less important than indices of actual quantities carried out since the former are changed more often. These data are important from the planning point of view of a future similar Project and they represent the basis for creating own experience-wise norms. Likewise, they are precious for obtaining a quick conceptual estimation of a Project on the basis of few input data only (total floor area, number of rooms, designed number of workers and/or staff, number of soldiers, number of pupils, plant capacity and alike).

(c) The statistical data on certain equipment functioning - average period of operation and failures, as well as an average period between the two failures. These data are required for analyzing the availability of plant/equipment thus to foresee any risks that may arise when carrying out the Works that require application of plant/equipment. The proper estimation of risks enables duly corrections to the offered price. By analyzing the availability of plant/equipment, the own indices of plant/equipment quality are obtained that may be utterly useful when purchasing and/or renting these.

(d) The data on applied designing, structural and technological solutions, on certain procedures and methods as well as on the effect of their application. It has the significance for both the Designing and Contracting Companies that are awarded the Contracts. By analyzing the completed Projects, a Contractor becomes aware of the data such as: average number of floors and floor areas for a specific type of Building on the particular markets, average level of equipping, average types (percentage wise) of rooms of various purposes (basement, penthouses, elevators, apartments, hospital wards, classrooms, etc.) and many other details. By analyzing the applied technologies, however, they are improved in the course of the following application and the choice of a technology procedure is properly made for future Projects. Moreover, the stored data may have significance for developing of science and, consequently, for professional training of the experts of a Company.

(e) The data relating to plant/equipment - the estimation of business contact accomplished with the plant/equipment manufacturers, periods of production/transport/installation, trial runs and warranty periods. The more significant technical data are to be stored for more important plant/equipment. The plant/equipment, particularly for Building Engineering Works, is a price component of a considerable importance and therefore, it is to be paid due attention to. The plant/equipment of Type A comprises unstandardized plant/equipment that affects all the other solutions, while the plant/equipment of Type B comprises some unstandardized requirements but the choice of manufacturers for this Type, is considerably wider. The Type C is standard plant/equipment for which the catalogue and manufacturer data exist and, if required, these data may be included in the Database.

(f) The Database on personnel - their participation on specific Projects and the results of their engagement for the type of job they performed. Sometimes it is of certain significance to include also some personal data, of course, with guaranteed secrecy and prevention from abuse.

(g) The data on Sub-Contractors and influential individuals among the Sub-Contractors whose decisions might affect the business activities of such Companies - the data on quality of their performance, their bearing in the course of Project implementation, selecting and re-selecting the plant/equipment of Types A and B.

(h) The up-dated technical means enable storing in a computer of complete texts of applied legal stipulations and regulations, as well as of expert regulations (standards and norms). Often, these are lengthy documents, therefore their entering and readily copying to a magnet media represent a considerable improvement.

A PRACTICAL ILLUSTRATION: A DATA BASE FOR TECHNICAL AUDIT OF DOCUMENTS IN THE COURSE OF PROJECT IMPLEMENTATION (Refs. 1, 2)

15. Prior to reviewing, in more details, the aspects of Technical Audit Database, it is necessary to indicate to the specific conditions where under the overall Project has been implemented. The carrying out of Works has been performed in an Arab country in accordance with the FIDIC-like Contract, however with numerous Special Conditions applied that favoured exercising of local laws and regulations. The value of contractual works has been made on the basis of the Preliminary Design only and it totalled to more than one Billion of US Dollars. The preparation of Main Design took place together with carrying out of the Works at Site and the Monthly Payment Certificates were submitted and certified in compliance with the Contract. The participants of Project, apart from the Client and Main Contractors, were also an Independent Consultants and more than 40 (forty) Sub-Contractors including a Designer, from more than 10 (ten) countries from all the world. The Works for the Project were carried out at three distant Sites comprising approximately 700 (seven hundred) Buildings of varying purposes, while designing was performed away from those Sites, at a fourth location, and the Head Offices of Client and Contractor were at the fifth location, all these location being far away from one another. Three complete plants of considerable capacities, for production of pre-fabricated concrete elements were installed to cover the requirements of that many buildings, and the Works of considerable scope were carried out for infrastructure. It was required to co-ordinate carrying out of more than

30 (thirty) different types of works, verifying their quality by applying the British, American and local Standards. For the illustration, the scope of Works was that large that the Contract for supplying of ceramic tiles had to be concluded with three Suppliers due to the quantities to be delivered, the stipulated design and quality, however, had to be necessarily followed. It is to be particularly pointed out to the quantities of imported and built-in equipment and, related thereto, to complex issues of complying various standards and regulations, especially customs regulations. In view of the simultaneous designing and carrying out of the Works as well as numerous participants, considerable quantity of modifications/alternations in respect of scope and quality were made thus causing substantial scope of additional Works. In a situation of colliding interests, it was to expect conflicts, disputes and disagreements as well as opposite interpretation of the contractual stipulations.

16. Preparing of a Contractor for a job that complex called for the detailed planning in respect of careful handling the paperwork at the Project. The abundant correspondence exchanged on the Client - Consultant - Contractor - Designer route is an integral part of the Contract Documents and, at the same time, the Database for the negotiations and claims, and, if required, for the arbitration as well. In order to back up well any claims and to be well prepared for negotiations, it was required to enable quick producing of technical files as per the subject negotiated. The only way to reduce any possibility to neglect an important document when making a decision, was to utilize computer recording.

17. Three basic types of documents were recognized: Technical Correspondence with the Client, Minutes of Checking and Approval and Minutes of Meetings and Minutes of Consultation Meetings. The input data were defined as well as the input forms for each of three Databases; the personnel responsible either for filling in the complete or specific part of the forms, were identified in the distribution scheme of documents. By establishing a singular system for collecting, storing and using of the documents within the overall Project, is essential for functioning of the Project. Also, the system of authorizing any enters, changes and access to data, has been determined. Due to expected abundance of documents, on one hand, and limited technical capabilities, on the other hand, it was decided not to enter in a computer the complete text of a document, however, the important data were selected such as: number of a file a document is located, reference number, date, code of addresser and addressee, area codes, the documents referenced therein, short description - subject, code of a Site, description of enclosed documents, code of a Building and some other data of less significance. By using the system of area codes, selected informing per various issues was enabled, which is similar to the system

of key words in large libraries. The area codes include for the following fields:

- The basic stages of Project implementation (designing, procurement, construction, equipping, transport, customs activities);
- More detailed classification within each type of Works (within the electrical installation, for example: lighting, telephone, services for the equipment, fire fighting system, internal communication system, computer communication, remote control system);
- Sub-Contractors abroad;
- Sub-Contractors in Yugoslavia;
- The obligations of Main Contractor;
- Code system as per Buildings and parts of Buildings;
- Contractual issues and settling of contractual disputes;
- Scheduling and monitoring of the Works carried out;
- Standards and Norms;
- Quality control of the Works;
- Issues arising in respect of Unit Rates;
- Payment and invoicing of the Works;
- Personnel issues;
- Import and customs clearing problems;
- Temporary registration and insurance of the vehicles and equipment;
- Trial runs and training of the personnel.

18. By combining of all these input data, the user is enabled to obtain any specific and detailed reports, and by using the reference document fields, searching may be made "deep", thus to connect the documents that deal with the same subject but in various periods of time. For instance, in order to obtain all the Client's correspondence received between January 1 and February 1, 1988, regarding the modifications to lighting of Mosque, it is sufficient to enter the following data in the mask for report creating:

- The Client's code;
- The beginning and end of the period we are interested in;
- The following area codes: DES (Designing), FIN (Preparing of the Final Design), ELE (Electrical Works). LIG (Lighting), F01 (code of Mosque Building), CHA (code that indicates to a modification to Design Documents).

19. The software enables the maximum automatic control of input data due to expected errors while entering them. The work with the Programme is organized as per the principals of dialogue and interactive works through the system of menus. The first version of the software consisted of more than 150 Files and of approximately 20,000 programme lines, while the Database contained, at the end of Project,

approximately 50,000 various documents significant for implementation of the Project.

20. When concluding the concise description of Database for Technical Audit, it is to be emphasized that such Database has had a significant role in settling the disputes with Client, and particularly when getting the payments for Claims. By using the created programme, it was enabled to have a quick observation of the documents containing the required data and independently from the personnel dealing with those issues in the course of Project implementation within the period of several years. When the first commercial Intelligent Databases appear (Ref.8), it would be enabled to handle efficiently the scanned images of complete texts and drawings as well as other components that traditional Databases do not aid. Consequently, creating of a more efficient system for handling Technical Audits in the course of Project implementation, shall be enabled.

CONCLUSION

21. When summarizing the foregoing, it may be stated that a supreme condition for creating a proper Databases at the level of a Company, is the existence of developed Information Systems at the level of Projects. Without up-dated Databases for specific jobs, it is impossible, upon completion of a Project, to commence analyzing of the data used and selecting of significant ones for future Projects. According to the author's experience, the creating of described Databases is to be made selectively and upon certain planning employing gradual personnel training, supply of software and hardware and creating additional programmes complied to the activities of a Company. The basic condition for developing of an Information System is to resolve organizational issues, both at the level of a Company and of a Project. Finally, it is to be mentioned that special care is to be taken for the engineering staff capable to systematize and computer process abundance of the data in respect of matters that they are well aware of.

REFERENCES

1. "Database for Preparing Technical Audits in the course of Project Implementation", Section for Construction Management and Technology, Faculty of Civil Engineering Beograd, 1989.

2. "CUSTOMS Database for Management of Customs Documents in the Course of Implementation of a Large Project", Instruction Manual for Using the Programme Package, Section for Construction Management and Technology, Faculty of Civil Engineering Beograd, 1990.

3. British Property Federation: "Manual of BPF System for Building Design and Construction", London, 1983.

4. Everest, G.C.: "Database Management-Objectives, System Functions & Administration", McGrow Hill, 1986.

5. Hughes, W.: "Modelling the Construction Process Using Plans of Work", International Conference on Project Modelling and Productivity, Cavtat, 1991.

6. Ivkovic, B.: "Relevant Input Data and Estimations in Construction Project Management", Baghdad, 1990.

7. Ivkovic, B.: "Reliability of Production Systems and Project Management", Proceedings of CIB 90, Vol. 4, pp.279-290, Sydney, 1990.

8. Parsaye, K.; Chignell, M.; Khoshafian, S.; Wong, H.: "Intelligent Databases", AI Expert, March 1990, pp 38-47.

9. RIBA: "Handbook of Architectural Practice and Management" RIBA, London, 1980.

Application of information technology to the site managment of trunk road contracts in Scotland

A.H. CRAIG, Partner, Babtie Shaw & Morgan

SYNOPSIS. In 1984 the Roads Directorate of the Scottish Office Environment Department embarked on a project which came to be entitled "Microcomputer Applications for Site Management". A development group was formed under the co-ordination of consulting engineers Babtie Shaw & Morton. The group's aims were to bring about improvements in aspects of contract control. The development group comprised consulting engineers and agent authorities and the work was undertaken by staff engaged on site in the supervision of construction of trunk road works. The applications developed have been incorporated into the Roads Directorate's standard procedures for the site management of all highways contracts and have been shown to be highly cost effective and of benefit to all parties to the contract.

INTRODUCTION

1.   In the United Kingdom approximately 1% of the gross domestic product is spent on maintaining and developing the trunk road network. In Scotland, the Roads Directorate of the Scottish Office is responsible for over 3,000 km of trunk road with a budget that exceeds £200 million per annum. This work is carried out through consulting engineers, agent authorities and contractors. The management of this large road network and supporting organisation is a complex operation requiring stringent budgetary control to ensure success and value for money. Some years ago the Scottish Office embarked upon a programme of introduction of computer systems into the decision making and project monitoring framework.

2.   The Microcomputer Applications for Site Management (MASM) project is one of these systems. The project commenced in November 1984 when approval was given for the installation of microcomputers in the resident engineers offices of selected trunk road schemes. The schemes selected were those under the supervision of consulting engineers and agent authorities who had each requested the introduction of microprocessor based technology into the field of contract control.

3.   The Scottish Office formed a development group under the co-

ordination of consulting engineers, Babtie Shaw & Morton whose aimswere to bring about improvements in certain aspects of site supervision. This was to be achieved through improved data collection, retrieval and reporting, resulting in an increased awareness of all aspects of the contract.

4.   This paper describes the experience of the co-ordinator of the project from its initial inception through design of the system and the issue of the user manual to its ongoing maintenance and development.

5.   It should be noted, at this stage that in the main, the basic development work described was undertaken by site supervisory staff concurrent with their normal site duties. The needs of these duties at all times took precedence over the development work. Only the final development and combining of sub systems together with drafting of the manual was carried out off site.

DESCRIPTION OF SITE APPLICATIONS
6.   As has been stated, the aim of the study was and still is to bring about improvements in aspects of site supervision and contract control. The intention is that the introduction of microcomputer based methods will improve contract control and reporting through better monitoring and forecasting.

7.   In this section of the paper a description will be given of the main areas of computer applications to site management as identified in the Microcomputer Applications for Site Management or 'MASM' manual dated August 1988.

8.   Within the MASM manual, the complete system is categorised in four sections:-

(a)   network analysis
(b)   measurement system and financial contract control
(c)   works records
(d)   data collection and setting out.

A flow chart of the fields of application is shown in Fig. 1.

9.   As can be seen the majority of site supervisory duties can be encompassed or related to the four categories of network analysis, measurement system, works records and data collection. As most of the reports to the client and resident engineer are generated from the network analysis and measurement system these will be the main areas discussed.

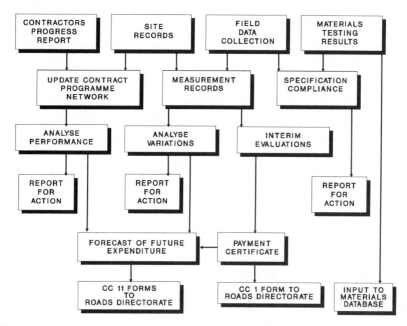

Fig. 1. Fields of application of microcomputer in site supervisory duties

10.   The Scottish Office contract control returns, known as forms CCI and CCII, can be regarded as the final output of the system. Form CCI is the payment certificate.   Form CCII provides a breakdown of the cumulative total of payments due to the contractor based on the section heads of the bill of quantities, variations, price fluctuation and the like, as well as giving details of the estimated final expenditure under the contract and the overall savings and excesses.   Form CCII is supported by three appendices. Appendix 1 gives details of the estimated costs of the variations. Appendix 2 gives information on the status and amount of claims.   Appendix 3, gives details of the actual and estimated expenditure over the remainder of the contract period. The information contained in Appendix 3 is fundamental to the Roads Directorate's budgetary control of the trunk road programme and hence the accuracy and reliability of the forecast information provided has a direct bearing on the successful management of trunk road expenditure.

11.   To enable the Engineer to make up-to-date accurate forecasts of future expenditure, he requires the following:-

(a)   up-to-date information on current progress and expenditure
(b)   the ability to assess the effects of current progress and changing circumstances on the future progress of the works.

The first of these requirements is fulfilled by an efficient site data collection and measurement system which maintains up-to-date records of quantities and costs as the work progresses. To satisfy the second requirement, the Engineer needs a full appreciation of the Contractor's approach to the construction of the works and his programmed intentions.

12.   The fulfilment of the first requirement is well within the Engineer's control. To satisfy the second requirement Clause 14 of the 5th edition of the ICE Conditions of Contract makes provision for the supply of the information that the Engineer requires. However, unless otherwise specified by the Engineer the form that the information takes is left up to the Contractor. Hence from the outset of the project the step was taken to specify that the Clause 14 programme should be provided in network form.

13.   From this the Engineer has the basis for developing the required understanding of the Contractor's approach to the works and for satisfying the second requirement for more accurate forecasting of expenditure.

14.   Having identified the objectives and the requirements to achieve those objectives, it is time to consider how computer technology was used to fulfil these needs.

Commercial Software
15.   With the exception of some user written applications programs to assist in field data collection and setting out checking, the majority of the MASM system is based upon three types of commercial software:-

(a)   Pertmaster for network analysis. Now replaced by Pertmaster Advance
(b)   Aladin for database applications. Now replaced by DBase III
(c)   Lotus 1-2-3 for spreadsheet applications.

Each of these packages have their own reporting capability which enables discrete reports to be issued from the direct applications of these programmes. In addition, reports can be transferred between these three programme modules for more advanced applications and it is in this area of development that the greatest benefits are to be derived.

Site Data Collection
16.   Comprehensive collection of site data is essential for the successful supervision of a contract. However, the usefulness of the data declines with increasing time lag between collection and processing for action. With the aid of the microcomputer, the rapid response to contractors consequent to field data collection for the assessment of

compliance with the Specification has been welcomed by them and leads to better relationships on site. There is other data of course which is collected for record purposes rather than specification compliance but here too the microcomputer facility is found to be advantageous in freeing staff to continue with site supervision rather than manually processing records.

17. The most major advances made in field data collection both for measurement and specification compliance purposes have been brought about by the use of data recorders. These computers, of which the Wild GRE 3 and the Husky Hunter were the models used, are programmable in their own right, but the greatest benefit is to be gained by utilising their ability to store data in the field and download it into the office microcomputer for processing and reporting.

18. With "total station" equipment, it is possible to go from field survey to plotted results without any manual transfer or processing of survey data other than that required to operate the programmes involved. In addition, suitable low cost software packages are now commercially available to take this data as input and enable the direct production of earthworks quantities for transfer to the earthworks data sheet and hence from there to the bill of quantities.

Measurement
19. The duties of the Engineer's staff in the measurement office lend themselves best to computer based methods. It is in this area, therefore, that much of the development work has taken place and around which the MASM system is based.

20. One of the benefits of introducing a computer based system into any suitable process is that it requires a clear systematic approach to the work. The benefits of such an approach are not solely confined to computer based systems and in fact once such a system has been devised it will operate just as satisfactorily manually as it will on the computer, albeit not as quickly. The system developed for MASM is the product of such an approach.

21. The role of the computer in the MASM measurement system based on the spreadsheet package is shown graphically in Fig 2 and is as follows:-

(a) Field measure sheets are produced for each bill item and the measured quantities are agreed and recorded in the field on these sheets by the Engineer's and Contractor's staff.

(b) Data from the field measure sheet is then entered into the bill sheet for that item. The bill sheet records the field measurement sheet number, the date and the quantity, together with a running total which therefore gives the cumulative total quantity measured to date.

(c)   At the time of the monthly measurement or any intermediate report, each bill sheet total is entered into the appropriate item in the bill of quantities.

(d)   When entering the measure to date, the estimated total is also amended as required to reflect any changing circumstances. Thereafter the quantity outstanding, the value to date and the value outstanding are also calculated automatically.

(e)   When the bill of quantities files have been updated, the final summary is produced and the total from each bill of quantities file is then automatically entered in the bill of quantities summary sheet.

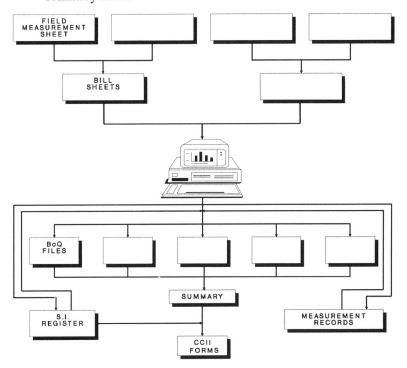

Fig. 2. Role of the computer in the MASM measurement system

22.   As an alternative or additional to the bill sheets, field measure data is also stored in the computer. Where appropriate, chainage is recorded and hence the records can be automatically resorted into chainage order thereby giving a readily assimilated statement of progress. At present, drainage, earthworks and roadworks progress records are all being maintained in this way.

23.   From these records information on, for example, uncompleted sections of formation, types of formation and date completed can be readily obtained. With the earthworks progress records, the individual bill items are broken down into the earthworks sections detailed in the earthworks data sheet and compiled to give an automatic earthworks data sheet update.   This is produced in a format which gives a comparison of quantities to date, tender quantities and projected final quantities and is very useful in identifying earthworks trends at an early stage.

24.   From the ongoing awareness of the current quantities for discrete sections of the works and from the comparison of these quantities with the anticipated tender quantities for these sections, ongoing savings and excesses can be readily identified at an early stage and monitored and any significant consequences assessed. While all of this can be done manually, the time involved in re-writing tables of information to enable the comparisons to be made is often prohibitive and therefore such exercises tend not to be carried out until a major change in circumstances is apparent. The virtually automatic recalculation of quantities enabled by the spreadsheet package greatly facilitates the estimation and awareness of these variations. Hence early consideration can be given to courses of action to ameliorate these changing circumstances.   There have been favourable reports from resident engineers to this effect in that they find the immediate availability of up-to-date measurement reports of great assistance at meetings with the contractor on the day to day running of the contract.

25.   When the final quantities from each of the bill of quantities sub-sections are automatically entered into the summary sheet, contract control reporting forms are automatically produced.

26.   A combined variation order and site instruction register is also held in the computer. To assist in the search for data, a database management system has been developed, with the accent throughout the system being to direct the site staff to the resolution of disputed works as they occur.

Network Analysis
27.   The greatest potential for improvements in contract control and forecasting of expenditure comes from the introduction of the computer based network analysis facility into the site organization.

28.   There are significant benefits in obtaining the network from the outset. The Engineer has at his disposal the facility to fully assess the Contractor's intentions at the Clause 14 approval stage and, as the initial Clause 14 programme is often the basis of any subsequent claims for increased payments it is essential to have at the outset an approved

contract programme in which there is mutual trust.

29.   Major subsequent benefits are also to be gained when the programme is updated monthly, thereby recording the Contractor's performance over the contract period. From this a record of a actual events is maintained. This provides an improved awareness of the effects of changing circumstances on the Contractor's programme and gives a better basis for the assessment of payments due. A monthly list of where the Contractor is falling behind programme has been found to be helpful in keeping the work generally on course. Certain software packages currently available allow progress to be recorded and a comparison made automatically.

30.   The improved awareness obtained from the use of network analysis is heightened by allocating resources to the network based upon the payments to the Contractor from the bill items. The resource costs are input into the program and used to produce reports containing details of the early and late start dates for each activity, the total time for the project and the cumulative expenditure.

31.   The usefulness of the network information is further extended by importing Pertmaster disk report files into the Lotus spreadsheet. This enables various additional calculations to be made and graphs produced to show expenditure forecasts based on both the earliest and the latest programmed start dates for each activity. These forecasts can be compared with actual expenditure and the forecasts revised accordingly.

32.   This linking of the network analysis with measurement progress enables the forecast expenditure figures to be extracted for financial reporting. When these links are formed, the Engineer's staff are then able to test the outcome of various events on the contract expenditure profile and from the range of values obtained, produce a monthly updated "best estimate" of future expenditure. The resulting reports are therefore based upon a full awareness of changing quantities, changing conditions and their likely effect on contract expenditure. As a result of the virtually automatic production of these reports from the interim measurements, speed of reporting as well as accuracy is improved.

33.   Evaluation of performance can be improved by storing resources of network activities in the progress network on the basis of measurement quantities and labour and major plant from site records. The facility is then available for assessing likely future performance on the basis of available or proposed resources and outstanding quantities. The facility is also available for the evaluation and analysis of claims, particularly those which are performance based.

34.   To enable actual plant and labour resources to be readily

assigned to the network, it is desirable to ensure that inspector's reports are structured such that they are referenced to network activities.

35.   Development work within the group is continuing in this area and the usefulness of storage of inspector's reports in a database is presently being examined. At present it can be reported that the simple structuring of the reports such that they facilitate subsequent input has been found to greatly improve the quality of reporting.

MARKET RESEARCH

36.   In June 1988 a user survey was conducted on the thirteen sites permitted to participate in the controlled introduction of microcomputers. The survey collected data on usage, problems encountered and recommendations for future developments of the systems. All sites were also requested to provide some indication of the benefits that could be achieved through the use of a microcomputer on site; the main benefit to the Department being a saving in staff or reallocation of staff from duties involving repetitive calculation to works supervision.

Computer Usage

37.   From analysis of the replies received the percentage usage of the site computer varied from 2 percent for a newly established site to 100 percent for a well established site with an average percentage usage of 50. From experience the maximum percentage usage for a well utilised machine is 80 to 85 before undue stress is placed upon the system. The excess of capacity indicated that all the site systems were not yet operational on the individual sites and the view was taken that once computers were accepted as the norm this spare capacity would soon be utilised.

38.   Examination of the average percentage allocation per work area produced the following ranking table:-

measurement	48% of computer in use time
financial control	19% " "
survey and data recording	13% " "
contract control	7% " "
works records	7% " "
material records	4% " "
others	2% " "

39.   The areas where further development can be expected are in contract control through the increased use of network analysis and inworks records. Growth will be brought about through staff familiarisation with computer systems and improvements in hardware and software allowing large volumes of data to be stored, sorted and

accessed rapidly.

Time Savings

40.   Given the above usage, the responses provided yielded average man power savings per work area as follows:-

measurement	23.0	man weeks per year	
survey and data recording	6.3	"	"
financial control	3.6	"	"
contract control	2.0	"	"
others	1.0	"	"
works records	0.4	"	"
material records	0.3	"	"

41.   The overall average man power saving, for the twelve contracts which completed that section of the pro forma, was 36.6 man weeks per year. The initial capital investment by the Scottish Office was of the order of £6500 per computer system and the average useful life expectancy of the system was assessed to be 4 years. The average annual staff saving of 36.6 man weeks per year produced a minimum cost saving of £8900 per year. This can be translated into an assumed net benefit of at least £5,000 per year per site. This saving when applied to the thirteen sites yielded a £65,000 reduction in site staffing costs at 1988 price levels.

42.   The savings do not necessarily represent the level by which the site staff can be reduced by the introduction of a microcomputer. For many of the sites the time savings represented the additional staff required if the microcomputer facility were to be removed and the current level of supervision and reporting maintained.

43.   These cost savings are easily quantified. However the use of computers on site offers the Directorate even more value for money through hidden cost savings.   By releasing staff from repetitive calculations the computer generates more time for site staff to spend on supervisory   duties,   with   a   resulting   increase   in   the   quality   of workmanship and site records. Improved workmanship reduces future maintenance costs while improved site records assists in the proper assessment of the value of claims awarded to the Contractor. Hence the use of computers on site can offer the Department savings far in excess of the apparent £5000 per year per site indicated from this simplistic analysis. In addition increased staff costs since 1988 and the significantly reduced costs of computer equipment now yield present day benefits of the order of £12,500 per annum.

OPERATIONAL CONSIDERATIONS

Setting Up

44. As might be expected, feedback from the market research indicated that sites which had the benefit of an early visit from an experienced user achieved greater savings than sites which attempted to set up the system without assistance. This is perhaps best illustrated by the comments received from two of the resident engineers:-

"Two month period at start of contract required for staff familiarisation and setting up worksheets".

"The hands-on guidance provided ... was most useful. Similar guidance for other programs would be beneficial".

The former was of course from a site which tried to do it for themselves. With the current trend for shorter contract periods, very few contracts can afford a two month period before reporting and forecasting facilities are operational. In addition, caution has to be exercised when determining the timing for delivery of the computer to the site. If the computer is not supplied until the contract is well underway it may prove difficult for site staff to convert from a manual system to an automatic system and many of the advantages will already be lost.

Problems Encountered

45. The general problems encountered were mainly associated with lack of staff familiarisation with the system. Early fears of the ability of micros to withstand the site environment were not borne out. The only additional facility to that normally required in the design office is the provision of a combined voltage regulator and temporary back up power supply.

46. The area where major problems were encountered in the early stages was in contract control. Most of these problems came from the inability or unwillingness of some contractors to submit a network programme. More recently this has become a diminishing impediment.

CONCLUSIONS

47. On the basis of the development work already undertaken, the installation of microcomputers on trunk road sites has been found to yield significant benefits.

48. Data collection has been improved and the resulting rapid response to contractors in sensitive areas of specification compliance has led, in itself, to better relations on site. In addition to this, the time saved by supervisory staff in processing collected data releases them to continue with the more important aspects of their work.

49.   In the measurement field, the development of a clear systematic approach and the avoidance of multiple handling of data is of benefit in releasing staff to concentrate on the resolution of disputed work at the time of occurrence.

50.   The benefits go beyond this however, in that the collected data can be automatically re-sorted to give up-to-date reports on progress based on comparisons of current quantities with tender values.   The timeous availability of this information considerably heightens the awareness of the effects of different events on the contract and gives early warning of variations which may prove significant.   This in turn assists in the resolution of contractual disputes as the Engineer or his representative is always able to be informed of the present situation.

51.   The availability of network analysis brought about by specification of Clause 14 requirements to this effect, improves the understanding of the Contractor's approach to the contract and clearly identifies where major requirements of the contract have been misunderstood or not allowed for.

52.   Costing of the network activities from bill items provides a basis for financial forecasting which can be further refined by monitoring of actual performance and comparison with predicted performance.

53.   The existence of an approved and regularly updated network provides a rational basis for the assessment of the effects of different events on the Contractor's programme and should therefore be of considerable assistance in the resolution of claims.

54.   The average saving identified from the introduction of microcomputers on site was established in 1988 as 36.6 man weeks per year.   This saving took no account of the benefits to the contract achieved by progress monitoring and the establishment of controls which came as a by-product of the computer facility and which would certainly require additional staff to achieve the same level of supervision.

55.   Benefits to the contract from the timeous agreement of the measurement quantities and the resolution of differences on disputed work are also difficult to quantify in terms of savings in man years. However, at the simplest level this will result in a reduction in the size of the site establishment required beyond the contract completion date.

56.   On the basis of the time savings as described above, it is estimated that at current costs, the provision of the microcomputer facility has yielded a basic increase in the level of supervision to a value of at least £14,000 per annum.   On the basis of present hardware and software costs, any scheme with a contract period in excess of six

month's duration would justify the provision of a microcomputer. However, it is suggested that these costs are insignificant compared to the benefits to be gained from the timeous resolution of disputes and the global improvement of financial forecasting. It has to be said, though, that all we have here is a system which, given reasonable co-operation from the Contractor, will enable the Engineer and his staff to improve their awareness of the contract - it will not do it for them.

ACKNOWLEDGEMENTS

57.   This paper is produced from work done under the control and direction of the Engineering and Procurement Division of the Scottish Office Roads Directorate and is published by the kind permission of the Director of Roads, Mr J A L Dawson. Acknowledgement is also due to the staff of Babtie Shaw & Morton, JMP Consultants Ltd, W A Fairhurst and Partners, Strathclyde Regional Council and Fife Regional Council whose close co-operation and contribution made the project possible.

Application of information technology and its impact on the education and training needs for professionals in construction

B. YOUNG, Lecturer, Department of Civil Engineering and Construction, University of Salford

SYNOPIS. This article reports on the findings of a study conducted in 1990 which established that there has been a significant increase in the number of contractors adopting IT. The spread of applications has also increased and that by 1993 the production function is most likely to benefit from increased investment in IT. The problems associated with the use of IT are different in kind to that of the 1980s. Aligning IT requirements with business strategy is senior management's concern. At the operator level user's training needs are identified. But professionals are inhibited from acquiring these skills and knowledge due to the pressure of work.

INTRODUCTION

1. How long will it be before the construction industry develops a real and sustained commitment to Information Technology (IT)? This question was posed in 1982, during Information Technology Year, when the Alvey Committee drew attention to the urgent need to improve the awareness, capability and understanding of IT users. The committee's report called for a massive input of research and development to alleviate misunderstanding and heighten the potential of IT for business use.

2. Certainly the 1980s have witnessed an overall increase in the use of computing by contractors (ref.10). Some would argue, however, that when compared to industries, such as travel, banking and insurance the construction industry remains the back marker (refs. 9,16).

3. The impact of IT on the construction industry depends upon the extent of use and the speed at which construction accepts new technology (ref.18). It is generally accepted that the initial period of penetration is slow, and each

application will have its own diffusion rate (refs. 15,6). Each application and rate of diffusion will be a function of factors prevailing in each industrial sector. Some inhibiting barriers have been identified, that limit the speed of IT amongst potential users (ref. 18). Most cited are the relative cost of software to hardware (ref. 1). Organizational size (ref. 5) and attitudal constraints (ref. 2). Collectively, these factors were evidently affecting the penetration and spread of IT applications in the construction industry during the 1980s.

4. This paper presents the findings of a study which investigated the penetration and diffusion rate of IT applications amongst building and civil engineering contractors. It forms the second part of an inquiry which took place with the same contractors in 1987. The study purposely sets out to establish whether there has been a significant increase in the number of contractors adopting IT, the spread of applications and projected changes, if any, by 1993. In addition, the problems encountered, and the impact of IT on training needs, formed major components of the study.

METHODOLOGY

5. Ten building and/or civil engineering contractors participated in the 1990 survey upon which these analyses are based. For consistency and comparability the contractors who took part in a previous study were selected (ref. 17). The study consisted of semi-structured interviews with directors or senior executives from each organization.

6. A questionnaire, listing various IT applications, compatibility with organizational needs, the main problem areas in the use of IT and professional involvement in IT was presented in structured format. The latter part of the questionnaire addressed training needs, and included an opportunity to add comment. This section was designed to encourage and stimulate in depth debate. When designing the questionnaire, care was taken to protect against invalidity.

THEORETICAL BACKGROUND

7. Gibson and Nolan's four stage model of data processing growth is represented by the S-curve. Each stage depicts a period of organizational learning and appears to be a function of the experience and progressive pressures of the previous stage (Figure 1).

8. In the initiation phase an organization decides whether computing is feasible, and conducive to the organization's business requirements. The applications which are obvious choice for automation are then developed, most accounting operations being considered viable.

9. Stage two, contagion, is marked by a period of expansion, expenditure on hardware rises sharply, accompanied by investments in a wide range of software applications. It is a period of unplanned growth with a proliferation of software acquisitions which may, or may not, be wholly suitable for the business's purpose. Rapid development is then moderated, and often ends in crises when senior management realize the explosive growth in expenditure and activity.

10. Phase three is characterised by moratoria on systems development and acquisition. Existing systems are finetuned, upgraded or restructured. Budgets are trimmed and users are made accountable for IT.

11. In the maturity stage, the organization regains confidence in managing IT. Usage becomes more sophisticated and is directed to enhance the service or product, as opposed to purely economic gain. It would appear that each stage lasts for three to five years, although it is not uncommon for an organization to get stuck in stage three for seven years or more (ref.7). According to Nolan 1979, the duration and movement from one stage to the other is greatly influenced by the organization's own internal body of knowledge as well as the professional body of knowledge external to the organization.

ANALYSIS OF RESULTS

12. To establish the trend in the general use of IT, a list of software packages was supplied. The interviewees indicated company usage for three time periods, 1987, 1990 and projected take-up by 1993. Figure 2 presents these data. In 1987, most of the contractors were using office

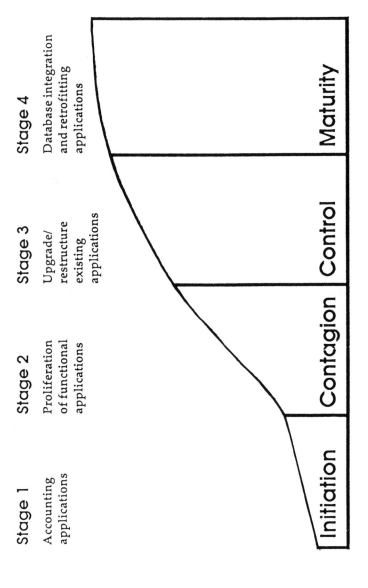

Stage 1
Accounting
applications

Stage 2
Proliferation
of functional
applications

Stage 3
Upgrade/
restructure
existing
applications

Stage 4
Database integration
and retrofitting
applications

Initiation | Contagion | Control | Maturity

Fig.1. Growth of applications

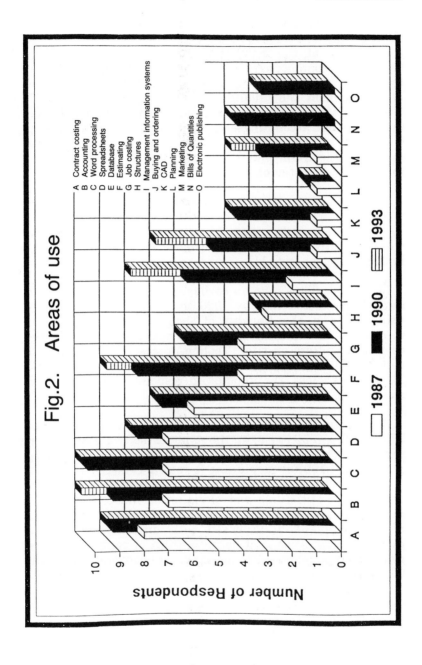

Fig.2. Areas of use

A Contract costing
B Accounting
C Word processing
D Spreadsheets
E Database
F Estimating
G Job costing
H Structures
I Management information systems
J Buying and ordering
K CAD
L Planning
M Marketing
N Bills of Quantities
O Electronic publishing

1987   1990   1993

automation systems. Contract costing, estimating and job costing were three operational packages most frequently in use. None of the contractors had electronic publishing facilities or computerized bills of quantities. Relatively few firms had extended IT to other functional areas. These results confirm the findings of the CICA survey in 1987. Over 85% of the 230 contractors participating in that survey indicated that accounting and contract costing were in use. Over three quarters of the sample employed word processing facilities. Electronic publishing appeared the least attractive in terms of investment.

13. These results are not untypical of industry as a whole. It would appear that in 1987 office automation systems were most popular across industrial sectors, whereas software specifically designed for operational tasks had less appeal (ref. 11).

14. The findings from an earlier study, conducted in 1987, (ref. 17) predicted that by 1990 the number of contractors using IT and the breadth of usage would significantly increase. At the time there were mixed views about the role of computers on site. Tooling-up costs and the lack of suitable software appeared to have dampened enthusiasm for IT. Nevertheless, the impetus to respond to economic and competitive pressure seemed inevitable.

15. Since 1987 the number of contractors using IT has risen and an increase in the type of software in use is reported (Figure 2). The difference over the three year period 1987-1990 is significant (t ratio p< 0.01). There are comparatively more contractors investing in IT. With the exception of structures and planning software, there is an increase in general usage. Within three years forty per cent of the sample had dispensed with manual methods for calling of quantities, and nearly a third of contractors used electronic publishing. These results are consistent with the CICA 1990 survey.

16. Computerized systems designed to enhance market strategy were considered important by all contractors. Although only three contractors claimed that they had recently introduced very simplistic systems to their marketing operations, it was acknowledged that marketing is an area ripe for computer technologies.

17. Discussion centred upon improving the knowledge base relating to company clientele and potential customers.

Several contractors expressed the view that data collection is an unfamiliar exercise and without prior knowledge and understanding there is little point in acquiring or developing software. They tended to rely on external consultants for marketing research and advice, or managed without. The companies relatively new to computerized marketing systems were clearly at the developmental and experimental stage. The interviewees maintained that it was too early to comment on the systems.

18. The consensus of opinion amongst contractors was that not all functions would invest heavily in IT over the next three years. The results shown in Figure 2 support the view that by 1993 the functions most likely to benefit from increased investment in IT are financial administration, procurement and purchasing and production, notably the latter. Management information systems were relatively unknown in construction during the 1980s (ref. 16). According to the majority of contractors the mid-1990s will witness a reversal of this phenomenon - particularly the organization of site labour, which is routine, but nevertheless a frequent and important management task (ref. 17). Once computerized information becomes accessible and accepted practice, there should be improvements in the speed and quality of decision-making on site.

19. The same is true for effective utilization and monitoring of materials, plant and equipment. It is anticipated that this facility will come on-line as the practice of networking increases. One senior executive enthusiastically described the effects of the introduction of IT on a major building site. The contracts manager and site manager were able to tap into the system and at a glance select information on labour, material stock, plant and equipment. For financial control and allocation of resources, the management team now enjoyed the benefit of new technologies, with heartening results.

PROBLEM AREAS IN THE USE OF IT

20. Directors were asked to identify the problem areas in the use of IT in 1987 and in 1990. In 1987 lack of suitable software and suitably trained staff posed problems for 3/4 of contractors. Off-the-shelf software was inappropriate to firms' needs and bespoke systems were considered costly in relationship to hardware. Directors admitted that few of their managers were trained in computer technology and

there was no strategy for encouraging the adoption of computer awareness.

21. The absence of an IT strategy has generated problems which contractors realize manifested from the mid 1980s when software and hardware were acquired in an ad hoc fashion. The difficulty is aligning IT requirements with business strategy. Stating business objectives and then formulating an IT strategy are major concerns. Contractors are also conscious of the fact that management awareness of IT is inhibiting progress.

22. These problems are shared by other industrial sectors. The OTR group conducted a detailed survey of 35 major organizations and discovered that technology awareness was lacking amongst senior management and boards of directors. OTR suggested that senior executives must be able to debate IT issues predominately from a business perspective. Recommendations included raising IT awareness through an Information Systems Function as a way of enlightening executives. The IT function should promote suitable seminars on the strategic use of IT.

PROFESSIONAL INVOLVEMENT IN THE USE OF IT

23. Discussion centred on the construction profession's involvement in the use of IT. The professional disciplines are listed in Table 1 below for the year 1987, 1990 and anticipated involvement by 1993.

Table 1. Construction Professional Involvement in IT

Professionals Using IT	No of Contractors		
	1987	1990	1993
Architect	1	4	4
Building/Civil Engineer	2	3	4
Construction Management*			
Senior Managers	2	3	7
Mid-level Managers	1	5	10
Junior Managers	2	4	8
Quantity Surveyor	-	4	4

*Senior Managers   -   Directors/Executives
Area/Regional Managers

Mid-level Managers   -   Project Managers
Contracts Managers

Junior Managers   -   Site Managers
Sub agents, assistants.

The table gives the number of contractors with professional involvement in the use of IT. The directors were unable to estimate numbers of staff involved. For example in 1987 only one contractor's mid level managers used IT. In 1990 half the sample had involved their project and contracts managers in the use of IT. By 1993 it is anticipated that if not all, the majority of contractors participating in this study will have invested in IT facilities for construction management. Ten contractors perceive the majority of their mid-level managers requiring computer skills and developing awareness. Marginally less firms perceive their senior and junior construction managers becoming familiar with computer applications. It would appear that the function most likely to be involved in IT by 1993 is construction management.

TRAINING NEEDS

24. Directors were invited to comment on the current and potential training needs of their staff regarding the use of computer technology including:

*   level of provision
*   course content
*   duration
*   inhouse/external training.

The consensus of opinion was that there is a need for two levels of provision - strategic/systems management level and operator level.

25. At the strategic level, courses should provide managers with an understanding of how IT can be used to gain competitive advantage and efficiency. IT requirements can then be aligned with business strategy. As the organization adopts, implements and manages IT, senior executives should be strategically aware of IT and its relationship to organizational change and the behaviourial aspects.

26. Opinions are divided as to whether managers should use IT systems directly themselves, or have others do it for them. If they decide to use IT, user skills most needed are:

* key board skills
* knowledge of computer language, conventions and limitations
* using computer manuals
* accessing and manipulating data
* using on line facilities - networking
* dealing with machine breakdowns and faults
* the capability of developing own systems.

27. Ideally, the duration for receiving training varied between a minimum of 2 days, and where necessary extended up to 1 week, preferably within the incumbents organization. The difficulty was in releasing individuals from their jobs. Operational staff are extremely busy people, "which is not altogether a valid excuse for not being able to attend courses", maintained one director.

28. Delivery methods best suited for distilling skills and knowledge encompassing computer based 'hands on' learning, videos and greater use of interactive videos are considered most appropriate solutions.

CONCLUSIONS

29. According to stage theory, organizational investment in IT applications is characterized by four stages of growth. The results from this study suggest that there is an increase in the number of contractors entering the contagion growth stage. Transition from initiation to expansion gathered momentum in the late 1980s as contractors sought ways of becoming more cost-effective. It is unlikely that any of the contractors in the sample will reach the control stage before the mid 1990s.

30. Even though attention is drifting towards formulation of an IT strategy, a lag will inevitably occur between strategists' thoughts and practice. Encouraging end users, particularly construction managers, to become more aware of computer applications is part of management's philosophy. Again there are inherent problems which prevail, notably the attitudes of senior management in releasing their staff

for training purposes. It is time the construction industry came to terms with the whole issue of education and training by implementing a fundamental strategy - that is, investing in the education and training of its workforce.

References:

1. BARRAS, R. and SWANN, J. Information technology and the service sector. New technology and the future of work skills, P. Marstrand Ed., Frances Pinter. (1983).

2. BEVINGTON, T. The barriers and opportunities of information technology. Kearney Consultants Report. (1984).

3. CICA. Building on IT. Report. (1987).

4. CICA. Building on IT for the 90s. Report. (1990).

5. COUSINS, W. B. "Looking ahead - future trends." A plain builders guide to computing, CIOB Occasional Paper, No.14. (1977).

6. CURNOW, R. The effects on employment.The managerial implications of micro - electronics, B.C.Twiss Ed., Macmillan Press, London. (1981).

7. EARL, M.J. Management strategies for information technologies. Prentice Hall, New York. (1989)

8. GIBSON C.F., and NOLAN R.L. "Managing the four stages of EDP growth." Havard Business Review, Jan/Feb, pp. 76-88. (1974).

9. HOLLINGWORTH, J. "Building and information technology." Construction Computing, January, pp. 14-18. (1985).

10. HOWARD, R. Building IT 2000. Development of information technology in building 1973-1988. (1989).

11. KOBLER UNIT. Does information technology slow you down? Imperial College, London. Report. (1987).

12. NOLAN, R.L. "Managing the crises in data processing." Havard Business Review. March/April, pp. 115-126. (1979).

13. OTR GROUP. What provokes creature use of
information technology - Is it management education?
Report. (1988).

14. RANCE. A.D. and SEDDON, F.H. "Adding new skills
to old". Proceedings of Computer Technology in
Construction, ICE, September. (1984).

15. TWISS, B.C. The managerial implication of micro-
electronics. Macmillan, London. (1981).

16. VICKERY, N. "Flying into the future." Construction
Computing, Winter pp. 18-19. (1988/89).

17. YOUNG, B.A. Career development in construction
management. PhD Thesis. UMIST December. (1988).

18. YOUNG, B.A. The Impact of Information Technology
on Construction Management. Occasional paper. RICS,
November. (1990).

19. YOUNG, B.A. "The perceived importance of present
and future construction management skills and knowledge."
Proceedings of Building Economics and Construction
Management Vol. 4, CIB W55/65, pp. 558-569. (1990).

Application of information technology to port management

D. BUCHANAN, Lecturer, University of Strathclyde

SYNOPSIS. This paper deals with the development of an information management system for the assessment of river and
estuarine sediments. The application of the system to port
management, with particular reference to maintenance dredging
operations, is discussed. Assessment of siltation rates,
identification of dredging needs, and evaluation of sediment
quality for comparison against disposal standards, are
considered.

INTRODUCTION.
1. A number of industrial cities within the United Kingdom
(U.K.) rely on shipping as a source of income and employment.
As such, there remains a need to maintain and dredge shipping
channels in ports, estuaries and rivers, in order to support
shipbuilding activities and transportation operations. In
recent years, the port authorities responsible for carrying out
these maintenance dredging works, have had to take an increased
interest in the environmental impact of dredging operations.
There is growing public concern in relation to the adverse
environmental effects of dredging operations and the subsequent
disposal of the dredged spoil.
2. Many of the unacceptable, environmental effects of
dredging can be attributed to the use of inefficient plant and
methods, resulting in fuel spillage, excessive emission of
exhaust fumes, noise and vibration, etc. These problems can
only be overcome by capital investment in new, more efficient
dredging equipment, and should be a future consideration of
port authorities and government.
3. Minimising the adverse, environmental effects, associated
with the disposal of dredged spoil, poses a management problem.
Legislative controls are being introduced which make it increasingly difficult for spoil to be disposed of in an uncontrolled
manner. Consequently, there is a need to undertake dredging
operations in a more efficient and economical manner. The need
to monitor and assess the quality of dredged spoil and the
evaluation of alternative disposal techniques, are now fundamental concerns in dredging management.
4. The future disposal of dredged sediment is a high priority
problem. The need to maintain shipping channels, whilst finding

Applications of information technology in construction. Thomas Telford, London, 1991 economical and environmentally acceptable methods to dispose of the dredged spoil, is of immediate concern.

DREDGING MANAGEMENT.
5. The creation of deep-water access channels, to improve navigational conditions, has been an integral part of port development. The depth of water available, at a given point in the tidal cycle, is increased, allowing larger ships to use the port facilities. The creation of such an artificially deep channel upsets the natural equilibrium of the water and sediment systems, which will in turn attempt to counter the induced change. Consequently, siltation will occur reducing the depth available for shipping. In order to maintain the depth of water available for navigation, an ongoing programme of dredging is required, periodically removing the sediment which has accumulated.
6. Dredging management is concerned with technical, commercial and environmental aspects of maintenance dredging. This relates not only to the removal of sediments to counter siltation, but also to the subsequent disposal of the dredged spoil.

Spoil disposal.
7. The majority of the spoil, arising from maintenance dredging works in the U.K., is disposed of by dumping at sea. The disposal site is in many instances situated a considerable distance from the actual dredging operation. Consequently, a considerable proportion of a port's total maintenance dredging costs, are attributed to the transportation and disposal of the dredged material. In spite of this overhead, disposal at sea is generally considered to be the most practical and economical option for U.K. ports (ref. 1).
8. A small number of ports currently dispose of their dredged spoil to land-based disposal sites (normally associated with land reclamation works). This particular option is only practical where suitable land areas are available, in close proximity to the maintenance dredging operations. Even in these cases, the capital cost of setting up an onshore disposal facility may be prohibitive, unless this can be offset against the tangible benefits accruing from the associated land development.

Environmental considerations.
9. Maintenance dredging operations, and subsequent spoil disposal, will result in changes (beneficial and detrimental), to the natural environment. The most obvious beneficial effect is in the creation of a deep-water channel, enhancing the navigability of the port. Other beneficial effects may include, the alleviation of flood risk and the removal of contaminated sediments.
10. Detrimental effects at the dredging site will be primarily of an aesthetic nature, these include, noise, vibration and visual impairment. The impact of these effects is dependent

on the dredging methods employed and, in most circumstances, can be reduced to an acceptable level. In the longer term, chemical and biological activity in the river system will also be affected by dredging activity (ref. 2).

11. Environmental impact at the disposal site is dependent on the method of disposal employed.

12. <u>Land disposal.</u> The controlled disposal of dredged spoil to land, may result in a number of beneficial effects. These include, the reclamation of land areas for future development and the reduction of flood risk by increasing flood plain levels. Adverse effects may be due to visual impairment, pollution of groundwater and pollution of the land surface. The impact of these effects will be dependent on the methods of working employed and on the unique nature and location of the disposal site.

13. <u>Sea disposal.</u> The disposal of spoil to sea results in permanent changes to the upper layer of the bed surface of both a physical and ecological nature. Where the spoil is contaminated, there may be a long-term deterioration of water and sediment quality. Turbidity, due to the suspension of fine-grained sediments, will slow down photosynthetic activity of plant life, with consequential depletion of available oxygen causing ecological change.

Governing legislation.

14. A number of legislative controls are currently existing, or are proposed, relating to the disposal of waste materials (including dredged spoil). The London dumping convention (ref. 3) and the Oslo convention (ref. 4), demand that a national authority be responsible for the issuing of all licences which allow the disposal of waste at sea. A disposal consent will only be granted, where the national authority is satisfied that this particular option, is the best, environmental option which is practically available (ref. 5).

15. The food and environment act, 1985 (ref. 6), takes account of the recommendations of the aforementioned conventions, and requires port authorities to make application for a disposal licence at frequent intervals. In arriving at a decision on whether or not to grant a licence, consideration will be given to the overall effect on the receiving environment.

16. The council of European Communities (EC), have issued a directive to member states, calling for the ultimate cessation of waste disposal at sea. No statutes presently exist to enforce this directive, however, the potential consequences to port authorities is apparent.

Disposal options.

17. Material arising from maintenance dredging operations has traditionally been considered as a waste product, to be disposed of in a manner which is most cost effective, in relation to the overall management of the port. Practically, this has resulted in material being disposed of at sea, or on land, in

it's as-dredged state. Material disposed of to land reclamation sites may be subjected to basic dewatering, otherwise no processing of the sediments will generally occur.

18. As a direct result of the legislative controls which have been introduced, innovative methods of spoil disposal have been investigated. Dredged material has been used to produce topsoil, landfill capping material, building products, including clay bricks and aggregates, and road grit. The dredged spoil is no longer treated as a waste product but as a resource, having a potential after-use and tangible value. The viability of using dredged material in this manner, is dependent on the quantity and quality (physical and chemical), of material available. Normally the as-dredged material will require to be dewatered or decontaminated (or both), either during, or as a prerequisite to, the manufacturing process. Processing and manufacturing costs must be offset against the economic and environmental benefits arising from the chosen disposal method.

19. Research has been carried out in the Netherlands (ref. 7-8) and in the United States of America (ref. 9), which gives a basis for classification of dredged sediments. Available disposal options can be evaluated, for particular classifications of sediment, allowing the best practical environmental option (BPEO) to be assessed (Fig. 1).

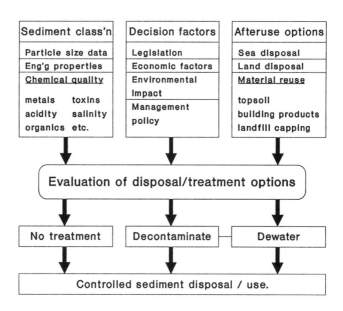

Fig. 1. Assessment of sediment treatment & disposal options.

Future strategy.

20. The dredging strategy of U.K. ports needs to be reviewed, taking due account of current environmental controls and the operational needs of individual ports. Maintenance dredging activity should be reduced to an operational minimum, thus reducing the total volume of spoil to be disposed of. In particular, an attempt should be made to eliminate contaminated, sediment recovery, during routine, maintenance dredging operations. These sediments should be recovered in a controlled manner, as part of an ongoing environmental improvement programme.

Information management.

21. Extensive data relating to the quantity and quality of in-situ sediments is required, allowing predictions to be made with regard to the volume and nature of the spoil arising from dredging operations. In particular, there is a need to identify areas of contaminated sediment which will present disposal problems.

22. An effective method of managing this data is also required, allowing the generation of information relevant to the identified problems. This is best facilitated by a computer-based, information management system (IMS), allowing the selective processing and interpretation of data, within a decision making framework. The technical aspects of the development of such a system are discussed in the following sections.

DEVELOPMENT OF THE DREDGING MANAGEMENT SYSTEM.

Identifying the system requirements.

23. Evaluation of the end-user requirements is an important aspect in the development of any IMS. Intended uses should be clearly defined at an early stage, allowing formalisation of data requirements, etc. The modelling approach to be adopted will also be influenced by the perceived end-user needs.

24. End-user requirements. The overall objective of the project was the development of an IMS which would enhance the technical, decision making capabilities of port authorities, in relation to the management of maintenance dredging operations. Specifically, the following concerns were identified.

- evaluation of siltation rates.
- assessment of maintenance dredging needs.
- assessment of in-situ sediment quality.

25. Data requirements. Evaluation of siltation rates and the assessment of maintenance dredging needs, require a historic record of bed levels within the shipping channel. Assessment of dredging needs also requires current "operational" data, defining the geographical limits of the navigation and maintenance depths to be achieved along the shipping channel. A record of the physical and chemical characteristics of in-situ

135

sediments is needed, allowing an assessment of sediment quality to be undertaken. The identification of contaminants and assessment of disposal options can also be facilitated with this data. Primary data requirements can be summarised:

- Hydrographic survey data.
- Sediment quality data.
    particle size data
    engineering properties
    chemical constituents
- Port configuration data.
    line of quay walls
    details of structures
    navigation limits
    maintenance depths

26. <u>System processes.</u> A number of integrated processes are required as an aid to the management and interpretation of information. Four major processes are identified.

- Hydrographic database manager.
- Spatial database manager.
- Digital terrain model.
- Information analysis module.

27. Each of these <u>major processes</u> contain a number of <u>detailed processes</u> which are used to carry out specific tasks; the most important of these are discussed later. The major components of the system are identified in Fig. 2.

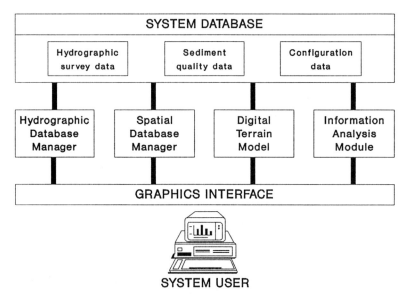

Fig. 2. Components of the information management system.

Development philosophy.

28. The overall philosophy has been the development of a system which will allow the rapid processing and presentation of information, providing an effective decision making tool. Additionally, a flexible system architecture has been adopted, allowing modifications to be made in support of future managerial policy.

29. The need to integrate data sets having a spatial and temporal dimension was a major consideration. This problem has been overcome in other areas of engineering by utilising spatial information system (SIS) technology (ref. 10), which was considered to be ideal for this particular project. The SIS environment allows all data to be related to a common spatial co-ordinate system, providing a basis for geographical referencing of information.

Database development.

30. The system, in addition to being used for information management purposes, is also intended to interface with a number of mathematical models, allowing the prediction of flood levels and channel scour and deposition. In order to minimise problems of "routine interfacing", and given the nature of the data to be handled, it was decided that the database manager would be customised. An overhead, in terms of development time and cost, was associated with this decision. However, it was felt that the ability to modify and maintain the system at a later date was a critical factor; a facility which would not be guaranteed if commercial data management software was employed.

Hydrographic database manager.

31. The hydrographic database manager (HDM) has been structured to take account of the current recording methods employed by the project sponsors, Clyde port authority(CPA). The main navigational channel is periodically surveyed at a series of fixed cross-sections, located at regular intervals along the channel. From a modelling viewpoint, the centre line of the channel can be represented as a series of linked nodes, each of which is coincident with a surveyed cross-section. The absolute position and orientation of the channel is defined at each model node by a pair of ground reference co-ordinates and a plan bearing, representing the direction of positive flow. The cross-sectional profile at any node, and at a specified point in time, is defined by a list of paired offsets (distance measured from the channel centre line perpendicular to the direction of positive flow) and levels. Each point can be reduced to full 3 dimensional co-ordinates using the spatial information provided at the appropriate model node.

32. The processed hydrographic survey data is stored in 3 linked files, the river description (RD), cross-section index (CSI) and cross-section data (CSD) files.

33. The RD file contains a series of indexed records, each consisting of an eight element string, giving positional and reference information relating to a single model node. An

additional field, containing a pointer to the CSI file, is incorporated for data management purposes.

34. The CSI file contains a summary of the hydrographic survey data available for each model node. Each record contains a model node reference and a survey date, together with a pointer to the record in the CSD file containing the relevant survey information. A field containing a link to the next record (for a specified model node), is included in the CSI file, improving file access time.

35. Hydrographic survey information, at a particular location and point in time, is fully identified by specifying the appropriate model node reference and survey date. The model node reference is a unique identifier of a particular cross-section which can be specified directly or implied from either the chainage, measured along the channel centre line, or the absolute spatial co-ordinates. The latter proves particularly useful when working in an interactive graphics mode.

Spatial database manager.

36. The spatial database manager (SDM) is presently dedicated to the management of sediment quality data. The physical and chemical characteristics of the sediment have been determined at a number of discrete sampling locations over a period of time. Sample points are spatially referenced by way of a location reference number, with which attributes (physical and chemical characteristics) can be associated. A date stamp is included to incorporate the time dimension.

37. The data management routines presently employed in the SDM are at an early stage of development and will be further improved as the SDM is refined.

Digital terrain model.

38. The digital terrain model (DTM) is used to process hydrographic survey data, allowing geometric calculations and graphical processing to be undertaken. The DTM contains a number of specific processes allowing the calculation of areas and volumes, surface contouring and graphical representation. These processes can be used in isolation or in an integrated manner within the information analysis module.

39. Area and volume calculation. This process provides a series of options for numerical integration, allowing the area between 2 profiles, along a common reference line, or the volume between 2 surfaces, located in a common spatial domain, to be estimated.

40. Contouring. The contouring option allows the value of a dependent variable $(z=f(x,y))$ to be estimated at any point in space. A series of contours can then be developed providing a complete spatial representation of the dependent variable for graphical analysis. At present the contouring option can only be used with bathymetric data.

41. 2 and 3 D viewing. Information presented in a graphical manner is generally easier to interpret than numerical data, enhancing the users understanding of a particular problem area.

The 2 and 3 dimensional viewing options are used for graphing
time and spatially variant functions, and for constructing
contour plots and colour coded surface representations.

Information analysis module.

42. The information analysis module (IAM) allows for the
selective processing of data, yielding information required in
the analysis of the problems previously identified. The IAM
utilises a menu-driven, graphical interface, allowing the user
to define all run options in an interactive manner. Extensive
data checking and error handling facilities are incorporated.

43. The methods employed by the IAM to undertake a number of
specific tasks are briefly discussed.

44. Evaluation of siltation rates. The net rate of siltation
over a defined area of interest (AOI) is estimated by consideration of data from consecutive hydrographic surveys. The
change in channel level integrated over the AOI yields the
total volume of siltation which has occurred over the inter-
vening time period.

45. The rate of siltation is calculated at each cross-section
in the hydrographic survey database, allowing the variation at
individual cross-sections (Fig. 3), along the length of the
channel, or over the AOI to be determined. This information can
be viewed using the graphics options available within the DTM.

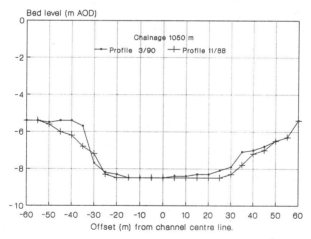

Fig. 3. Evaluation of siltation at specified cross-section.

46. Assessment of maintenance dredging needs. Dredging needs
are estimated in essentially the same manner as siltation
rates. However, in this case the most recent hydrographic
survey data is compared to an idealised channel at each cross-
section (Fig 4). The idealised channel is based on the limits
of navigation and maintenance depths required within the port.
The DTM option for area and volume calculation is used to
determine the total volume of sediment lying above the idealised channel, representing the maintenance dredging commitment.

Again, this information can be viewed using the various graphics options of the DTM.

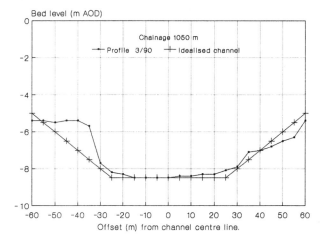

Fig. 4. Evaluation of material lying within shipping channel.

47. <u>Assessment of in-situ sediment quality.</u> An estimate of the physical and engineering properties of the sediment, at any point on the channel bed, can be made by consideration of the data collected at discrete sampling points. The user has the option to use data from the nearest sampling point or to perform a local interpolation using a maximum of 3 specified sites.

48. The spatial and temporal variation of particular quality parameters can be evaluated and presented in a graphical manner (Fig. 5). These parameters can then be compared against known quality standards allowing immediate identification of problematic areas.

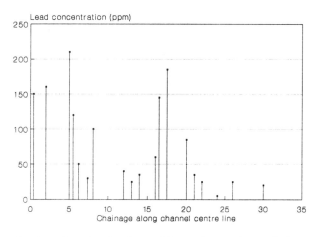

Fig. 5 variation in chemical quality along channel length.

Further development.
49. The present system is no more than a prototype, requiring considerable upgrading before it is applied in a serious manner. A number of developments are proposed for future implementation. These include:

(a) Optimisation of data management routines and incorporation of an SQL interface.
(b) Porting of software to a UNIX based workstation with increased graphics capabilities.
(c) Incorporation of a knowledge base and rules processor, increasing the decision making capabilities of the system.
(d) Incorporation of models to simulate flood levels and siltation, allowing the system to be used as a forecasting tool.

CONCLUSIONS
50. The need to undertake maintenance dredging operations in a manner which limits adverse environmental impact, whilst remaining viable form a technical and economic point of view, is a problem which is currently facing ports throughout the U.K.
51. There is a need to reduce dredging activity to an operational minimum and to evaluate alternative disposal options for dredged spoil. Effective interpretation of hydrographic survey data and the assessment of in-situ sediment quality are fundamental concerns, if these objectives are to be achieved.
52. The application of information management techniques and, more generally, the application of information technology, will allow the development of effective, computerised systems, which will be invaluable to port managers in the future planning and engineering of maintenance dredging activities.

ACKNOWLEDGEMENTS.
53. The Clyde Port Authority (CPA) provided funding for an industrial lectureship at the University of Strathclyde (department of civil engineering), for a period of 3 years commencing October 1987, during which period initial development of the dredging management system was undertaken. The author formally acknowledges the support of CPA and thanks them for there financial and technical contribution to the research.

REFERENCES.

1. Finney N.H., Maintenance dredging and spoil disposal at UK ports, Proceedings of the conference on maintenance dredging, Institution of civil engineers, Bristol, 1987, 6-20.
2. Rees C.P., Environmental impact of dredging operations, Third international symposium on dredging technology, Bordeaux, France, 1980, 373-388.
3. Final act of the intergovernmental conference on the convention on the prevention of marine pollution by dumping of wastes and other matter, London, 1972, Her Majesty's stationary office, London.
4. Convention for the prevention of pollution by dumping from ships and aircraft, Oslo, 1972, Her Majesty's stationary office, London.
5. Parker M.M., The future for the disposal of dredged material in the UK, Proceedings of the conference on maintenance dredging, Institution of civil engineers, Bristol, 1987, 249-262.
6. Great Britain - Parliament, Food and environment protection act 1985, Her Majesty's stationary office, London.
7. De Waaij A.F.C. and Van Veen H.J., Processing of contaminated sediments in the Netherlands, Contaminated soils 88, 1988, 1277-1283.
8. Van Veen H.J. and Stortelder P.B.M., Research on contaminated sediments in the Netherlands, Contaminated soils 88, 1988, 1263-1275.
9. Hummer C.W. and Lazor R.L., Overview of dredged material disposal options or alternatives, Proceedings of the conference on maintenance dredging, Institution of civil engineers, Bristol, 1987, 241-247.
10. Chidley T.R.E. and Drayton R., Remote sensing and spatial information systems in civil engineering, Report to SERC environment committee (civil engineering sub-committee), 1989.

Imaging in sewer systems

D. J. J. WOTHERSPOON, Research Assistant, and
R. M. ASHLEY, Reader in Civil Engineering, Dundee Institute of
Technology, and S. P. WOODS, Detectronic Ltd

SYNOPSIS. The instrumentation available to engineers involved in the assessment of the performance of sewerage systems, particularly for purposes of hydraulic renovation, has changed radically during the last decade. New, legislation driven, requirements to account for quality as well as hydraulic performance have necessitated further development of more precise equipment to overcome many of the known deficiencies and limitations of existing instruments. Development initiatives for enhanced equipment have originated from the UK Water Industry, through the Water Research centre (WRc), and have also been supported by research funding from the Science and Engineering Research Council (SERC) and manufacturers such as Detectronic Ltd.

INTRODUCTION

1.   The design of any civil engineering artefact is based on received knowledge which is embodied in standards, codes of practice and other sources. Such knowledge bases are continually undergoing modification as further scientific and technological advances occur. In parallel, and as a consequence of, the growing knowledge base, new tools and techniques are also being developed to assist with the design process. Knowledge growth and tool development are each dependent upon the acquisition of information concerning the natural and man-made environment. Data relating to the performance of designs are also essential to ensure that the civil engineering profession can maintain an appropriate level of service to fulfill the needs of society. For example, in response to society's growing demand for a cleaner environment, the performance of sewerage systems must be monitored and assessed in order to develop improved and more cost-effective designs and better methods of operation.

SEWERAGE MANAGEMENT

2.   The present day U.K. sewerage engineer has inherited an infrastructure which has gradually evolved over the last 150 years. Most urban conurbations have very old core sewer networks comprising a variety of storm and foul pipes in combined, separate and partially-separate networks. Thanks to the skills of our Victorian forebears, most of these systems are still serviceable and have operated satisfactorily with little maintenance, despite increasing urbanisation and consequent increases in the demand placed on them. The sophistication of the hydraulic design methodology has also evolved with time, with significant advances in the most recent past as a result of the availability of computer technology. The use of computer-based hydraulic simulation models such as WALLRUS (ref.1), to model the performance of sewerage systems has now become routine.

3.   These techniques, together with the publication of the WRc Sewerage Rehabilitation Manual (ref.2), which sets out a formalised planning strategy, have allowed engineers to pursue more cost-effective renovation measures for hydraulically overloaded sewerage systems, rather than the traditional and more costly wholesale replacement programmes (ref.3). This approach, based on the optimisation of the use of existing infrastructure and the assimilative capacity of natural water bodies, has been adopted by the UK water industry as a fundamental tenet for wastewater flooding and pollution control (ref.4). Having developed new methodologies and computer-based models to solve the problems relating to the hydraulic analysis of sewerage systems, the water industry has more recently turned its attention to the quality aspects of sewerage system performance. New strategies for the control of intermittent discharges from combined sewer overflows, for example, are now emerging which are based on recent research studies of the problems caused by in-sewer deposition and subsequent wash-out of these highly polluting materials. A new sewer flow quality computer model, MOSQITO (ref.5), has been developed, which when used in conjunction with the WALLRUS hydraulic model will be able to simulate dynamically the polluting performance of sewerage systems.

4.   It is essential that good quality data are obtained relating to rates of flow and in-sewer sedimentation if sewerage performance analyses using models such as WALLRUS and MOSQITO are to be accurate and robust enough for design and management purposes (ref.6,7). Theoretically, flow in a sewer can be calculated from depth using values for diameter and pipe gradient, and an estimated roughness, and by assuming that flow is at normal depth and unaffected by backwater. The uncertainties involved in these assumptions however, make such an approach inaccurate for all practical conditions. Methods of measuring flow in sewerage systems have advanced significantly over the past decade, with the development of in-sewer ultrasonic flow survey packages, which are generally regarded as being adequate for the purposes of verifying the performance of most computer-based hydraulic models when used correctly and with regard to their recognised limitations (ref.8). However, confidence in the assessment of the performance of critical areas of a sonar network may be limited, with the consequence that any renovation works may have to be overdesigned.

5.   The current development and application of models which include sediment and other pollutant transport parameters require a more precise definition of hydraulic conditions, with, for example, allowance for velocity variations within the flow cross-section in large sewers (ref.9). The current generation of in-sewer flow survey packages do not always measure accurately the velocity distribution in a flowing sewer, as these rely on an averaged value obtained from a 'snap-shot' of part of the flow cross-section. Enhanced instruments are now under development specifically to ensure that more precise measurements of velocity can be made. These instruments will improve the precision of total flow measurement, from the current uncertainty levels of typically 20% in larger sewers, down to some 5%.

6.   Sewer sediment considerations and sewer structure integrity assessment require systems which can be used to 'picture' the in-situ sewer boundaries. In a typical brick sewer at a particular cross-section there may be loss of mortar at joints and sediment deposits sitting in the invert. The monitoring of these may be complicated by the necessity to maintain flows within the sewer, and unless over-pumping is possible the use of CCTV (closed-circuit television inspection) systems will be limited. Accurate measurement of sewer shape below the flow surface, together with any sediment deposit, is now feasible whilst maintaining flows, due to the development of

sonar systems which can be used to scan the sewer cross-section. Such systems are in use in conjunction with CCTV surveys to obtain a complete and, most importantly, dimensioned picture of sewer decay and sediment build-up (ref.10).

MEASUREMENTS IN SEWER SYSTEMS

7.   Sewerage systems are a harsh environment in which to take measurements, with the ubiquitous biological hazards, dangers of operating in confined spaces with restricted access and potentially corrosive, poisonous and explosive atmosphere. In particular, the measurement of flow in such systems, which can have a wide variety of shapes, sizes and alignments, presents numerous difficulties for the reliable operation of monitoring equipment.

8.   The range of hydraulic conditions encountered in sewers is broad, encompassing all types of flow states. Any measurement system must either be able to accomodate such variability or be sited to avoid unfavourable conditions. These may include non-uniform flow conditions, large velocity and depth ranges and variable conduit shapes, sizes and materials. Flow patterns may be low, dry weather conditions, which vary only gradually with a diurnal pattern, to high storm flows which may vary rapidly.

9.   Any instrumentation developed for in-sewer use must be robust enough to withstand the environment, and also utilise a measurement system which is cognisant of the nature of the fluid being monitored. Sewage flow arises from a number of sources, i.e. domestic, trade effluent, stormwater and groundwater, the proportions of which depend on the type of sewer (separate or combined) and on the degree of groundwater infiltration. The liquid contains suspended and floating material possibly with dissolved or immiscible corrosive contaminants. Within sewers, deposits of solids in the invert are common. Such deposits may occupy up to one third of the cross section of the sewer (ref.11), and may be erodible.

FLOW MEASUREMENT

10.   The usual systems for monitoring flows in streams and rivers are of only limited application for sewer systems. For example, surcharged flows cannot be monitored using the weirs or flumes traditionally installed at sewage treatment works. Because of the problems caused by debris collection, it is essential to utilise systems which are not mechanically operated and are minimally intrusive. Due to the depth of sewer placement, it is not normally practical to use the types of measurement systems developed for external pipe flow study. There are exceptions to this, however (ref.12), but these require massive investment in providing an external chamber for access. Practical sewer flow measurements are based on separate measurements of flow depth (or surcharge pressure) and velocity. Depth may be measured using a pressure transducer immersed in the flow, a sonar system located above the water surface, or as is common in the rest of Europe, by use of a 'bubbler' pressure tube (ref.13). The depth aspect of measurement is the most accurate, with current velocity measuring systems failing to achieve the same precision. There are two techniques for velocity measurement currently in use for commercial instruments: electromagnetic meters (EM) and ultrasonic meters (UM). In sewer systems, such instrumentation has been confined largely to portable systems which are installed intrusively within a sewer to monitor the flow for a relatively short period, usually up to two months.

Electromagnetic meters

11.   The electromagnetic flowmeter utilises the same basic principle as the

electrical generator: when a conductor moves across a magnetic field a current is induced in the conductor, and the magnitude of the current is directly proportional to the speed of the moving conductor. Electrodes may be mounted in or on a sewer-wall at appropriate positions to monitor the velocity of the flowing sewage 'conductor'. As the EM system only measures the velocity within about 25mm of the sensor head (and hence sewer wall), to determine the flow, the velocity profile must be symmetrical and definable (usually assumed logarithmic) across the sewer. In practice, magnetic fields are not completely uniform nor are velocity profiles symmetrical or logarithmic. Consequently, if high accuracy is required, EM flowmeters must be calibrated on site. The best accuracy obtainable is approximately ± 1% over a velocity range of 5:1, with accuracy deteriorating for velocities below 20% of full scale.

12.   EM units have been found to be largely unaffected by variations in fluid density, viscosity, pressure, temperature, and to some extent, electrical conductivity, for example (ref.14), a 30% change in conductivity was found to cause only a 1% change in velocity measurement. Upstream flow disturbances also lead to very little effect unless the velocity profile becomes seriously asymmetric (ref.15,16). Other problems can occur due to air bubbles, radio signals and even water waves (creating electrical noise) (ref.17). The most significant problem for the user is that of 'fouling' of the electrodes, by for example, grease deposits from sewage. These will insulate the electrodes from the flowing fluid.

13.   Very little information has been published relating to the use of EM velocity meters in sewerage systems, despite their almost exclusive use in the USA, where two systems are manufactured by Montedoro-Whitney (M-W) and Marsh-McBirney. Both systems are similar in application, with electrodes fitted into a small debris shedding wedge, which is mounted intrusively on the wall of a sewer. The Marsh-McBirney EM has been used for flow velocity measurement in sewerage systems with apparent success (ref.13,18,19). The M-W is currently in use in Brussels to measure velocity at the flow surface of the main trunk sewer, and also in smaller sewers by the Belgian road research laboratory. Equipment problems have occurred, however, particularly due to greasing of the electrodes.

Laboratory and field tests of EM units in Dundee

14. Studies of sewerage system performance and sediment provenance, occurrence, erosion, movement and polluting potential are currently underway in Dundee (ref.3) funded by WRc, SERC, and Tayside Regional Council. As part of this work, detailed measurements of velocity gradients over a short length of 1.5m high interceptor sewer have been required. Consequently an appraisal of existing and required velocity measurement instrumentation has been made for this type of application. Initially it was believed that an EM type of system would give the most accurate measurements, particularly close to a sediment bed, and consequently a hybrid version of the Marsh-McBirney (M-M) Model 201D portable flowmeter (ref.20) was tested. A second EM system has also been tested, the 'SENSA' produced in the UK by Aqua Data Systems Ltd (ref.21), which has an improved operational specification in comparison with the M-W and M-M systems.

15.   Laboratory and field tests were carried out in Dundee to assess the suitability of the M-M and SENSA EM units in sewage flows. Simple laboratory studies using "clean" water in a hydraulic rig with a recirculating pump showed both units performed satisfactorily. Field tests were carried out by installing the unit in the 1.5m diameter brick sewer in Dundee. Results were compared with those obtained from a doppler-

shift ultrasonic unit mounted approximately 2m downstream. The field trial did not prove to be successful as the M-M display readings inconsistently fluctuated with no apparent mean value.

16. Further tests were carried out in an attempt to explain the poor performance of the M-M system. These included an evaluation of: the rate of grease build up on the electrodes; the electrical interference caused by metal in the sewage flow; changes in conductivity; interference from the mounting and other adjacent instrumentation; and ambient conditions, for which spectral analyses of the electromagnetic fields in the sewer were carried out. The results from these tests were inconclusive. The SENSA EM system was also tested in the field and found to operate satisfactorily. It has not been possible to explain the difference in performance of the M-M and SENSA units without full access to details of their design and operational characteristics, although it is known from spectral analysis of the signals, that the units have different electromagnetic operational characteristics.

Ultrasonic Meters

17. Ultrasound can be used in different ways to measure the mean velocity or flowrate of fluid in a conduit. The ultrasonic signal is generated by electrical excitation of a thin piezo-ceramic crystal at a typical frequency of 1 Megahertz. There are two commercially available systems, one in which the principle of operation is based on the speed of the sound wave moving faster or slower when going with or against the current respectively. Although used extensively for river studies, there is no published information regarding the system's usage for sewers or sewage flows. In the second, more popular system, the principle of operation is based on the Doppler effect. The Doppler effect works on the principle that the frequency of a sound vibration emanating or reflected from a moving object changes in frequency, with the magnitude of the frequency change being proportional to the speed of the object. The Doppler-effect ultrasonic meter works by measuring the velocity of dirt particles or small air bubbles conveyed in a moving fluid, and assumes that on average, these are travelling as a wash-load at the same rate as the fluid. Ultrasound from a transmitter is reflected from a large number of the particles and picked up by a receiver, whence the signals are averaged. It is inevitable that the mean of the frequency signals will not always be correctly weighted, and thus the system is sensitive to flow profile variations and to the distribution and concentration of particles in the cross-section of flow. A further disadvantage of this type of meter is that, unlike the other types of ultrasonic meter, its readings are affected by changes in the velocity of sound in the liquid, so that it is both density and temperature sensitive.

Ultrasonic velocity meters

18. Despite the limitations mentioned above, ultrasonic (Doppler-shift) velocity systems have become the standard for short-term surveys of sewerage systems in the U.K. (ref.6,8). Units incorporating ultrasonic twin sender-receiver crystals, together with pressure transducers, as manufactured by Detectronic Ltd (Fig.1), have been used successfully for the last six years. Several thousand such units have been purchased by UK sewerage investigators in that time. This type of instrument has the capability to provide flow data under both free surface and surcharged conditions. Programmable control software allows the operator to preset the solid-state logger to vary the recording interval to suit flow conditions; a slow rate for low (dry weather) flow conditions and a fast rate for storm flows, initiated by changes in flow level. Recorded

data can be retrieved using a portable computer. The accuracy of the standard flow survey unit is of the order of ± 10% when expressed in terms of volumetric flowrate (ref.23), in ideal conditions. The lower limits of accuracy of the instrument's depth and velocity readings are approximately 80mm and 0.3m/s respectively. However, these results are based on the individual effects of the pressure and velocity transducers, and do not explicitly account for the effect that the depth of flow can have on the measurement of velocity. Tests in a laboratory flume indicated that velocities recorded could be affected by a flow depth of 100mm or less. When the flow depth is low, the degree of scattering of the ultrasound beam from the liquid/air interface was found to significantly affect the readings. The relative accuracy of these instruments may be summarised (ref.23):

(a) individual instruments have different error ranges;
(b) an accuracy of flow measurement to within 20% is attainable, provided the flow depth is greater than 100mm, and the velocity is between 0.3 m/s and 2.5 m/s;
(c) shallower sloping pipes give more precise results, non-uniform conditions and steep velocity gradients give poorest results;
(d) pressure (depth) measurement transducers are subject to zero drift errors.

The WRc "Guide To Sewer Flow Surveys" (ref.8) states that velocities given by this type of instrument are repeatable to ± 5% and flows accurate to ± 10 to 15%, the measurement technique being particularly efficient in small diameter sewers up to 600mm.

19.   Ultrasonic velocity measurement using a single transmit/receive unit cannot be very accurate as the instrument has a wide (15 to 20°) ultrasound beam divergence and it is therefore impossible to determine precisely where in the depth of flow the velocity is being measured (fig.1). The instruments look at the vertical velocity distribution as being representative and the limitations are thus minimised if the vertical velocity distribution is 'square', i.e. if the profile is only gradually changing across the section, there are no discontinuities, and the profile relates consistently to the mean. This usually pertains in free gravity flows only, with backwater effects and surcharging causing problems.

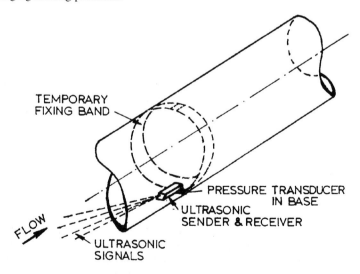

Fig. 1. Typical ultrasonic sewer flow survey unit installation.

Recommended Use Of Ultrasonic Flow Survey Units

20.   WRc (ref.8) recommend the installation of loggers and the in-situ calibration of the sewer rather than the logger, by measuring the peak velocity (and where possible the entire vertical profile) with a portable probe and comparing this with the logged mean velocity. Installation must be in a good hydraulic location where there are no backwater effects, and where covering of the transducer with sediment deposits is unlikely. These peak/mean velocities are calibrations of the flow with respect to depth. However, calibration adjustments made to surcharged measurements can only be theoretically based due to the impossibility of calibrating loggers in surcharged sewers. Fig.2 shows the WRc recommendations as to acceptable monitoring sites in terms of flow depth, sewer size and velocity.

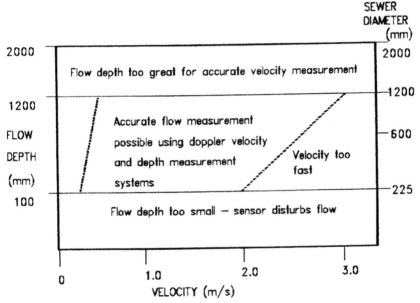

Fig. 2. Regions of validity for flow measurement using standard flow survey units.

21.   The known deficiencies of the standard instruments relate principally to the area of the flow 'viewed'. A vertical profile is averaged over an area which is (relatively) close to the sensor and bed of the sewer. Existing instruments are thus recommended only for sewers up to 1200mm high.

NEW DEVELOPMENTS

22.   Work is currently being undertaken by WRc (ref.24) to provide some form of velocity profiling or averaging in an effort to obtain improved accuracy (± 3%) of flow measurement in large diameter sewers. Range gating (using only reflected ultrasound signals from around a set time delay) has been considered, but found to have only a limited applicability due to problems with signal processing and the maximum resolution of doppler frequency at a given distance from the transmitter. A geometrical array system is also under development, whereby the transducers are arranged such that the transmit and receive beams cross in predictable positions.

Development of an array system

23.   In view of the deficiencies found when testing existing EM and ultrasonic systems in the sewers in Dundee, an alternative system was sought which would provide as full information as possible about the velocity distribution in the large Dundee sewer. A prototype system has been developed by Detectronic Ltd in conjunction with Dundee Institute of Technology, whereby a circumferential ring of Doppler-shift ultrasonic transducers have been installed at a section of the sewer, as illustrated in Fig.3. The 'array' is designed to operate on the principle that velocity information from a transmit/receive pairing of transducers is received from a limited area where the transmit and receive beams cross. This principle has been used in biomedical and other applications (ref.25,26), and has potential for the three-dimensional imaging of velocity fields. A number of transmit/receive pairs of transducers have been mounted around the circumference of the sewer with different transmit/receive angles to provide an overlapping sequence of information envelopes.

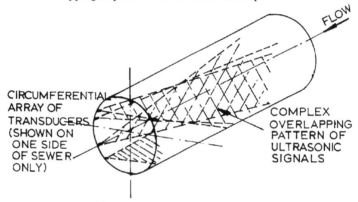

Fig. 3. Section of sewer showing ultrasonic array.

24.   Testing and calibration has been based on laboratory and field tests. Following laboratory testing and calibration of the individual sensor heads in a small sized laboratory flume, the system has been tested in a large flume (1m width), at a sewage treatment works inlet channel and in the sewer. The instrument initially installed in the sewer consisted of eight individual sensor heads supplied by Detectronic Ltd, subsequently an additional two sensor heads were added to enhance the data collected in the dry weather flow and near-bed region. The frequency/velocity relationship for the individual sensors was verified by testing each head under a number of near-uniform flow conditions in a laboratory flume.

25.   Using the frequency/velocity relationships derived from the individual transducer tests, it was possible to calibrate the site data, relating velocities to the frequency signal received at any one of the sensor heads. As can be seen from fig.4, each of the individual sensors receives velocity signals within definable limits, these limits being related to the height of the sensor head above the invert of the sewer. Also, from the signals received at any one head, as shown in fig.5 for transducer 1A, the range of velocities may be attributed to the source of the signal, i.e. each transmitter's signal appears within definable limits at an individual receiving transducer. Thus the technique is able to identify differences in velocities across the cross-section of a large diameter sewer.

150

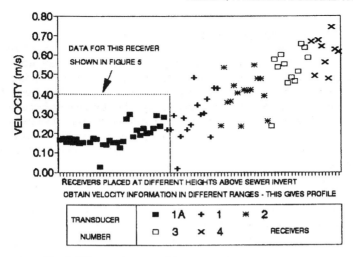

Fig. 4. Ultrasonic array. Murraygate interceptor sewer.

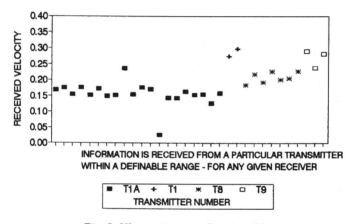

Fig. 5. Ultrasonic array. Receiver 1A.

26.   Skew velocity profiles may also be detected by the sensor heads, the velocity one one side of a sewer being shown to be higher than that on the other. However, a more sophisticated analysis of the signals will have to be carried out to examine the relative influence of the velocity profiles, both with depth and across the section, on the frequency signals.

27.   Further development of the imaging of flow velocities in sewers using this system has two possible options. The first is based on locating the coordinates of the intersection of the centrelines of the transmit/receive cones to assign the appropriate velocity. The second is based on identifying those flow volumes within different cones of intersection responsible for creating differences in the velocity signals between alternate pairings of transmit/receive transducers, and by relating these to a common datum point, construct a tomographic image of the velocity field across the sewer section.

MEASUREMENT OF SEDIMENT IN SEWER SYSTEMS

28.   The monitoring of sediment deposits and movement in sewerage systems requires the measurement of patterns of erosion and deposition. Measurements of the pattern of bed deposits are usually made (ref.27,28) by physically measuring the deposit depths at certain points if the sewer is of man-entry size. However, this approach does not reveal how deposit depths vary with time and flow conditions. To address this problem, WRc have developed two sonar based sensor systems, one, in conjunction with DIT, to provide continuous monitoring of sediment bed deposits at a point in a sewer. This instrument also provides the possibility for a linkage into a telemetry system, such that sewer cleaning operations may be optimised by monitoring deposition at critical locations.

Sonar depth gauge - point measurements

29.   The fixed instrument comprises a sonar head mounted in a rigid plastic tube of known length as shown in Fig.6. The tube is attached at the upper end to a pivoted clamp for mounting to the soffit of the sewer, and the lower end floats on the surface of the sewage. At the pivot point, an inclinometer is attached to monitor the position of the arm. The signals from both the sonar head and inclinometer are recorded by a solid-state logger. For general use the arm and pivot must be constructed as site-specific elements. To avoid access, maintenance and fouling problems, the pivot point has to be kept as close to the soffit of the sewer as possible. This limits the amount of counterbalance achievable in order to allow the sonar head to operate just submerged under all conditions, and a buoyancy aid will usually br required.

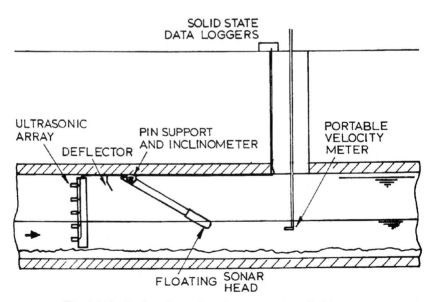

Fig. 6. Velocity & sediment imaging systems installed in sewer.
(Data loggers are installed above ground)

Calibration and installation

30.   The voltage signals from both the sonar and inclinometer were initially calibrated in the laboratory prior to installation in the sewer in order to provide voltage/ distance and voltage/angle relationships. Once installed it was necessary to measure accurately the total height of the sewer section and the relative distance of the pivot axis from the sewer soffit. The sonar arm was installed in the Dundee interceptor sewer which is 1.5m in height, and a standard sewer flow survey doppler ultrasonic logger was placed at an upstream manhole to monitor flow depth and velocity. Typical results are shown in Fig.7. Further results have illustrated that fine materials deposited during night-time dry weather flow are eroded during storm flow events and peak diurnal flows. Similar studies in France (ref.28) have utilised a larger sonar unit mounted on a 'boat' which floats at a point in a sewer. Both the Dundee and French work has shown that the system is reliable, robust and able to measure sediment depths to within a few millimetres.

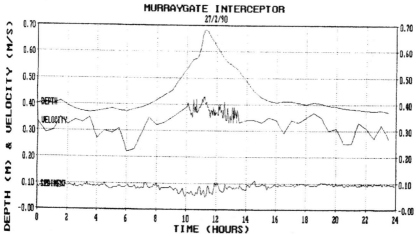

Fig. 7. Fixed sonar results showing sediment bed response in sewer to diurnal flow.

WRc 'PYPSCAN' - Mobile sonar

31.   WRc have also developed a portable sonar, in conjunction with Marine Electronics Ltd., which may be used to minitor sediment deposition along a pipe length or in ancillary structures such as silt traps. The device may be used to detect flaws in the pipe structure below the water level which would otherwise require over-pumping and sewer cleaning. The equipment consists of an Underwater Acoustic Scanning Profiler (which may be skid, tractor or ROV mounted), a cable reel with an incremental payout sensor, a surface control unit and a high resolution colour monitor. The 2MHz acoustic signal is amplified, logarithmically compressed and converted to a digitally generated 16 colour screen display. Generated images may be fixed and stored to a miniature tape cartridge or standard VHS video monitors may be connected. Figure 8 shows an example of the results from a study of silt trap sedimentation in Dundee. The 3-D graphics were produced from a series of images generated by the PYPSCAN instrument.

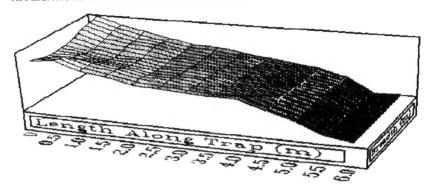

Fig.8. Portable sonar results - sediment build-up.
Blackscroft silt - trap study.
(Length & breadth are shown in metres)

CONCLUSIONS

32.   Increasingly sophisticated design tools and methodologies rely on the collection of extensive and reliable data. Design to precisely defined factors of safety, for example, requires data which accurately illustrate the details and performance of a system. Techniques and instruments for the acquisition of data for the design and management of sewerage systems have advanced considerably during the last decade, thanks mainly to computer-based technological developments. It is now possible, using robust electromagnetic, ultrasonic and acoustic systems, to obtain on-line data about the performance of a sewerage system in terms of flows and sedimentation. Such systems are increasingly being used for sewerage operation and management in real-time, via telemetry links to computer control systems.

33.   Despite the general availability of sewer monitoring systems, further developments are required if quality and polluting aspects of wastewater management are to be dealt with adequately. The system described for three-dimensional imaging of flow fields, coupled with simultaneous sediment monitoring, is only an initial step in this process. There is also a need for additional instrumentation for the rapid assessment of chemical, and possibly bacteriological, characteristics of sewage flows if wastewater system management is to become a fully established and cost-effective activity.

ACKNOWLEDGEMENTS

34.   The authors would like to express their appreciation to the following for support, financially and practically during the last five years over which the described studies in sewers have been undertaken: Tayside Regional Council, Water Services Department; the Water Research centre; the Science and Engineering Research Council.

REFERENCES
1. HYDRAULICS RESEARCH LIMITED. WALLRUS User Manual - Version 1.3, 1989.
2. WATER RESEARCH CENTRE. Sewerage Rehabilitation Manual, Second Edition. Water Research Centre/Water Authorities Association. 1986.
3. ASHLEY, R.M. and GOODISON, M.J. The development of best optimum solutions to drainage problems. To be presented at the 2nd. Int. Conf. on systems analysis in water quality management, University New Hampshire, June 1991, IAWPRC. (Published in J. Wat. Sci. Tech.)
4. CRABTREE, R.W. and CLIFFORDE, I.T. Sewerage pollution control: UK research programme. U.S. Eng. Foundation Conf. Proceedings, "Urban stormwater quality enhancement: source control, retrofitting and combined sewer technology", Davos, 1989.
5. MOYS, G.D.; OSBORNE, M.P. and PAYNE, J.A. MOSQITO 1 -Modelling of stormwater quality including tanks and overflows - Design specification. Hydraulics Research Report No. SR 184, August, 1988.
6. GREEN, M. The role of flow surveys in the hydraulic analysis of sewerage systems. Proc. I.C.E. Conf. Sewerage '81, June 1981.
7. WILLIAMS, D.W. Hydraulic analysis - the role of sewer flow surveys. WRC External Report No. 136E, April 1984.
8. Water Research Centre. A guide to short term flow surveys of sewer systems. 1987.
9. DAY, H. and ORMAN, N. Hydraulic Modelling in the 1990's. Wallingford Procedure Users Group, Autumn Meeting, 1990.
10. WATER AND SEWERAGE INTERNATIONAL. Combined sonar and CCTV surveys of sewers in use, p.24, August 1990.
11. CONSTRUCTION INDUSTRY RESEARCH AND INFORMATION ASSOCIATION. Sediment movement in combined sewerage and drainage systems. Research project 366, 1987.
12. GREEN, M.J. Storm sewer data. Foundation for Water Research, Report No. FR 603, October 1990.
13. BRULL, A.; PETERS, J.J.; VANDENBERGH, J.M. and VANSLAMBROUCK, A. Hydrometry in sewer systems: 3, Reliability of hydraulic field systems in sewers: Intercomparison of instruments. Proc. Int. Symp. on measuring techniques in hydraulic research, IAHR Section on Hydraulics Instrumentation, Delft, April 1985.
14. BAKER, R.C. Effects of non-uniform conductivity fluids of electromagnetic flowmeters. J. Phys. D: Applied Physics,1970,3,637.
15. HEYWOOD, N.I. and MEHTA, K. A survey of non-invasive flowmeters for pipeline flow of high concentration non-settling slurries. 11th Int. Conf. on the hydraulic transport of solids in pipes. BHRA, 1988.
16. REINHOLD, I. Velocity profile influence on electromagnetic flowmeter accuracy. In: Flow Measurement of Fluids, North Holland Publ. Co., 1978.
17. ROWSE, A.A. Measurement of flow in part-filled sewer pipes using the electromagnetic technique. Int. Conf. on the planning, construction, maintenance and operation of sewerage systems, 1984. WRc/BHRA.
18. WALTON, E. et al. Assessing a sewer network in the Middle East. Int. Conf. on the planning, construction, maintenance and operation of sewerage systems, 1984. WRc/BHRA.

19.   ZECH, Y. et al. Control and operation of sewerage systems - problems of instrumentation and measurement. Int. Conf. on the planning, construction, maintenance and operation of sewerage systems, 1984. WRc/BHRA.

20.   MARSH-McBIRNEY INC. Model 201/201D portable flowmeter instruction manual. Maryland, U.S.A.

21.   AQUA DATA SYSTEMS LTD. Chippenham, Wiltshire, U.K.

22.   JEFFERIES, C. and ASHLEY, R.M. The use of a microcomputer for the simulation of flows in the Dunfermline sewerage system. Proc. 2nd. Int. Conf. on civil and structural engineering computing, Vol.2, pp 229-236, 1985.

23   ASHLEY, R.M.; JEFFERIES, C. and STEVENS, G.S.W. Overloading of the Dunfermline sewerage system due to peripheral urban expansion. Proc. Int. Conf. on infrastructure renovation and waste control. I.C.E., 1986.

24.   PINKARD, D. WRc developments in doppler flow monitoring for large diameter sewers. Wallingford Procedure Users Group conference and workshop, Scarborough, Nov. 1989.

25.   BRODY, W.R. and MEINDL, J.D. Theoretical analysis of the CW doppler ultrasonic flowmeter. I.E.E.E. Trans. Biomed. Eng., BME -21, 1974.

26.   COUSINS, T. The doppler ultrasonic flowmeter. In: Flow Measurement of Fluids. Eds: Dijstelbergen, H.H. and Spencer, E.A. North Holland Publ. Co., 1978.

27.   ASHLEY, R.M.; COGHLAN, B.P. and JEFFERIES, C. The quality of sewage flows and sediment in Dundee. Proc. 2nd. Wageningen Conf. on urban storm water quality and ecological effects on receiving waters, Wageningen, 1989.

28.   LAPLACE, D. and BACHOC, A. Programme de recherche sur le transfert des solides en resaux d'assainissement: suivi des dépôts dans le collecteur 13 à Marseille méthodologie et mesures. IMFT/ESL Report No. 401/1990.

Developments of a software house for technical engineering software in hydraulics and water resources

R. K. PRICE, Manager, Wallingford Software, Hydraulics Research Ltd

SYNOPSIS. Hydraulics research has set up a software house to address the problems and opportunities of developing computational hydraulic software for the design, construction and operation of civil engineering works. The organisation of the software house depends intimately on research and development in open channel hydraulics.

INTRODUCTION.

There is a rapid takeup of information technology in the Civil Engineering Industry as engineers appreciate the improvements that can be gained in design, analysis, construction and operation. Management information systems are being used on large civil engineering construction projects, geographic information systems offer potential savings to the water utilities in operating their sewerage and water distribution networks, digital ground models provide better tools for road design and construction, SCADA systems are being implemented on treatment plants and distribution networks, CAD is now being used extensively in design offices, and design and analysis software is being introduced into all aspects of the design process.

The Water Industry has been responsible for commissioning a number of major civil engineering construction projects such as the Thames Barrier, the London water distribution supply main, as well as numerous sewerage and water distribution rehabilitation works. Many of these projects depend intimately on the use of design and simulation software to reproduce the behaviour of the flow before and after the construction of civil engineering works or the operation of such works.

In addition software is being used to predict the effect that the flow under existing or design conditions will have on pollution and sediment transport.

Even before privatisation the Water Industry placed strong emphasis on the introduction of IT into all aspects of its business. So far as engineers in the industry have been concerned there has been considerable benefit and job enhancement to those engineers who have taken advantage of IT in their areas of work. One particular area has been sewerage rehabilitation. Along with the development of comprehensive procedures for planning sewerage rehabilitation schemes (ref 1) has been the wide-spread use of complementary computational procedures involving a sophisticated hydraulic simulation of free surface and pressurised flow in pipe networks (ref 2). Similar benefits have been gained in using software to simulate flows in water distribution networks, rivers and estuaries and coastal waters, as well as reservoirs, irrigation networks and groundwater.

The remainder of this paper considers the problems and opportunities in developing software to model open channel and closed pipe hydraulics, particularly as it affects the design and construction of civil engineering works.

COMPUTATIONAL HYDRAULICS

Computational techniques in structures have been well developed for over fifty years in that the basic equations have been well defined and algorithms for their solution have received considerable attention. Finite element techniques were a natural basis for calculating stresses and strains in complicated structures. With the advent of commercial computers in the 1960s the development of software to implement these techniques was rapid and there has been a wide-spread use of the resulting products.

The development of rigorous computational hydraulic techniques began more recently in the 1950s and were greatly enhanced in the 1960s. Because the basic equations are non-linear and essentially hyperbolic in nature the algorithms used at first were an extension of the graphic techniques based on the method of characteristics. However, developments of research done by Stoher (ref 3) and Priessman (ref 4) lead to commercial software based on implicit techniques, and these have remained the basis of the more sophisticated software now in regular use. Despite such developments the use of computational hydraulic software has lagged somewhat behind structural software. This is because of the greater concern and investment in civil engineering structures and also because the fundamental hydraulic equations are more complex and difficult to solve and the modelling requires large amounts of data which are expensive to collect or derive and which can have significant errors or uncertainty.

As with the modelling of any physical situation there is the need to go through various stages, namely, building, calibrating and/or verifying a model as well as applying it. Each of these stages requires considerable experience on the part of the engineer. For example the building of a model can consume large amounts of data, much of which has to be collected deliberately for a particular study rather than is available in the form of plans and charts. It is vital that this data is properly verified. Often however the data can be too much to handle and the discretisation of the model process means that only a limited subset of the data is required. Then there comes the problem of how to make a proper selection of this limited data from the complete set. An example of this choice is the simplification of a model of a sewerage network.

Model calibration is a crucial aspect of the development of a model for, say, a particular river. Attempts have been made to automate this process but the best models are developed by careful individual selection of roughness values for the channel or flood plain. Verifying that the choice of calibration values is appropriate is usually another essential part of river model development. So far as a model of a sewerage network is concerned verification is the means whereby the data for the network model is refined in the absence of a comprehensive and accurate set of basic data for the network.

Once a model has been verified there is then the need to apply the model, first in appraising the performance of the existing system and then in determining the effect that proposed civil engineering works will have on the performance.

For these and other reasons the development of computational hydraulic models has been the preserve of research organisations or civil engineering consultants who have the sizable resources to develop or use such models.

Until comparatively recently clients for feasibility or design studies of civil engineering works involving computational hydraulics have been content to recognise the sophisticated nature of such studies and to leave them to the developers of the software. This situation is now changing as clients are more used to software in other areas of civil engineering and as they perceive better opportunities for them to take direct responsibility for the use of computational hydraulic software. For example there is a trend for consultants to be commissioned to build computational models and for the end-client to then use them for engineering application or for planning or operational purposes. The end-client expects to have sufficient resources in-house to implement this strategy, whether hardware in the form of micros or graphics workstations or staff with training and experience in operating computational models. In turn this places a number of requirements on the software such as to be user-friendly with a good graphics interface, to have links to databases, GIS or MIS, and to have good reporting facilities. This has meant a radical change in the way the software has been developed and made available to end-users. In particular the development of the software can no longer be the single responsibility of the experienced hydraulics engineer but now involves an important contribution from other professionals, including software engineers for interface development and data modelling, knowledge engineers, graphics designers for interface design, and technical authors for the documentation among others. For this reason it has been recognised by Hydraulics Research, as one of the leading laboratories world-wide for open channel hydraulics, that a new approach is needed to the development of computational hydraulic software, particularly if reliable and user-friendly software is to be made available to end-users in the water and civil engineering industries.

COMPUTATIONAL HYDRAULIC SOFTWARE

HR Wallingford carries out research and consultancy

PRICE

work in civil engineering hydraulics applied to
areas such as urban drainage, river and catchment
management, estuary and coastal waters modelling,
and wave analysis with emphasis on water quality,
sediment transport and environmental implications.
Traditionally HR Wallingford has carried out its
research and studies using physical modelling and
laboratory experiments. However as one of the first
international laboratories to use computational
hydraulic modelling techniques at least half of its
work now involves such techniques. Despite the
complexity of computational modelling HR Wallingford
has a history of making its software available to
consulting engineers as part of its mission to
assist the UK civil engineering consultants in open
channel hydraulics research and application. In
1982 HR Wallingford, formerly known as the
Hydraulics Research Station within the UK Department
of the Environment, was privatised. In that year HR
Wallingford also released a package of computer
programs called WASSP to implement a new design and
analysis procedure for urban storm drainage.
Released for mainframe application the software was
subsequently ported to the new micro computers which
were becoming available and distributed as
MicroWASSP. This package had a straight forward
text-based interface, which ensured much better
access to the design and simulation software than
was convenient with the mainframe software.
Additionally the package became an important
component in the Sewerage Rehabilitation strategy
developed by the Water Research Centre (ref 5), with
consequent economies in construction work on
rehabilitation of sewerage systems nationwide. Over
450 copies of MicroWASSP were sold with possibly as
many as 1000 copies in regular use. This became the
basis of a new business at HR Wallingford, namely
the development of packaged software for
computational hydraulics.

The WASSP software was developed during an extensive
research project with the Institute of Hydrology and
the Meteorological Office during the 1970s. As such
the software was put together for research purposes
and then subsequently refined for release. It
lacked formal design and strict coding standards.
Immediately after release the software was
extensively enhanced to model the very complex
sewerage networks found in the UK. These
enhancements were difficult to implement because of
the inadequate design of the software, and a number

161

of problems were experienced by users despite the considerable support given by HR Wallingford. It was apparent that further enhancement was impossible with the existing code and much of it was rewritten for a new product called WALLRUS. This product used the same hydraulic algorithms as WASSP but was adapted for general use world-wide. Some improvements were also made to the interface and the graphics facilities, but they still fell short of the capabilities of a full graphics interface that were beginning to be introduced in CAD and other software.

To meet the challenges of new developments in software engineering HR Wallingford therefore set up in 1988 an internal software house, called Wallingford Software, with the specific mission of developing and marketing top quality computational hydraulic software.

The scope of the software under development or on release covers the areas of investigation at HR Wallingford, including river, tidal and maritime engineering. In terms of application the software is concerned with the simulation of flows in 1D networks and 2D and 3D domains. The 1D applications cover hydraulic transients in pipe lines, urban drainage networks, streams in treatment works, stream networks in rural catchments, and river, estuary and irrigation networks (water distribution networks could also be included but Wallingford Software does not develop its own products in this area). The 2D and 3D applications are to problems such as tidal and surge flows in coastal waters, and circulation in reservoirs and tanks. In all cases there is strong interest in pollution and sediment transport and the influence of, or the effect on, civil engineering structures.

In view of the wide range of applications in the 1D area, for example, it makes sense to economise on software development and to make the range of software more accessible to engineers by using a common graphics interface and data structures. In the past, with the emphasis on research, the software was developed for particular applications by different researchers which meant that there was little in common between software, say, for urban drainage and for river modelling. Therefore recent software concentrates on using the same or very similar interfaces between the 1D products. Also, undergirding any network application is the data structure for the network itself. Again it is desirable that this is common between the products.

The common graphics interface is built out of sets of library routines specifically developed for the purpose. Ultimately a suitable database will be necessary to give suitable consistency and flexibility on the data structure.

As with mechanical and other products there is a need for software products to be developed under strict quality assurance procedures. British Standards 5750 and ISO 9003 are two particular standards which are being used for QA on software. There are still difficulties in implementing these standards but increasingly clients are looking for certification of software by a responsible body to act as a guarantee of proper development of the product. What cannot be guaranteed of course is the accuracy and reliability of the product. This requires extensive testing, and the necessary procedures for doing this are still not developed. Modular and integration testing of software is part of the QA procedure, but precise and accurate testing of the software is impossible because of the very large number of separate paths through the software and the infinite number of alternative configurations of a network that can be devised. Testing is however important and it is likely that testbeds of data will have to be developed whereby each individual hydraulic element addressed by the software is tested individually together with a number of distinct sample networks including the hydraulic elements in a variety of combinations.

ORGANISATION

Hydraulic code depends on a number of factors including a sophisticated analysis of the mathematical equations describing the hydraulics of flow and the movement of pollutants and sediment, the development of appropriate numerical algorithms, and an appreciation of the way in which the algorithms are applied to solve for the flow within a civil engineering environment. Obviously a high degree of mathematical and civil engineering insight are required. For these reasons hydraulic code is probably best developed within a research environment by personnel in close touch with new developments in hydraulic modelling and processes in their particular areas. So, for example, there is value in having different researchers working on estuarial and river type problems. However it is important for the resulting products that the development of the code is done within strict QA procedures monitored by software engineering staff. Additionally the software should conform to data structures and formats used generally with the particular type of application. HR Wallingford continues to use Fortran 77 as the standard high level coding language for hydraulic code.

Because the graphics interface across a range of products for, say 1D network models should be common then it is preferable to centre its development in a team within the software house which specialises in software engineering and is cogniscent with the latest developments in interfaces and database. They specify the interface to meet the needs of end-clients, as well as the underlying data structures to which the developers of the hydraulic code work. In addition they are responsible for the implementation of interface modules which assist the user in building, calibrating and/or verifying, and applying a model, together with the links to external software such as corporate databases, GIS, MIS, weather radar, SCADA systems etc. Wallingford Software largely uses the C high level language for its interface development.

The QA procedure requires formal development of documentation of the software. Similarly there has to be appropriate user documentation which, because the software will be used in an engineering context, requires particular attention so that the engineering background can be clearly described.

The construction of suitable testbeds of data is largely the responsibility of the developers of the hydraulic code. Formal testing at alpha (in-house destruction testing) and beta (in-house and external application testing) test levels is handled by the software house.

Besides the software engineering department the software house then has other departments specialising in marketing, sales, product production, product distribution, customer support, and training. The remaining area is software maintenance. This depends on having strict control on the total code with software review meetings agreeing on code fixes and improvements prior to the next release of the software. Again proper testing of the code is required before a new release is made. The expertise for customer support and training and maintenance of hydraulic code largely resides with the original researchers. Therefore there has to be a mechanism for drawing on that expertise when the first line of contact with the customer is via the support team in the software house.

Many of these features of the organisation of Wallingford Software can be found in other software houses developing and releasing off-the-shelf products for other areas of application. What is particular about Wallingford Software is its intimate dependence on research and development within civil engineering hydraulics and the complex nature of computational modelling.

There is a school of thought that argues strongly that computational hydraulic modelling is too prone to abuse by inexperienced engineers and that the release of software will only lead to poor, if not inadequate, civil engineering design. This is probably the greatest danger in releasing the software. To overcome this danger there has first to be a ressponsible ddevelopment of the software based on sound research. This is best achieved by the international hydraulics laboratories or using academic expertise based in universities. In the latter case it is very important that the software itself should be developed by a professional software house with experience of computational hydraulics. So far as the software is concerned there should be a considerable number of checks on the accuracy and validity of the data input during the model building process and of the computations. In particular there is usually a need for rigorous checks on volume or mass conservation and on the stability of the results during a simulation. Even then there is no guarantee that the results are accurate or reliable. This depends on the expertise of the user in interpreting the results. Some expertise can be built into the software to assist the engineer in this interpretation, though the formal assistance will probably depend on having expert system modules incorporated within the software products and containing relevant expertise culled from existing expert users. Wallingford Software also runs a telephone hot-line service for users and puts considerable emphasis on providing a quality training service both at Wallingford and at customer sites. In this way it is hoped that the software on release will be used reliably and responsibly. In the last analysis, as with any tool, it depends on the skill of the user if the software is to be used successfully.

CONCLUSION

A software house has been set up within HR Wallingford to promote the development and sale of packaged computational hydraulic software for the Water an Civil Engineering Industries. This software house imitates the way in which similar organisations have been set up to serve other industries. However in this instance there needs to be close cooperation between researchers working in the field of computational hydraulics and those developing the final software products. This ensures that the latest research results are incorporated in the software and that the best available expertise in applying such models is captured for others to use.

The effect on civil engineering construction, whether on sewerage rehabilitation or the design of estuarial barrages, of good quality computational software has been profound. In the case of sewerage rehabilitation there are catalogued economic benefits of millions of pounds. There is also little doubt that in many other areas the reliability of civil engineering designs could not have been justified without such models. The widespread use of these models in the future will make it all the more necessary that the software is responsibly developed to the highest standards. The organisation of Wallingford Software within HR Wallingford ensures that such standards are both promoted and maintained.

The views expressed in this paper are those of the author and do not necessarily represent those of HR Wallingford.

REFERENCES

1.   HYDRAULICS RESEARCH LTD, Design and Analysis of Urban Storm Drainge - the Wallingford Procedure, Hydraulics Research, Wallingford, originally published by the National Water

Council, London, 1981

2. PRICE R K, A New Computer Package for the Design and Analysis of Storm Sewer Systems, Adv. Eng. Software, 1982, Vol 4, No 3

3. STOKER J J, Numerical Solution of Flood Prediction and River Regulation Problems - Report 1 - Derivation of Basic Theory and Formulation of Numerical Methods of Attack, Report no. IMM-200, New York University, Institute of Mathematical Sciences, New York, N Y, 1953

4. PRIESSMANN A, Difficulties Rencontrees dans le Calcul des Ondes de Translation a Front Raide, Proceedings of the Eleventh Congress, International Association for Hydraulics Research, Leningrad, USSR, 1965, Paper 3.5

5. WATER RESEARCH CENTRE, Sewerage Rehabilitation Manual, Water Research Centre, 1984

A geographical information system for flood risk assessment

P. H. MILNE, Senior Lecturer, and D. BUCHANAN, Lecturer,
University of Strathclyde

SYNOPSIS. Predicting the frequency of occurrence and consequences of major flood events (flood risk), is an important
aspect of the planning, design, operation and management of
lowland developments. This paper considers the application of
information technology to flood control practices, and in
particular, describes the development of a geographical information system for flood risk assessment. The integration of a
river basin model, a flood routing model, and a digital ground
model are discussed.

INTRODUCTION.
1. The problems of flood prediction, flood alleviation and
flood risk assessment, have been active concerns of engineers
for many years. Recent advances in computer technology, have
enabled mathematical modelling and information management
techniques to be applied, in developing an advanced understanding of flood processes. However, it is still the case that
flood prediction and flood warning methods employed are often
inadequate, exemplified by the extensive flooding experienced
throughout the United Kingdom (U.K.) in the early months of
1990.
2. This wide spread flooding of lowland areas has long been a
problem in the U.K. An ever increasing demand for new land
holdings has led to the development of flood plain areas for
commercial and residential purposes. Consequently, destruction
of property, livestock and human life is often associated with
extreme flood events. This represents a significant economic
cost, and can be the cause of much grievance to communities and
individuals at large.
3. The need for adequate flood risk assessments at design and
planning stages of proposed developments, and for effective
managerial controls, enabling timeous flood predictions to be
made, is clearly evident (ref. 1).
4. Current research has the basic objective of applying
information technologies in data capture, data abstraction and
information analysis, to the improvement of river management
and flood control practices. The development of a geographical
information system (GIS), incorporating a river basin model and
a flood routing model, with digital ground modelling (DGM)

capabilities, is a fundamental aim of this research (Fig. 1).

5. The intended uses of this system are in undertaking flood risk assessments for proposed land developments, enabling the geographical limits of flood plain inundation to be identified. Additionally, the system may be used in a decision support role, for implementation of flood warning schemes, by providing rapid and accurate predictions of impending flood in a real-time mode.

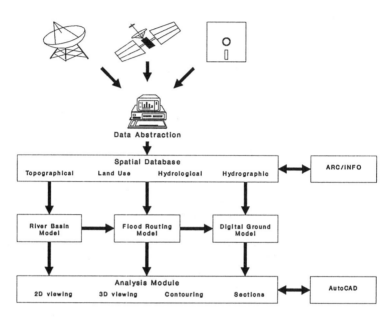

Fig. 1. A GIS for river management and flood control.

FLOOD RISK AND FLOOD PREDICTION.

6. Flood risk may be defined as, "The long term probability (or risk) of a flood occurring at a defined geographical location". In this sense, a flood is any natural event which leads to the submergence of a land surface area, which, in 'normal' circumstances, would neither store nor convey water. Explicit in this definition is the notion of flood plain inundation.

7. Flooding of lowland areas may result from a number of physical processes; runoff from upland areas due to rainfall or snowmelt conditions; tidal influences, e.g. storm induced surges; indirect causes, e.g. as a consequence of earthquake or landslide. The first two are directly influenced by local meteorological and climatological conditions. Hence, the probability of occurrence of these events, in the longer term, can generally be estimated from historic rainfall and tidal records. It is possible, by consideration of catchment and channel network characteristics, to make a quantative assess-

ment of flood levels (associated with a particular flood event) along a given river channel. Subsequently, the flood risk for all points on the land surface, within the river valley, can be identified.

8. Probabilistic methods of flood prediction regard isolated flood events as belonging to a data set having an underlying statistical distribution. Where a sufficient historic flow record is available, the statistical distribution of the data set can be estimated and subsequently employed to predict the probability of occurrence of given flood events. Such methods have an inherent limitation in that, it is assumed that unrelated flood events, of equal magnitude, occurring at different points in time, have the same probability of occurrence. The basic data set is very often inhomogeneous due to changes in catchment characteristics, as a result of land use changes, etc., in which circumstances the above assumption will be invalid (ref. 2).

9. Deterministic methods of flood prediction, which consider flood magnitude as being a direct function of effective precipitation and catchment characteristics, can often be used to generate a homogeneous data set for statistical analysis. This method is preferred, as meteorological data (precipitation and evaporation), although subject to climatic change, is generally more stable than other forms of hydrological data.

10. River basin modelling (RBM) techniques are used to generate synthesised flow data. The river basin is defined by a number of parameters which relate to physical catchment processes, allowing streamflow data to be predicted from meteorological inputs. In general, the RBM will be calibrated to the present situation, taking account of current land uses etc. Alternatively, the effect of proposed land use changes can be estimated by effecting appropriate changes to the relevant model parameters. A further advantage of this streamflow synthesis approach, is that flood predictions can be made on ungauged catchments, i.e. those where no historic record of streamflow is available. Empirical techniques are used to estimate model parameters, with meteorological data from local sites used as model input.

11. Having developed and calibrated a model, a series of simulations, using rainfall events of varying probability of occurrence, is undertaken to yield a flood probability distribution (Fig. 2).

12. The catchment parameters and hydrological data required are dependent on the particular model chosen, as are the complexity of the simulation techniques employed. The basic concept, however, is consistent, and having developed a model a flood frequency curve can be constructed from storm frequency data. Conventionally, catchment characteristics have been derived from archived data, e.g. O.S. Maps. This process is both time consuming and of limited accuracy, in that the data contained on the O.S. Map is a simplification of the real situation (at some historic point in time), where geographical parameters are constantly changing. There is likely to be

little gain in evaluating changes of a minor nature. However, major change, e.g. large scale urbanisation or deforestation, may have a dramatic effect on catchment response (ref. 3).

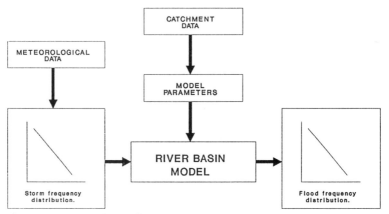

Fig. 2. Generation of a flood frequency distribution.

REMOTE SENSING TECHNIQUES.

13.   Remote sensing refers to the collection (by earth observation satellites), and processing, of electromagnetic images emitted or reflected from the land surface. Surface and sub-surface characteristics can be inferred from the images obtained, and catchment parameters estimated for use in the river basin model (ref. 4). Land use, soil type, vegetation characteristics, and soil moisture conditions, affect the reflective properties of the land surface; the spatial and temporal variation of these parameters can be estimated using appropriate image processing techniques (refs 5. -7).

14. Data obtained from the satellite image will be related to a ground reference grid of cellular format, generally having a size of 30 or 80 metres square. Processed data, giving a detailed description of the catchment at some point in time, is stored in a spatial database, which can be accessed to evaluate appropriate parameters for the RBM.

THE RIVER BASIN MODEL.

15. River basin models (RBM's), attempt to define the land phase processes of the hydrological cycle in a simplified quantative form. The general concept is that of a series of interrelated surface and sub-surface storage reservoirs, each representing a distinct physical element of the catchment. Semi-empirical mathematical statements, describing the transfer mechanisms between these storage reservoirs are employed. A number of the parameters required in these equations, can generally only be found by model calibration; the process of fitting simulated output to recorded data.

16. RBM's are of two general types, lumped and distributed

parameter. Lumped parameter models use a single representative
value of all variables and parameters, for each catchment or
subcatchment modelled. Distributed parameter models take
account of the spatial variation of model variables and parameters within each catchment, by allowing unique values to be
specified at the nodal points of a ground referencing grid. The
latter provides a more realistic description of the catchment.
However, such models are almost impossible to calibrate, hence
a lumped or semi-distributed model will be employed.

17. The model presently used is the Strathclyde river basin
model (SRBM) (ref. 8); a deterministic, lumped-parameter model,
based on the Stanford watershed model (ref. 9). The SRBM
requires daily precipitation and evaporation data as input,
together with other climatic data where snow processes are to
be simulated. Simulated daily streamflow is produced as output,
which is used to construct a flow frequency distribution.

THE FLOOD ROUTING MODEL.

18. The most common method of modelling the flow in natural
channels assumes a one dimensional flow case. The velocity of
flow is averaged with depth and across the width of the
channel, and is thus only assumed to vary along the length of
the channel at any point in time.

19. The average velocity and depth of flow can be estimated
at any channel cross-section by considering the geometric
configuration and roughness of the channel at that point. The
entire stream network is modelled as a series of linked nodes
in X-Y space. The depth of flow, and subsequently the level of
the free surface is evaluated at each node point, allowing the
water surface profile to be represented as a 3-dimensional
(X,Y,Z) string (Fig. 3).

20. The limits of inundation of the flood plain can be
estimated by projecting a series of normals from the water
level string-line, and determining points of intersection with
the ground surface ; this is facilitated by interfacing with
the DGM. These points of intersection are connected to form the
free surface model.

21. In undertaking flood risk assessments, the steady state
profile associated with a flow of given probability of exceed-
ence can be evaluated and the limits of the flood plain determined. Where a river channel is subject to tidal influences
the probability of occurrence of a given tidal condition
contributes to the overall risk of assessment. The method of
determining the level of the free surface does not however
change (ref. 2)

22. The prediction of floods in real-time, requires a full
hydrodynamic simulation to be undertaken; velocity and depth of
flow are, in this case, spatially and temporally variant. The
hydrograph generated from the RBM (and tidal conditions, if
applicable), should be updated at an appropriate time interval.
The modelling time-step chosen is a function of catchment
response time, and must be sufficient to allow timeous warning
of pending floods. Numerous models are available for real-time

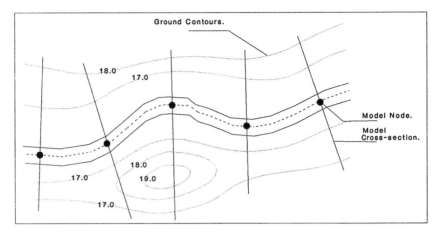

Plan of river channel & flood plain.

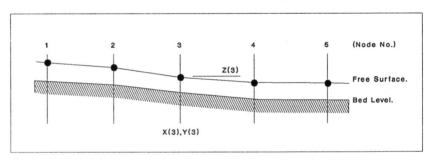

Section along centre line of river channel.

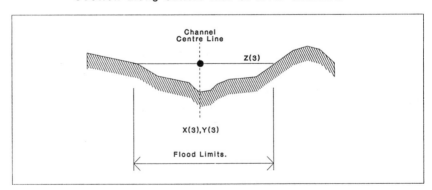

Cross section at model node No. 3.

Fig 3. Identification of flood plain limits.

flood forecasting, the most appropriate in any given situation will be dependent on a number of problem specific factors (ref. 10)

23. Many situations cannot be adequately modelled using 1-D flow assumptions. In such cases a 2-D flow model (velocity averaged with depth only) is required. The 2-D model will generate a 3-D free surface model, giving a direct indication of flood plain inundation.

THE DIGITAL GROUND MODEL.
24. Ground data for the digital ground model (DGM) can be obtained in several ways: as digitised maps, as contours from maps, plans or aerial survey photographs, or from land surveys of the area (Fig. 1). These data inputs, together with river cross sectional data (Fig. 3), are compiled in a database for use in both the DGM and the GIS. In the latter, the rivers or streams are split into segments, e.g. between tributaries, or where cross-sectional properties are similar. This information is stored under a stream identity number, name, stream code (depending upon size), shape and flowrate. These combined data inputs are then used to model the topography of the river valley to accurately determine the flood storage variation along the valley. The formation of the DGM automates the extraction of these data for the flood routing model, (ref. 11)

25. In one-dimensional flood routing models, data is held on a grid basis, where ground co-ordinates are fixed but water level is variable in time. In the vicinity of river banks where the contours are irregular, grid modelling techniques are unsuitable (ref. 12) as the grid tends to smooth out surface irregularities. This smoothing of the contours tends to disguise sharp changes in the topography in the vicinity of the river banks. As the distance between contours indicates the local ground gradient, this smoothing will lose any sharp changes in the ground slope.

26. The triangulation based method of terrain and surface modelling, often referred to as TIN (triangulated irregular network) is now favoured. All measured data points are used and honoured directly, as they form the vertices of the triangles used to model the terrain and construct the contours (ref. 13). Breaklines can also be defined in a TIN model, to represent irregularities such as sharp ridges, embankments, river banks, etc. The TIN method currently employed by the Department (ref. 14) is based on the Delaunay triangulation method.

27. Once the triangulation is complete, contours can be threaded through each triangle using a linear interpolation. Although the data may only have been entered at 1.0m or 0.5m intervals, the advantage of the DGM is that the area can be contoured at smaller intervals, e.g. 0.1m, giving a much better visual representation of the very flat terrain associated with flood plain areas.

28. In flood risk assessment, two main types of output are available; numerical data for the flood routing model and visual output in the form of 2 dimensional maps and 3 dimen-

sional surface models. The latter output may also include the flood limits corresponding to predicted water levels. Subsequently the DGM can generate a predicted water surface over the flood plain, and then calculate and plot the water surface intersection for 3 dimensional visualisation.

29. The DGM can also be used to calculate areas and volumes relating to the river's flood plains, thus building up very accurate information on the water retention profile of the river and surrounding area.

FORMATION OF THE GEOGRAPHICAL INFORMATION SYSTEM.

30. To merge the output from the flood routing model with the DGM, use has been made of ARC/INFO GIS software, which has facilities to integrate map and attribute information in a common spatial database.

31. Background topographical data for the area can be input in a variety of forms, as Ordinance Survey digital data (if applicable), as digitised data from existing maps, as land survey data or from photogrammetric machines and image processing systems. ARC/INFO will also accept output from other digital mapping systems such as AutoCAD. From this information, a 3-D digital terrain model can be formed using ARC/INFO's TIN software, which describes the surface as a series of irregularly shaped triangles. Once formed, the TIN model provides functions for surface analysis, slope calculations, contouring, watershed and 3-D display. Attributes may be associated with the polygons defined by the triangles, the line segments forming the triangle boundaries and the elevation points where the triangles intersect. The slope utility is ideal for identifying drainage networks for merging with the main stream network. An ARC/INFO GRID digital terrain model is then formed by interpolation from the TIN data, and stored in a cellular format.

32. The GIS data is held in several layers. The most important ones in flood risk assessment are, landuse (e.g. urban, agricultural, brushland, forest, water, wetlands and barren), soils (type, infiltration potential, etc.) and streams (identified by name, stream code, shape and flow rate). The landuse and soil layers are stored as polygons and the streams stored as lines. Other layers which are useful in the development of the GIS, for administrative purposes, are a road layer (stored as lines) and a building layer (stored a points), allowing buildings and roads at risk to be identified.

33. Data from the rivers and streams in the area are stored in a stream NETWORK model. The stream network is made up of intersecting line segments, stored topologically in the ARC/INFO data base. Attributes are associated with the network to describe the size, shape and flow rate of the stream along each line segment. For given flood flows, the level of the stream can then be computed (Fig. 4), and by combining the GRID and NETWORK models, buffer zones showing those areas at risk due to flooding can be immediately computed and displayed. A set of flood risk contours can then be computed for flood flows

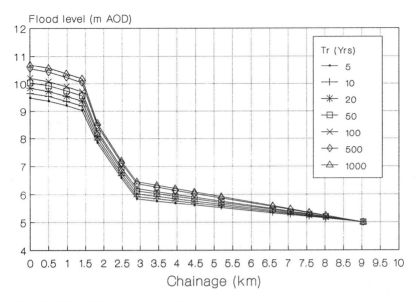

Fig 4. Flood level variation along channel.

at various return periods, e,g 10, 20, 50 and 100 years. Flood risk contours can be used as a development tool in planning and design of flood alleviation schemes. These risk contours can then be viewed in 3-D, as TIN has the same structure as the 2-D ARC/INFO maps, allowing maps of flooding, etc. to be draped over the 3-D surface. Flooded areas can then be computed accurately and attribute data combined for flood risk analysis.

CONCLUSIONS.
34. Mathematical modelling provides a powerful tool for use in many engineering situations. Areas where the proposed GIS could be employed include; the identification of present and future risk of flooding due to existing and proposed developments; effects of implementing flood control and flood alleviation schemes, allowing cost/benefit analysis to be undertaken for proposed schemes; implementation of flood warning schemes, etc.
35. The GIS environment provides the optimum operating platform for management of the extensive spatial database, required by the various models, allowing information to be rapidly processed and displayed in a manner which supports effective decision making. The ability to selectively extract information from the extensive database, in relation to a user-defined problem, allows decisions to be taken with increased confidence, and in general, increases operational efficiency.

REFERENCES.
1. HILL J.M., SINGH V.P., AMINIAN H. A computerised database for flood prediction modelling. Water Resources Bulletin, 1987, vol. 23 (1), 21-27.
2. OGINK H.J.M., GRIJSEN J.G., WIJBENGA A.J.H. Aspects of flood level computations. Delft Hydraulics Communication No. 357, 1986.
3. FLEMING G., HYNES C. The influence of land use on flooding in the river Oykel, Scotland. 2nd international conference on the hydraulics of floods and flood control, 1985, 221-234.
4. RANGO A., FELDMAN A., GEORGE T.S., RAGAN R.M. Effective use of Landsat data in hydrologic models. Water resources bulletin, 1983, vol. 19 (2), 165-174.
5. SCHMUGGE T. Remote sensing applications in hydrology. Reviews of geophysics, 1987, vol. 25(2), 148-152.
6. FLACH J.D., CHIDLEY T.R.E. River basin surveillance using remotely sensed data. 13th annual conference of the remote sensing society, 1987, 417-425.
7. RANGO A. Assessment of remote sensing input to hydrological models, Water resources bulletin, 1985, vol. 21(3), 423-432.
8. FLEMING G. Computer simulation in hydrology - user guide for the river basin model, University of Strathclyde, Scotland, 1986.
9. CRAWFORD N.H. and LINSLEY R.K. Digital simulation in hydrology: Stanford watershed model IV. Stanford University, U.S.A.
10. POWELL S.A. and CLUCKIE I.D. Mathematical hydraulic models for real-time analysis of floods. International conference on the hydraulics of flood and flood control, 1985, 457-472.
11. SAMUALS P.G., PRICE R.K., WILDE J.S., CORMACK W.J. A digital model of river valley topography. Advances in engineering software, 1982, vol. 4(2), 58-63.
12. MILNE P.H. Computer graphics for surveying, E & F.N. Spon, London, 1987.
13. INSTITUTION OF CIVIL ENGINEERS. Surface modelling by computer. Proceedings conference of institution of civil engineers, London, 1977.
14. MILNE P.H. Survey software for digital terrain modelling, in Terrain modelling in surveying and civil engineering (eds. Petrie G. and Kennie T.J.M.) p 171-185. Whittles Publishing, Caithness, Scotland, 1990.

Information technology in coastal zone management

C. A. FLEMING, Director, I. TOWNEND and R. DEAKIN
Sir William Halcrow & Partners Ltd

SYNOPSIS. A geographic information system (GIS) has been used to develop a shoreline management strategy, covering the east coast of England from the Thames to the Humber. In the initial stage the system was used to map relevant variables, and analyse the inter-relationships between variables in order to produce interpretive maps. The system is now being developed as an integrated management tool, with uses which include: retrieval of information; provision of summary data; classification into management zones; and predictive modelling. One of the major problems being addressed is the maintenance of the system, where variations in time are a crucial aspect of the data.

INTRODUCTION

1. In 1953 a major storm surge in the southern part of the North Sea caused severe flooding in south east England, leading to the loss of some 200 lives, as well domestic' livestock, wildlife and devastating damage to property and agricultural land. As a result there was a major reconstruction of the sea defences along the east coast and England. These defences have been maintained, extended and rebuilt during the ensuing years, but the time has now come to re-think the sea defence system as a whole and make some major reinvestments for the security of the future.

2. It is also evident that coastal engineering has evolved rapidly over the last twenty years, and now there is a vastly improved understanding of process in the sea and its effect on the coastline. Many of the traditional techniques of protecting the coastline, such as groynes and sea walls can be complemented or replaced by softer techniques such as sediment supply, which is the means of placing sufficient material on a beach to absorb wave energy, the building of off-shore breakwaters or the creation of artificial headlands. All these methods are feasible, provided the processes occurring on the beach are fully understood.

3.   Anglian Water, realising the problems that must be faced
        in the future, and being responsible for one of the
        longest and most vulnerable coastlines in Britain
        stretching from the estuaries of the Thames to the
        Humber, commissioned a study of the foreshore, which
        could help them to establish a coastal management
        strategy based on sound scientific principles. Thus the
        Anglian Sea Defence Management Study emerged and is
        probably the most extensive study of coastline
        properties and processes to have been carried out in the
        UK.

4.   The Anglian coast is some 750 kilometres in length and
        has been the subject of many studies and investigations
        in the past. It was therefore recognised that a vast
        amount of information was dispersed in various archives
        throughout the region. The philosophy adopted for the
        study was to try to make maximum use of these existing
        data sources by gathering them together into a unified
        format which would permit rapid manipulation and
        analysis. This was achieved by setting up a geographical
        information system (GIS) incorporating a database with
        enquiry facilities designed to meet the projects
        analytical needs. This aspect of the work is described
        in Fleming and Townend (1989).

5.   In all, 19 main variables were included in the GIS
        database and each of these have complex data structures
        in order to provide a comprehensive description of any
        particular variable. The main variables were selected on
        the basis that they either provide information on the
        direct influences and responses of the coast (eg waves,
        coastal morphology, rate of retreat, etc) or on their
        implications with respect to the impact of the erosion
        and any protection strategy that may be implemented (eg
        present coastal works,ecologically and environmentally
        sensitive areas, land use etc).

INFORMATION SYSTEMS

6.   At its most basic an information system provides access
        to data through some form of referencing. Traditionally,
        this is through an index system to an archive of records
        and documents. The alternative now available is to use
        some form of computer database to store and retrieve
        information. For coastal studies a convenient and
        relatively quick approach is to define a reference
        coastline and chainages along this line from some
        arbitrary start point. All attribute entries into the
        database are then referenced to this fixed chainage
        system. This imposes a reduction on the data to either
        point or line type on the fixed reference line. Its
        advantage is that it readily allows spatial correlations

in the alongshore dimension and can be used to develop both maps and x-y plots showing values of variables against chainage along the coast.

7. The processes, the resources, and the uses we make of the coast all have a clear spatial dimension. By using GIS it is possible to describe real world objects in terms of their spatial description (point, line, area), their attributes (eg name, value, classification*, and their relationship with other objects (ie topographical relationship). The fundamentals of GIS and the concepts involved in the related issues of data structures, storage techniques, modelling (eg terrain models), data analysis, classification and most importantly data quality issues have been comprehensively set out in the book of Burrought's (1986). The specific application of GIS to coastal and shoreline management has been considered by Law (1990), Townend (1990), Mitchener et al (1989), and McCue (1989), amongst others.

8. Within coastal management applications one is usually trying to satisfy the requirements for analysis and the requirements for management. The capability of a GIS are however, dependent on the scale at which data is captured because detail cannot readily be removed or added. This may require compromise to meet the needs of different users, or alternatively multiple sets of graphics linked to a common database to meet differing presentation and analytic needs. In either case, the user requirements must be clearly specified and the data model designed to meet these needs. This has always been recognised when building large relational databases (see Martin, 1983 for example) but is often overlooked when setting-up a GIS because of the apparent definition provided by real world objects. This, however, is something of an illusion because within a GIS they are represented schematically as points, lines or areas (eg when mapping a river one could use the water surface area, the two banks, a centre-line, or even a point when working at very large scale). The right choice depends on how the data is to be manipulated and presented.

9. As a basic data retrieval tool a GIS can be used to find where items are, what an item is, or to obtain a summary of all occurrences of an item. The real advantages are gained from the analytic capability. The tool can be used heuristically for classification, by comparing different data sets to seek patterns of combinations which suggest some form of relationship. By starting with known problems or phenomena one can adopt a more inductive approach, to seek more general relationships. Finally it is possible to work in a deductive manner, starting with an accepted principle and seeing if this

can be substantiated by the available data. In all such analysis, it is important to seek the underlying physical explanation for any relationships observed (usually by means of carefully focused modelling), and to be aware of spatial and temporal limitations of the data within the GIS.

DEVELOPMENT FOR ANALYTICAL USE

10.   The rationale of the approach adopted was to extract a coherent picture of the dominant processes from the wide range of information that was already available. This philosophy was appropriate because it was felt that over such a large and diverse area, any attempt to apply numerical models to examine processes and coastal genesis would inevitably be constrained by limited knowledge of the governing mechanisms. The prime objective was therefore to structure the data in such a way that it could be rapidly manipulated. A thorough analysis of existing sources of information could then be made, to both gain insights and focus the objectives of future field work and numerical model studies.

11.   A GIS was therefore used to meet the following objectives:

    i)   to map relevant variables for the entire coastal region
    ii)   to use the graphical output of the system to present each variable or combination of variables on a series of maps
    iii)   to assess the inter-relationships among variables and their contribution to coastal erosion
    iv)   to produce interpretive maps which form the basis of coastal management policy.

12.   The software used in the initial stage of the project was developed for use on a micro-computer with two screens, one for text and another for graphics display. The configuration was established to provide facilities to create, display, edit, report, plot and query the data. Two forms of query facility were available. The first provided the ability to make enquiries of a single variable (eg waves, or morphology, or coastal works etc). The second enabled the results for a number of enquiries, using different variables, to be combined (eg waves and morphology and coastal works, etc). This is achieved by plotting the result of each enquiry at an offset from a "coastal reference string", thereby permitting the spatial coincidence of different fields within the database to be rapidly tested.

13.   Where data has been measured or calculated at a point then it has been defined as point data. In a number of cases the data could possibly have been interpolated onto a linear string along the coast (thereby assigning measurements as "representative" of a given length of coast). This would, however, have introduced an element of interpretation and it was felt better to avoid this until an initial evaluation of the 'raw' data had been made. Point data was recorded to the nearest metre, or to the level of accuracy with which the position of the data was recorded and documented.

14.   A large proportion of the information obtained has been incorporated as line data. For these data a 'coastal string' has been established. This is a single line running the length of the coast from Flamborough Head to the Thames. In general it follows the coastline as given on the 1:50,000 Ordnance Survey Maps, although some coastal features, such as the barrier beaches on the North Norfolk coast, do not form part of the string. This is because as far as possible the coastal string represents the backshore/hinterland interface and coastal features are mapped onto the string.

15.   It is important to recognise that this does not follow conventional practice within GIS, in that items are not being mapped in a literal geographical sense. However, given that relationships are being sought with respect to the coastline, there is the problem of how these can be identified. Plotting items in their actual geographical locations would mean that, except when using small scales to look at 'local' details, the data would largely overlap on or about the coastline. The ability to look at whole regions and then move in to study a particular site is an important aspect of the analysis method. Thus some means of displaying a selection of items drawn from different variables, at any desired scale, is an essential requirement for this application. By relating the data to a single coastal string, a number of items can be displayed by using a series of offsets from the reference line. This thereby provides a picture of spatial coincidence, whilst retaining the geographical location of the data.

16.   The final type of data has some areal extent and is recorded as area 'boundaries'. Where the areas are on the coast then a part of the polygon will be formed from the coastal string. This therefore provides a direct means of reference. In a few cases, such as dredging and dumping sites, the areas are remote from the coast and there is no obvious means of reference to the coastline.

17.   Using the approach outlined, a number of insights into
       coastal behaviour were obtained. By looking at the coast
       as a whole and then moving in to particular localities,
       the various qualitative descriptions led to many
       conclusions with respect to local processes. In contrast
       the quantitative data were best examined as x-y plots,
       so that the peaks and troughs in different data sets
       could be compared and related to coastal chainage. Such
       comparisons led to a number of conclusions about the
       governing processes on a regional scale.

18.   Based on the experiences gained in the first stage of
       the Study, the following enhancements to the system are
       now being introduced for this application:

       •   access to time series data
       •   x-y plots of time series
       •   x-y plots of magnitude against chainage
       •   statistical analysis facilities
       •   capture of satellite imagery
       •   a surface modelling capability

19.   Of these the first four are seen as the most important
       for the system to be used as an analytical tool. Coupled
       with an appropriate user interface this provides a
       system which can be used for routine analysis by those
       responsible for managing the coast.

DEVELOPMENT FOR MANAGEMENT USE

20.   The ability to undertake analysis for interpretive
       purposes has been demonstrated (Fleming and Townend,
       1989), and the additions noted above should further
       enhance this particular capability. Application of the
       system as a management tool has been limited and it is
       therefore worth defining what might be provided. The
       uses envisaged are:

       i)   Retrieval of information for a specific site.

       ii)   Provision of summary data for planning purposes
             (eg the regional extent of a feature or
             attribute).

       iii) Preparation of graphical displays for educational
             and public relations exercises.

       iv)   Classification of the coast into management zones.

       v)   Sensitivity testing of the classification system.

       vi)   Predictive modelling to determine:

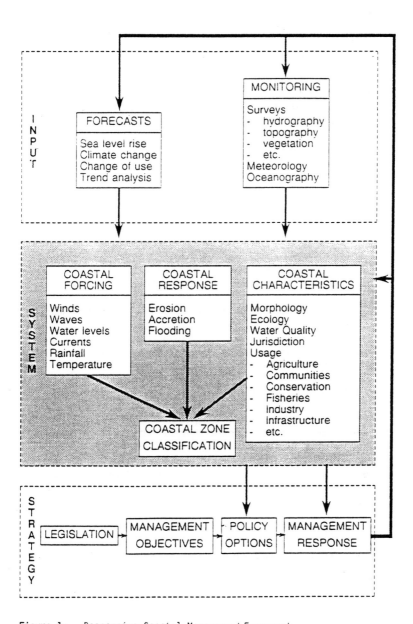

Figure 1:   Responsive Coastal Management Framework

- projections of coastal change
- impact of individual schemes
- impacts from change of use
- economic consequences (eg of sea level rise).

21.   The first three uses can be provided by a number of GIS's and make use of routine enquiry facilities. Options (iv) and (v) are essentially a development of the Policy Option and Coastal Unit concepts established in the first stage of the study (Townend 1989). Here the "management system" forms a part of the management framework, providing the information needed to develop and evaluate the appropriate management strategy (Figure 1). The main difference would be that rather than being developed externally and then input to the system as data sets, they would be derived from the data within the system. This requires the ability to combine different data sets spatially (using overlays) according to some algorithm and with the option to weight the different contributions. Sensitivity tests are then performed by altering the weightings associated with each of the attributes which make up the classifications.

22.   The final option (vi) is intuitively appealing but it is also likely to be the most difficult to achieve. With the appropriate data, the last two predictive capabilities could potentially be developed as extensions of the management zone classification. The first two capabilities suggested are however far more dependent on rules, which may be implicit in numerical models used to derive the required inputs, eg beach plan shape. Whilst it may be possible to develop these for specific instances, a generalised capability is likely to require extensive research into the links between the fundamental processes involved.

23.   Considering the uses outlined above, the capabilities that a GIS will have to provide for the combination of analytical and management requirements are:

Project management tools	-	greatly facilitate the rapid set-up and subsequent control of projects developed within a GIS environment.
Data Security	-	the ability to control read/write access is vital in multi-user/multi-disciplinary GIS application.

Data documenting and audit facilities	-	essential if sources and definitions of the data are to be documented as an integral part of the system. Audit trials allow the data integrity to be tested.
Features definition, create and edit	-	standard on GIS's but these features need to be examined carefully as they can greatly influence productivity.
Enquiries on attributes	-	as above.
Spatial analysis	-	enables overlays, feature synthesis and complex spatial queries to be made. In conjunction with arithmetic transforms this is required to implement coastal zone classification.
Arithmetic transforms	-	allows data attributes to be manipulated according to user defined relationships (eg $A = \log B + C^2$).
Areas to lines or areas and chainage	-	if features are mapped more literally to provide for coastal zone classification (eg map the morphology as areas rather than on a linear string), then some means of deriving the multi-line presentations that were the focus of the initial study is required. An elegant solution would be to derive the line feature from the areas when required using 'feature generalisation'. However such facilities are only at the research stage. Thus one either has to attach the attributes to both an area and a line or store the attributes against the area feature and create a chainage table in the database to assign each feature a position on the coastal reference string.
x-y plots of magnitude against chainage	-	identified as an important requirements for studying coastal processes.

Access of time series data	-	as above.
x-y plots of time series data	-	as above.
Regression and correlation statistics	-	as above.
Summary statistics	-	needed for planning purposes.
Satellite image capture	-	not an immediate requirement but likely to play a role in long term monitoring.
Perspective views	-	useful for visual presentations.
Interactive surface model	-	not an immediate requirement but would be needed to test process models interactively within the system.
Interactive use of predictive models	-	the ability to run numerical models interactively using information in the database, are needed for the predictive capabilities to be developed.
Graphic attributes	-	some attributes could be presented and displayed more effectively using graphics (eg geological cross-sections, sea wall details, etc).
Measurement of areas/lengths	-	for analysis this facility is used from within statistical routines. For management such measurements may be required for planning or as the basis of economic appraisals.
Attribute reports	-	the ability to construct ad hoc reports, suitable for printer output, enables specific data to be extracted from the database as required.
Plots	-	screen dumps and annotated maps are essential in order to provide hard copy of the graphics.

High quality maps - facilities to produce colour maps are important for presentation of results.

SYSTEM MAINTENANCE

24. The facilities described above provide a comprehensive range of tools for the coastal manager. The coast is however a very dynamic interface between land and sea. There is therefore a need for continual updating of the system with new information. This requires information gathered around the region, as part of a co-ordinated monitoring programme, to be processed and ported to the management system. In consequence the process of updating the system is of particular importance, if the GIS is to have a sufficient life to justify the initial costs of establishing the system.

25. The nature of updates varies from one data category to another. This is because the importance of variations in time varies. There are five types of update to be considered:

    i)   fixed definitions - no updates required
    ii)   edit features or attributes
    iii) edit features or attributes but retain access to original entries
    iv)   add graphical features with a time stamp
    v)   add new records/attributes with a time stamp

26. The first two types require no special treatment. Type (i) is a most unlikely case but may apply to 'standard' data sets, whereas type (ii) will apply for corrections and where historical information has no relevance. Following on from this, type (iii) applies to changes in time which are occasional, where the main interest is in the current description, but where specific studies may require access to historical descriptions (the sea defences are a good example of this type of update requirement). The (iv) and (v) types apply where a 'time series' record is sought so that changes in time can be interrogated using the enquiry facilities and/or spatial analyst capability. Examples of these types of update are saltmarsh vegetation and annual wave statistics for (iv) and (v) respectively.

27. These various update requirements necessitate careful structuring of the GIS at the project planning stage. Updates to attributes can be handled by the appropriate use of a revision control system for text file recovery and the provision of the relevant 'time' definition within the database table and field structure. Graphical attributes which change with time, can be handled within

TABLE 1 - STAGE III GIS REQUIREMENTS

MANAGEMENT	ANALYSIS
	----Project management tools----
Data Security----	
	----Data dictionary and audits-
	----Feature definition, create and edit-
	----Enquiries on attributes-
	----Spatial Analysis
	----Arithmetic transforms
	----Areas to lines or areas and chainage
	----x-y plots of magnitude against chainage
	----Access to time series data
	----x-y plots of time series
Summary statistics----	
	----Regression and correlation statistics
Perspective views----	
	----Satellite image capture----
	----Interactive surface model
	----Interactive use of predictive models----
Graphic attributes----	
Raster with Vector----	
	----Measurement of areas/lengths----
	----Attribute reports-
	----Plots----
High quality maps----	

the GIS's which are currently commercially available, by judicious allocation of layers. This can however be extremely cumbersome, particularly when a consistent register in time is required between different data sets, where recordings have been made at a variety of time intervals. As a consequence the ability to handle a third dimension - that of time (rather than the vertical dimension) -would significantly increase the potential of GIS for environmental applications.

CONCLUSION

28. The first stage of the Anglian Study evaluated the use of GIS for shoreline management. To begin with this focused on the use of GIS as an analytical tool. This proved to be particularly successful, allowing a wide range of information to be gathered together in a form which enabled rapid manipulation and inter-comparison of data sets. As a consequence of this initial study a number of facilities to enhance the analytical capability within the GIS framework were identified.

29. In planning the further development of the GIS for use as a management tool, consideration has been given to a wider range of functions. These relate to data manipulation procedures which will provide management with information in an appropriate format to meet their needs.

30. Much effort is being focused on the development of the GIS based, "coastal management system". This however is only the beginning and for the proposed approach to succeed, these tools must form an integral part of routine management. They must therefore be available for use by those responsible for the day to day management of the coast and must be capable of regular updating with newly acquired monitoring information. This requires a well designed user-interface, provision for the time varying nature of the data in the system design, appropriate training and a commitment to regional rather than local management.

ACKNOWLEDGEMENT

The staff of the National Rivers Authority, Anglian Region have provided much advice and support for this development, which has been much appreciated.

REFERENCES

BURROUGH P A, 1986, Principle of Geographic Information Systems for Land Resource Assessment, Clarendon Press, Oxford.

FLEMING C A, Townend I H, 1989, A coastal management database for East Anglia, ASCE, Coastal Zone '89, Charleston, SC, USA.

LAW M N, 1990, Application of GIS to local shoreline management issues, Ontario Ministry of Natural Resources, Toronto, Canada.

MCCUE J C, 1989, The use and potential use of geographic information systems in coastal zone management, MSc Thesis, Dept of Biology, Uni of Newcastle-upon-Tyne, UK.

MITCHENER W K, COWEN D J, SHIRLEY W L, 1989, Geographic Information Systems for Coastal Research, Coastal Zone '89, ASCE, Proc of 6th Symp on Coastal and Ocean Management.

ROBERTS S I, 1989, Problems of Developing a GIS data base for the FMG, Coastal Zone '89, ASCE, Proc of 6th Symp on Coastal and Ocean Management.

TOWNEND I H, 1989, Frameworks for Shoreline Management, PIANC.

Geographical information systems in civil engineering

T. GIDDINGS, Director, Posford Duvivier, and T. JEFFRIES-
HARRIS, Manager, GIS Group

SYNOPSIS. Geographic Information Systems use modern computer technology to combine electronic databases with powerful spatial analysis and graphical display techniques. The use of GIS is growing rapidly, and has the potential for wide application in civil engineering and related fields. This paper describes the power of GIS and gives some examples of its application in civil engineering related projects in the last 3 years.

INTRODUCTION

1. More than 80% of the information that civil engineers use is geographic in nature. That is to say, the vast majority of data has some form of spatial reference and can be fixed to x,y co-ordinates in one way or another. This is hardly surprising, given that civil engineers are essentially involved in the concrete world of development and construction rather than the more abstract world of, say, banking or economics.

2. From the time of Thomas Telford, civil engineers have estimated, measured, designed and communicated their ideas by means of maps and plans. Paper was the traditional medium for both storing and displaying this information. However, with the advent of modern computer technology, information can be stored electronically, easily edited or amended and then communicated and displayed either electronically or on paper. Word processing and CAD are common examples of this technology.

3. Geographic Information Systems, commonly referred to as GIS, use the power of modern computer technology to combine electronic databases of spatially referenced data with graphic analysis and display capabilities. So what, you may ask. However, that simple description of GIS is deceptive.

4. Many civil engineers are using electronic databases, ranging from the excellent library system at the Institution's headquarters at Great George St. in Westminster to the household accounts set up on their home PC's ! Even more are using graphic displays of digital data of their plans and drawings in CAD. So they have a good understanding of the two basic functions of GIS.

5. What is extremely difficult to comprehend, however, until you have seen GIS in action is the extraordinary power of combining those two basic functions. By providing the data

contained in an electronic database with a spatial reference, i.e., with x,y co-ordinates, and then being able to access the data with software which allows you to query, analyze and display that data in geographic terms, a spectacular 'third dimension' is added to the information. If it is true that a picture is worth a thousand words, then a pictorial or graphical representation of complex data is very often worth several thousand numbers.

6.   This paper attempts to show how this 'third dimension' of GIS can assist civil engineers, by giving a few examples of how we are using GIS in civil engineering related projects to solve problems and provide answers that would otherwise not be possible.

RESOURCE MANAGEMENT

7.   Management of the precious resources of our world lies very close to the heart of civil engineering. The description of the profession of a Civil Engineer, dating back to the Royal Charter in 1828, as '....being the art of directing the Great Sources of Power in Nature for the use and convenience of Man' might need a bit of repolishing in the light of present day attitudes to green and feminist issues, but essentially every civil engineer strives to utilise the earth's materials in a careful and economical way, increasingly aware of the need to take into account the widest interpretation of the long term '...use and convenience of Man'.

8.   GIS is ideally suited to resource management, since the resources are on or in the ground and therefore the information relating to those resources can be spatially referenced. We are using GIS in two completely different parts of the world to provide essential management · support for natural resource extraction vital to the civil engineering industry. The first of these is the management of the marine sand and gravel aggregate around the United Kingdom. The second is for part of what will arguably become the largest civil engineering project of the 1990's, for management of up to 400 million cubic metres of marine sand required for reclamation for the many separate projects comprising Hong Kong's huge Port and Airport Development Strategy (PADS).

Marine sand & gravel in the U.K.

9.   The United Kingdom is one of the world's largest users of marine sand and gravel for construction industry purposes. In 1989, for example, some 25 million tonnes of marine aggregate were landed, nearly 20% of the national total demand for sand and gravel. The use of marine aggregate is much higher in the south east of England, providing some 40% of the total in the region increasing to 80% of consumption in the London area. It clearly is of vital importance to the nation's infrastructure.

10.   Marine aggregate is extracted by dredgers varying in capacity generally from 500 to 5000 tonnes, small enough to land their cargoes in a wide number of wharfs around the UK coast. Dredging technology has developed rapidly in recent years, and most extraction is now carried out using specially designed trailer suction vessels with dry self-discharge equipment. The industry fleet totals about 50 ships, with 5 major companies owning the majority and several minor operators having one or two dredgers.

11.   The Crown Estate.   The UK marine aggregate industry is administered by The Crown Estate which in addition to major land holdings owns about 50% of the country's foreshore, all the seabed to the 12 mile territorial limit and all the non-hydrocarbon mineral rights out to the UK continental shelf.   This is an area exceeding 200,000 km^2 off the coast of England and Wales.

12.   The Crown Estate, although originally under the direct control of the sovereign, passed in the eighteenth century to the control of Parliament and is now directed by a board of Commissioners under the Crown Estate Act of 1961.   The Crown Estate Commissioners are charged with ensuring that the value and income of the Estate are maintained and enhanced, using sound estate management practices.   All surplus income goes to the UK Exchequer.

13.   The offshore assets are controlled by licences granted by the Crown Estate.   A potential extraction area is first licensed temporarily for prospecting by the companies, and if commercial reserves are found, an extraction licence may be granted to that company after very thorough consultation with all organisations concerned.   The licence will set down special conditions which must be met by the operator, and will specify a royalty to be paid to The Crown Estate for each tonne of material extracted.

14.   Managing agents offshore.   Posford Duvivier has acted for several years as Dredging Adviser to The Crown Estate, originally dealing with the vital issues of ensuring that no seabed extraction adversely affected the coastline.   This role expanded to providing technical support on a wider range of topics.   With the substantial increase in demand for long term marine aggregate reserves in recent years, The Crown Estate decided to appoint Posford Duvivier as Managing Agents to deal on their behalf with all day to day management aspects of the dredging companies.

15.   The role of Managing Agents requires both strong commercial and technical management skills.   Commercial management involves a thorough understanding of the dynamics of the economic and market related factors influencing the supply and demand of all aggregates, both land and marine, to enable new areas of growth to be developed for the benefit of all parties, and to facilitate commercially correct royalty rates to be negotiated. In addition the commercial function administers all issuing of licences, recovery of royalties and dredging audits of the companies to ensure correct records are kept and compliance with licence conditions achieved. Access to accurate and up to date information is essential to be able to fulfil this function properly.

16.   The technical management main tasks include resource assessment, resource recovery and resource monitoring functions. Regarding resource assessment, the Crown Estate has a very large amount of historic data on its seabed resources from prospecting surveys carried out by companies over the last 30 years.   It also has commissioned extensive area studies from British Geological Survey, is receiving detailed information from current company prospecting activities, and will continue to receive ever more detailed information in the years and decades ahead.

17.   In order to manage the resource effectively in the long term, it is necessary to carry out assessments of the quantity and quality of the resource on an on-going basis. This is a very major and important technical management task.

18.   The recovery of the material from the seabed to the wharf is an increasingly high-technology field of operation. For effective asset management it is essential for the management team to have a thorough appreciation of present and likely future technologies. These include material quality and quantity measurement, vessel positioning systems, information technology and data transfer.

19.   One of the most important functions is that of resource monitoring. The extraction licences for sand and gravel require the licensees to carry out regular bathymetric and re-prospecting surveys, and to submit the information for evaluation. There is an input to the technical data from the dredging audits of the companies, on quality and quantity of materials extracted. In addition, an electronic monitoring system (EMS) is being established for all extraction vessels on Crown Estate licences, requiring the companies to provide electronically recorded data on position and dredging status so that any disputes on illegal dredging can be resolved, and to provide the companies themselves with improved management information.

20.   It can be seen that a vast amount of information is required to be processed, analysed and evaluated for effective resource management. Faced with this problem three years ago, we investigated which high technology management tools were most appropriate to help us. We came to the conclusion that GIS was the answer.

The U.K. Offshore Database

21.   Before setting up a system, we investigated very carefully the options available. The prime requirement, since we were tackling issues which no one had faced previously, was for a flexible system. We did not know and indeed could not know before we started where we might finish, and therefore a system which could be adapted and added to if necessary without wasting time, effort, money and data already invested in the project, was essential. The second requirement was the ability to run a low-cost pilot GIS study to test out assumptions and feasibility and confirm the extent, resources and cost of a full GIS database.

22.   An initial pilot project was undertaken using GIS software ARC/INFO running on a 386 PC platform. This was extremely valuable in proving the viability of GIS to handle the complexities encountered in managing the marine aggregate resources. It also highlighted the need to use workstation technology. The PC environment proved too restrictive in terms of time, space and processing power for the outlined objectives. The offshore database was then designed on and for use with workstation ARC/INFO using Sun's SparcStation as the hardware platform.

23.   The system has been established as a specialised tool and been tailored with a user friendly windowing system to facilitate reporting, on screen querying, analysis and plotting.

24.   The database was set up in two parts.   Firstly for management control, records of past extraction from each licence area are held and updated with each new set of monthly extraction figures.   This enables the dredging activities of companies to be carefully supervised, and is used in the accounting system for revenue returns.   The system has been designed to accommodate the day to day queries required of it, as well as the complex annual and bi-annual reports.   In addition the system is used to record the rapidly changing prospecting situation.   Its map production capabilities are used to generate high quality output required for reports to The Crown Estate.

25.   The second part of the system is concerned with geological and resource analysis.   The system has been designed to store the huge amounts of borehole information accumulated by The Crown Estate over many years.   This information, in conjunction with geological information from both company surveys and sources such as BGS, is used to obtain the volume of potential resource. Information regarding physical and environmental constraints is then incorporated with the analysis to determine the actual available resource.   These results then link back to the management system in determining policy for extraction to meet future requirements.

26.   The Data. Admiralty chart data is used as backdrop data for the system.   This necessitated digitising 25 Admiralty charts (mostly at 1:150,000 or 1:200,000 scales) as none were available in digital form.   Admiralty feature information such as seabed cables and pipelines, shipping channels and navigation aids all provide important information regarding other sea uses affecting an area. To our knowledge it is the first digital map of such extensive Admiralty coverage.

27.   The offshore maps of seabed sediment being compiled by British Geological Survey under joint contract for The Crown Estate and DOE are digitised as they become available giving an area indication of the geological trends.   However, the majority of geological data used in the system comes from detailed surveys carried out by the dredging companies.   Survey data includes charts of survey tracks, bathymetry, isopachytes and sample site (boreholes and grab samples).

28.   Text records comprise licence agreements, extraction records and geological sample data.   Entry of the licence and extraction records offered little difficulty.   The information was well documented, relatively simple, and had been logged using a standard format.   The co-ordinates of each licence area were entered at the keyboard along with its associated statistics.   This information is the basis of the management system.

29.   Geological samples data is the basis for the resource analysis.   This proved to be a problematic data set, as methods of collection and classification have varied considerably over the last 20 years.   This obviously has considerable influence on the quality of the data.   Conversion of the data into a standard digital format was complex.   A variety of conversion programmes was established to assist the process and maintain data integrity.   Each sample is assigned a degree of confidence.   The data has necessitated the

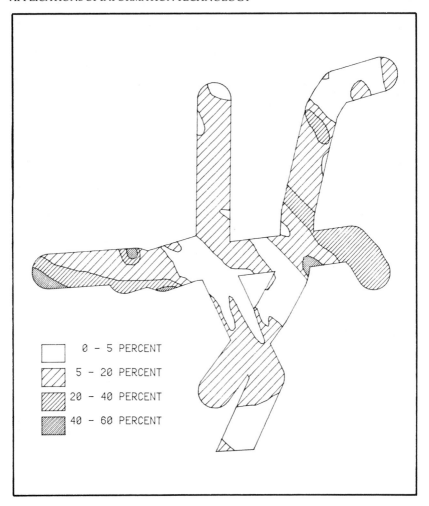

Fig. 1. Example of buffer zones, showing percentage of gravel
on seabed which might be affected by cables.

establishment of a sediment classification system based around
British Standard 5930. The latitude and longitude co-ordinates of
each sample are recorded as attributes and are used to create the
location map of sample sites. Data entry uses a series of
programmes incorporating special input forms which enables data
validation. Data structure of geological sample information has
been established to conform to the existing structure of the BGS
borehole database as far as is possible.

30.   Implementation. The UK offshore database took 2 years to
implement fully, from the initial decision to run the pilot study to
the time when essentially all the current and historic data had
been entered. By carefully phasing data entry and database module
design, to ensure that areas of greatest importance were addressed

first, benefit was obtained from the system at a relatively early stage, soon after the first year.

31.   The system is operated on a day to day basis by Posford Duvivier's Managing Agent team to obtain the information, analysis and reports they require.   The firm's separate GIS Group was responsible for all development work and most of the initial data entry, and can provide on-going support for any training and development work which might be required in the future.

32.   A simple example of one of the features of the system is illustrated in Fig.1.   Cables on the seabed effectively 'freeze' marine aggregate resources in the vicinity, since dredging vessels must be kept a safe distance away to prevent possible accidental damage to the cable.   The GIS can easily examine the quantity and quality of marine aggregate in any 'buffer' zone.   The operator can query the system for various buffer widths, and obtain quantities of aggregate affected.   This information can be used to assist the leasing valuation for the seabed cables, and to plan future resource extraction after the cable lease has expired.

Marine fill for reclamation in Hong Kong.

33.   The Hong Kong Government are embarking on one of the world's largest series of reclamation projects as part of the development of the Territory's airport and port facilities.

34. The Information Management System (IMS) project forms part of the Fill Management Study being undertaken by the Geotechnical Control Office (GCO) of the Civil Engineering Services Department in Hong Kong.   About 400 million cubic metres of marine dredged sand fill are expected to be required for reclamation purposes in the next 20 years or so.

35.   The Fill Management Study will be generating very large amounts of detailed information on the quality and quantity of the marine and alluvial deposits lying below Hong Kong waters.   Much reconnaissance work has already been carried out, with marine seismics and several hundred boreholes.   Further investigation will generate thousands of kilometres of additional seismics and many hundreds of extra borehole records.

36.   How could this huge amount of information best be handled to enable optimised management decisions to be taken on allocation of fill resources to infrastructure projects in the next 10 to 20 years, given that many of the Port and Airport Development Strategy (PADS) related projects are on very tight time schedules, and reclamation fill is inevitably in the first phase of project construction?   Clearly the answer lay in the use of computer databases and information technology systems.

37.   Posford Duvivier through their GIS work for the Crown Estate are at the forefront of the application of information technology to the management of marine sand and gravel.   Au Posford, the Hong Kong office of Posford Duvivier, were therefore appointed by Civil Engineering Services Department in September 1990 to establish, on a turnkey basis, an information management system which could then be operated by GCO to manage the marine fill resources of Hong Kong.

38.   The System. With the Hong Kong Government's selection of ARC/INFO GIS software on a linked Sun SparcStation and PC 386 hardware platform, flexibility to facilitate future enhancement and development is assured.   The capacity and speed of the system is more than adequate for the current and anticipated data set.   The system is also compatible with the system introduced in 1989 by the Building and Lands Department of the Hong Kong Government.

39.   The Data. It   is   essential   in   developing   an   information management   system   that   the   data   structures   for   the   various elements   of   the   database   are   very   carefully   designed.   Therefore considerable   attention   has   been   paid   in   the   start-up   stage   to defining   data   structures   particularly   for   the   geotechnical   and seismic   information.   Full   Admiralty   chart   data   has   also   been entered, e.g. bathymetry, cables pipelines and other seabed services, navigation   data   and   dumping   areas.   Details   of   all   reclamation projects   and   contracts   will   be   entered.   The   system   is   also compatible   with   Timeline,   the   PC   based   project   management software, and will therefore be able to receive and output project related data via widely based sources.

40.   Implementation. Implementation   of   the   system   is   being carried   out   under   a   tight   time   schedule,   in   order   to   be   ready   to receive   data   from   the   detailed   investigations   of   the   Fill Management Study. The major element of the project has been the development   and   customization   stage   in   which   various   modules   of the system were established to deal with different aspects of the management   process.   These   modules   include   data   entry,   data validation, analysis, management and output plotting and reports.

COASTAL ENGINEERING

41.   In addition to resource management applications, we have also used GIS to assist in planning coastal defence strategies. By ensuring close liaison between the GIS specialists and the coastal engineering specialists and designing the database with great care, extremely valuable analysis capabilities can be achieved.

42.   Database design.   Basic maps can be digitised into the system from Ordnance Survey sheets.   The 25000 series are usually the most convenient for such strategy studies. Particular features include coastline, line of MHWL and MLWL, mud areas along the shore, groynes, roads, spot heights, contours, town outlines, railway lines (used and unused), and sand dunes.   Additional digitised engineering data can also be entered, such as drainage lines.

43.   In addition to basic map data, other valuable information is also essential.   This can include bathymetric data from sea bed surveys, borehole data on seabed materials, seawall information including   data   about   the   frontages   along   the   seaside, environmentally protected areas, recreation areas, assessment of the status of the sand dunes, and assessment of the status of any piles or groynes along the seashore.

44.   It is outside the scope of this paper to go into great detail on the minutiae of data structure. An example of the types of data that can be entered, however, would be helpful to illustrate the practicable range of information to be stored and accessed in such a database.

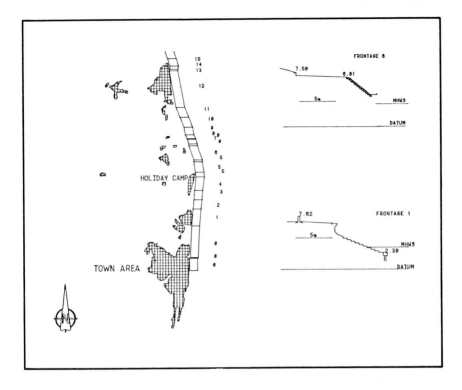

Fig. 2. Example of database seawall cross section display from selected frontages in coastal study.

45.   For a condition survey of existing seawall frontages, the following data items would typically be recorded:

Identity Number (a unique number for the system)
Co-ordinates of each end of the frontage
Frontage Number
Part Number (if frontage has more than one type of wall)
Description of the frontage
Description of the type of defence
Construction date
Level of the crest
Level of the toe
Description of vegetation behind the seawall
Indication of any previous defence
Condition of the toe
Condition of the revetment
Condition of the wave wall
Condition of the crest
Overall condition of the frontage
Name of the cross section associated with the frontage

46.   This data as well as all other data in the database can then be queried in spatial as well as numerical terms. A simple example of the output is illustrated in Figure 2, to show how individual

cross sections can be displayed for any particular frontage. The use of colour, not available in this paper, greatly enhances GIS output, since colour coding of maps and displays directs the human eye to the essential interpretation of complex data.

PORT & HARBOUR ENGINEERING & PLANNING

47. A further example of the use of GIS in which we have been involved is that of port planning. The technical issues involved in developing a port are extremely complex, and cover many areas that are not directly linked to civil engineering. However, most of them are related to spatial data and therefore a GIS approach provides an extremely effective method of helping to solve many of the problems.

48. Port planning will frequently involve the following disciplines and particular issues:

Land use planning
- policy planning and property valuation
- urban design and town planning
- landscape architecture

Transport & traffic
- traffic engineering
- transportation analysis
- public transport planning

Port planning
- port engineering
- cargo handling and dockyard operations
- reclamation

Marine impact
- harbour operations, navigation and craft manoeuvering
- hazardous cargoes
- risk analysis
- dredging

Engineering & infrastructure
- geotechnical engineering
- railways, highways, utilities
- public health and waste management
- hydrology
- marine structures

Environmental
- air, noise and water quality
- pollution control
- terrestrial and marine ecology
- visual impacts
- archaeology

Financial
- privatisation options
- financial modelling

49. Although each discipline brings its own specialist expertise and experience to the project, and therefore needs to act independently on the issues involved, like all multidisciplinary teams there is a vital need to ensure that the final results reflect the combined skills of the group.

50. Furthermore, the data and information available to the different disciplines has large areas of overlap. Some of the information needed by one team will certainly be required by one or more of the other groups. All this clearly signals the value of having a common database of project and site information which can be accessed, updated and maintained as the planning project proceeds. GIS provides the ideal tool for this purpose, since it is flexible enough to be tailored to the precise requirements of any particular project.

51. However, GIS is not just a powerful spatial database. With project data stored in that spatial database, the data can be analysed and displayed in spatial and numerical terms, and the real power, the 'third' dimension of GIS really comes into its own.

52. Analyses of demographics, distribution networks, transportation, navigation restrictions, marine sediment distribution, dredging volumes, urban and rural planning options, and environmental impacts, to name a few, can be quickly carried out and a whole variety of alternatives examined.

53. A final value of GIS is the cartographic capabilities inherent in a geographical system. This means that very high quality output of drawings, plans, layouts and maps to a whole variety of scales and colours can be produced for communicating the results of the planning exercise to the large number of organisations inevitably involved in any major port development. Fig. 3 gives a simple example of a 3D view, although the inevitably severe restrictions in this paper on size and colour of illustrations doesn't do justice to the powerful graphics output of GIS.

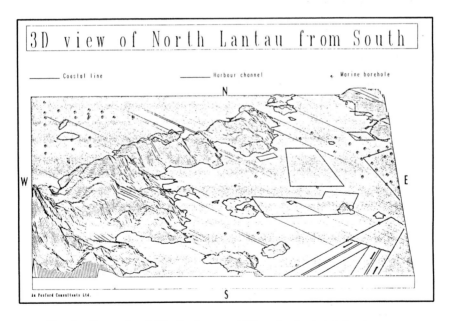

Fig. 3. Example of 3D display capability of selected datasets

THE FUTURE

54.   The very rapid developments in computer technology in recent years will continue at an ever faster rate in the future. This means that more and more computing power, in hardware terms, will be available at lower and lower cost.

55.   The challenge facing civil engineering managers now and in the future is how to harness this power to help them do their jobs more effectively.   If managers simply delegate complex decision making to computers they run enormous risks because they are then in essence abdicating their responsibility to those who put the computer systems together.   We will never completely escape from the GIGO (garbage in-garbage out) syndrome, and no one can predict the future in the management environment with such certainty that the unique human qualities of synthesis, evaluation and problem solving can ever become redundant.

56.   We believe that the future lies in developing powerful computer tools for civil engineering managers, so that they themselves can evaluate complex data simply and effectively and then make their decisions.   GIS is one of the most powerful tools in this respect now available to those managers who have to deal with large amounts of spatial information.

ACKNOWLEDGEMENTS

57.   The authors wish to acknowledge the major contributions being made by the Crown Estate in UK, and the Civil Engineering Services Department in Hong Kong, towards the development of Geographic Information System technology in civil engineering, and thank them for their permission to publish certain details regarding their GIS projects.

Traffic congestion modelling within the EC-funded DRIVE programme

S. DRUITT, Director, and D. McARTHUR, Senior Software
Engineer, SIAS Ltd

SYNOPSIS

The efforts of a small company to contribute to and gain from a large
bureaucratic research programme are described. Written from a historical
perspective, the author discusses some early considerations to be made
before funds can be obtained. The directors of the EC-funded DRIVE
programme have recognised the IMAURO research project as offering an
appropriate challenge and potential for wide application. The concepts of a
future traffic information and control environment which have emerged
from early research are fully embodied within DRIVE, and this has
stimulated a new approach to traffic simulation modelling, an element of
which is described below.

EC RESEARCH FUNDING

1.1   The DRIVE programme is one of a large number of EC research
funding initiatives which are attempting to strengthen competitiveness by
fostering cooperation between European commercial and academic bodies.
Although open to potential hijack by large commercial operators, EC
research programmes stimulate the interest of small companies which lack
personnel and capital to participate in the establishment of standards and
procedures. Funding for commercial organisations is at a rate of up to fifty
percent of costs, and some profit making concerns may not find this
sufficiently attractive to be of interest. One hundred percent funding is
available to academic organisations, for whom EC research grants are
becoming an increasingly important lifeline.

1.2   The requirement for proposal and contract deadlines varies between
research programmes, and the degree of bureaucracy varies between the
EC administrative bodies known as Directorates General. This tends to be
underestimated, and is the principle reason for participants not wishing to
continue with a second term of funding, although there are a number of
organisations who are very good at fielding eccentric EC directives.

1.3   Projects are usually required to be undertaken by consortia, and
rules stipulate the academic/non-academic mix and minimum number of
participants' countries of origin. Putting a multi-national consortium
together is the first test, and holding it together long enough to write a
proposal within very strict and often incomprehensible guidelines is a task

for a seasoned "Lead Contractor". The trick is to be a subcontractor to a Eurospeak linguist with EC insight and sufficient stature to keep the group together for the two to three years necessary to show a result and fulfill the terms of the contract.

THE DRIVE RESEARCH PROGRAMME

2.1   Like many acronyms, DRIVE is a bit of a forced misnomer, because the *safety* aspect of the "Dedicated Road Infrastructure for Vehicle safety in Europe" takes a back seat in what is more of a programme to address the problem of congestion, and how to best make use of rapidly diminishing European road space. DRIVE is mainly about "Road Traffic Informatics" (RTI), which will come with or without DRIVE simply because the pressure from the World's electronics industry is too great to resist.

2.2   The use of telecommunications is central to DRIVE's vision of a future road environment. The development of suitable technologies will result in vehicles being imbued with "intelligence", by which they may sense and respond to movements of neighbouring vehicles or obstructions to vehicular flow. The term IRTE (Integrated Road Traffic Environment) describes the infrastructure enabled by the new RTI technologies.

2.3   The EC's injection of 60 million ECU into a shared cost research programme to coordinate research and set standards also provides impetus to computer traffic modelling, a subject which has seen surprisingly few advances since its inception in the late 1960s. For those with the enthusiasm to continue, "DRIVE-II" offers potential from 1992, although this is expected to dwell more on aspects of implementation, and to be dominated by electronics and automotive concerns.

2.4   To get on in the EC, a consortium needs a good acronym, preferably related to a character from ancient Greek history or mythology. Names such as PROMETHEUS, SOCRATES, ICARUS, ATLAS, ULYSSES, CASSIOPE, PANDORA abound, although it is not clear why the representatives of chaos and disaster should be so honoured. Naturally, Euro-names are popular, as are female names, and the DRIVE programme upholds this tradition, spawning a new autostrada strain for good measure.

2.5   Knowledge of the nomenclature may be demonstrated at the frequent "concertation" meetings, at which all contractors are expected to attend. Administration and coordination functions are conducted here, and papers presented to a theme chosen during the course of a previous concertation meeting. All proceedings are in English, the official language of DRIVE, although this is of a Euro-technical variety which needs its own dictionary to decipher. Consequently, concertation meetings are very dull, with delegates airing convoluted policy statements rather than communicating at a working level. Some find this the least attractive aspect of the programme, although the meetings can spawn more useful impromptu secondary events.

THE IMAURO CONSORTIUM

3.1   The author's company, SIAS, is participating in the DRIVE programme as a subcontractor to a project sporting the acronym IMAURO (Integrated Model for the Analysis of Urban Route Optimization). This was invented by our Belgian colleagues, and is unusually descriptive. The IMAURO consortium was initially composed of six concerns, one academic, four commercial, and one quasi-governmental. The latter, the Belgian Road Research Laboratory, acts as the lead contractor. One Belgian commercial partner has gone out of business, while the largest (German) partner has dropped out. Intellectual leadership comes from the Mathematics Department at the University of Namur, whilst the RTI hardware interest is maintained by the Belgian company Devlonics.

3.2   The project's objective is to build a traffic modelling system to test the effects of RTI strategies, and to complete it in demonstrator form by December 1991. Seen as an essential tool for traffic planning, the system will be used in simulation testing of incident detection, the flow of traffic information and advice, route planning, route guidance and collision avoidance. To do this, the IMAURO partners are pioneering new traffic modelling techniques. The challenge is recognised by Stergiou and Stathopoulos (ref.1) who write "..the most marked effect of RTI systems in modelling practice will be the adoption of drivers' performance and reaction to the new driving conditions, which means that a new philosophy should be adopted in traffic models sensitive to the impact of RTI systems".

3.3   SIAS's contribution to the DRIVE effort is outlined below. In particular, a new methodology based on behavioural modelling required to encompass the RTI concepts within the IMAURO simulation system is described, and its role is identified within an IRTE. The IMAURO system will consist of three cooperating subsystems, each capable of modelling traffic but to different geographical scales.

THE DRIVE IRTE AND RTI CONCEPTS

4.1   The traffic scenario shown in figure 1 symbolizes a possible DRIVE vision of a future traffic environment. Vehicles, suitably warned of upstream obstructions (such as road works, tailbacks or accidents) may plan diversions well in advance. Rather than contribute to the growth of congestion centred about the incident, traffic is dispersed.

4.2   The portion of IRTE shown may be considered part of a wider urban road network, on which broadcast devices and traffic condition information processors are superimposed. IMAURO's view of an IRTE consists of the superposition of two networks:
1. The physical road network (eg. roads, lanes, junctions, traffic lights).
2. An information network consisting of :
   a) DETECTORS : roadside sensors which detect vehicles with suitable onboard RTI devices.
   b) SOCKETS : roadside beacons which broadcast traffic information.
   c) A TRAFFIC INFORMATION CENTRE : which receive incoming data from detectors, sort the information according to priorities and transmit the data to the sockets.

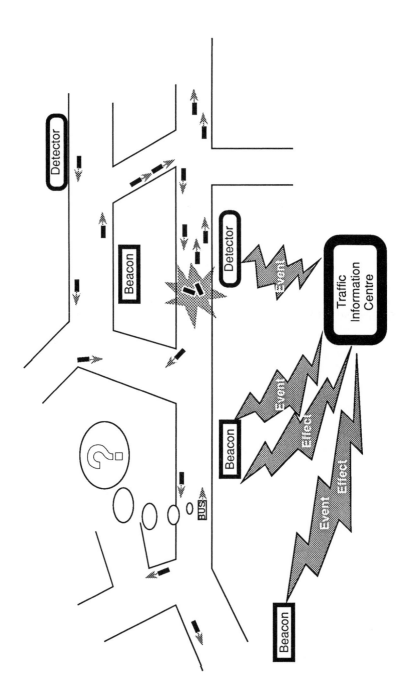

Figure 1: The DRIVE IRTE

d) A TRAFFIC CONTROL CENTRE : which assesses the traffic situation by monitoring data passing through the traffic information centres, composes advice for motorists and transmits advice to the sockets.

4.3   To make use of such a flow of traffic information within an information network, vehicles must have onboard communication devices which can ideally both receive and transmit information. As part of the DRIVE effort, the SECFO consortium headed by Daimler Benz have identified the technologies which will play a leading role in an IRTE (ref.2). These are :
1. Radio Data Systems, allowing parallel transmission of digital data and VHF/FM.
2. Systems based on Cellular Mobile Telephone technology.
3. Intelligent Cruise Control by which vehicles will be equipped to "sense" other elements of traffic within their proximity zones.
4. Interactive Route Guidance, providing vehicle position identification and route optimisation.
5. User Financing For Infrastructure, featuring time-dependent charging for effective use of roads.
Variable Message Signs technology, already in widespread use, should be added.

4.4   Drivers investing in RTI will benefit in terms of speedier and less stressfull travel. With suitable inducements and infrastructure investment the market for RTI can be stimulated by national governments. DRIVE expects the RTI elements to be in widespread use by the end of the century, although much painstaking work has to be undertaken to set international standards on RTI and the IRTE so that drivers may draw the same benefits across national boundaries.

THE IMAURO MODELS

5.1   A transport system may be modelled as a very large set of interacting variables. Traditionally, transport planning models tend to be "macroscopic" or "microscopic", the former considering traffic in terms of flows in roads with given capacities and the latter attempting to model individual or groups of vehicle s as discrete units. IMAURO attempts to bring the two approaches together in the form of a three stage dynamic model comprised of subsystems named TOPSORT, PACSIM (Packet Simulation), and SIAS's contribution MICSIM (Microscopic Simulation).

Background to MICSIM (ref.3)

5.2   Traditionally, highly deterministic solutions have been derived in traffic analysis for situations where the consequences of inputs are not precisely known. It has long been recognised that the achievement of "simulation", the modelling of individual vehicle movements, provides the best basis for the study of dynamic systems, which consider both the variations in travel demand and the fluctuations in the resulting traffic conditions through time.

5.3   In being "dynamic", IMAURO is consequently "non-equilibrium". Complete model cycles are measured in small numbers of minutes, within which most vehicles do not complete their journeys. There has been some disagreement among the team on the degree of dynamism and whether or not IMAURO should contain an element of equilibrium.

5.4   Apart from computer power, simulation models face severe calibration problems due to complexities resulting from their hybrid deterministic/stochastic nature. The principle behind MICSIM is to combine algorithmic simplicity with analytical sophistication, in the belief that this will provide a valid modelling platform more able to exploit the emerging computational infrastructure. While obeying basic rules dictated by network geometry, kinetics and the law, MICSIM's operation is almost entirely governed by driver perception of gap acceptance.

5.5   Inevitably, such a simplistic approach will be modified as the realities of validation become apparent. MICSIM's predominantly non-deterministic mode is essential if computational time is to be found to address some difficult problems, such as overtaking, parking, route deviation from PACSIM, and RTI input.

5.6   The principal function of MICSIM is to examine local vehicular flow at the microscopic level and determine the values of parameters required by TOPSORT's strategic modelling algorithms. To do this, MICSIM simulates individual vehicles, and models their interaction and the interaction with the network description derived from the IMAURO infrastructure database. MICSIM reacts to irregular events derived from RTI data, and transmits parametric consequences to TOPSORT. Through MICSIM, IMAURO is reactive, in varying degrees of real time.

5.7   The flow of information between the three models is shown in figure 2 :

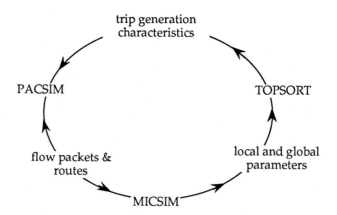

Figure 2: IMAURO relationships

5.8   TOPSORT, PACSIM and MICSIM each operate on different geographical areas of an urban network such as those in figure 3. Affordable computers are not yet available to enable MICSIM to function on a large geographical scale, so it acts as "moving cursor" under user or software direction. MICSIM is concerned purely with drivers' immediate intentions and perceptions, modelling the movement of individual vehicles using simple car following rules and behaviour modelling to maintain safe distances on highway links and observe gaps at junctions.

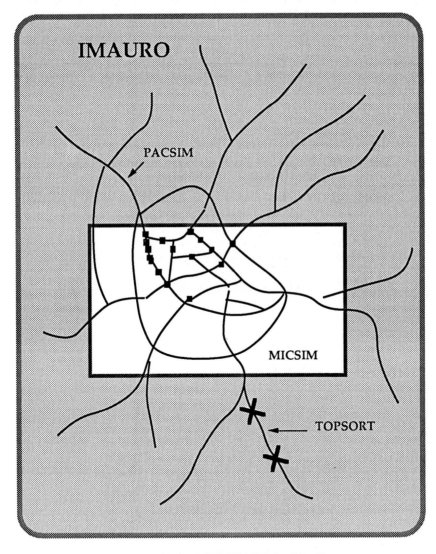

Figure 3: IMAURO Relationships II

5.9   PACSIM operates at the more aggregate level of "packets" of vehicles with common objectives, and is an even mix between policy or strategy and practice. TOPSORT is concerned with "higher level" matters, and is biassed towards strategy. It considers a large number of parameters in determining the relative attractiveness of highway links, from the more obvious level of congestion to the less obvious potential for environmental damage.

5.10   Within IMAURO, the three subsystems will operate in a loop, currently requiring three networked computers, subsystems activating each other by the transmission of data. TOPSORT will determine initial highway network costs and capacities, passing these to PACSIM, which uses a simple model of traffic demand to simulate packet flow. PACSIM can also obtain more accurate information regarding vehicular movements and the formation of tailbacks within a smaller area by initiating MICSIM, which separates packets into vehicles, and displays movements at a graphical interface. Thus MICSIM provides a window on the PACSIM simulation.

5.11   Established macroscopic and microscopic traffic modelling techniques employed within the three sub-models of IMAURO are sufficient to model current urban traffic. With reference again to figure 1, complications are seen to arise when attempting to incorporate RTI. Drivers in receipt of broadcast traffic information are likely to modify their speeds, safe distance, routes or even their destinations. In addition, traffic incidents such as tailbacks or congestion must be modelled dynamically, so the flow of data in the information network cannot be determined in advance.

5.12   The developers of PACSIM argue that established modelling methodology fails in the face of such complexities and that new techniques must be employed to model driver behaviour directly (ref.4). The belief that new modelling techniques must place an emphasis on behaviour is shared by Steriou and Stathopoulos who also claim "..coordination of several RTI systems, such as traffic controls and individual vehicle guidance, will require any traffic network control models to deal with traffic flows at the individual vehicle/driver level". The onus of developing the new techniques clearly lies with the developers of MICSIM, the microscopic sub model.

A FORMAL FRAMEWORK FOR DESCRIBING DRIVER BEHAVIOUR

6.1   A formal framework has been developed by SIAS to represent driver behaviour within a traffic modelling system. Supported with software tools, the framework consists of three independent components which are outlined by examples below. (A formal description can be found in ref. 5.) It should be noted that the components are independent, some or all of which will be used in future traffic modelling projects.

Formal Data Structures For Describing RTI Data.

6.2   The numerous forms of information that might feature in RTI broadcasts may be cast into one of three data types, each with a fixed set of attributes :
   1. EVENTS may be used to describe the remarkable traffic conditions that are occurring at certain roads or junctions. The EVENT data type

specification has attributes:
a) NATURE, one of ACCIDENT, ROADWORKS, SPILL, FLOOD, FOG, RAIN, SNOW, ICE, WIND, TAILBACK.
b) TIME, ie the clock time at which the event occurred.
c) POSITION, ie the point on the road network where the event occurred.

2. EFFECTS which describe the impact the event has on the road network. The EFFECT specification contains components:
a) TYPE, one of CONGESTED, TAILEDBACK, MAXSPEED, PARKING, BARRED, NOLANE.
b) VALUE associated with an effect (eg. the identity of the closed lane or speed value).
c) HORIZON, or clock time at which the effect ceases (24:00 if unknown).

3. The ROUTE UPDATE represents positive advice to motorists and contains components:
a) TARGETS: Set of destinations (ie.junction names) for which the route update is relevant.
b) SUBDESTINATIONS: Sequence of junction names which the road user is recommended to follow en route to the TARGETS.

6.3   Note that it is not intended that a SUBDESTINATIONS component of the route update should fully describe a new route for relevant vehicles. It might take the flavour "..vehicles bound for junction X from road Y should proceed via junctions W and Z..". Conversely, for the purposes of directing vehicles with route guidance equipment, the SUBDESTINATIONS component might consist of a complete sequence of contiguous junctions which fully determine a route from the road user's current position.

A Formal Behavioural Rule Language.

6.4   The rule language permits the specification of behavioural response of road users in particular traffic situations described in terms of objects of the traffic model (eg.vehicles, route updates, effects, events etc.) and their attributes. The 'when' part of each rule stipulates conditions on values of one or more attributes of such objects. If these conditions are satisfied then the 'follow' part of the rule is enacted. In the 'follow' part new values are assigned to attributes of objects.

For example, the bus driver in figure 1 may consider a short detour necessary, outwith the peak hour when informed by Radio Data Systems that the next road on the intended route is barred. The formal language description is:

```
WHEN    USER.MODE              =  BUS
        USER.RTITECH           =  RADIO_DATA_SYSTEM
        EVENT.EFFECT.TYPE      =  BARRED
        EVENT.EFFECT.POSITION  =  USER.ROUTE.FIRST
     (NOT NOW                 >= 16:00 OR
      NOT NOW                 <= 18:00)
```

```
FOLLOW    $DETOUR              =  MINCOSTROUTE(
                                     USER.POSITION TO
                                     USER.ROUTE.SECOND
                                     EXCLUDE =
                                     (EVENT.EFFECT.POSITION))
          $RESTROUTE           =  BREAK(USER.ROUTE FROM
                                     USER.ROUTE.SECOND)
          USER.ROUTE           =  JOIN($DETOUR $RESTROUTE)
```

6.5   The objects referred to in the rule are USER, EVENT and EFFECT (namely, the first event and effect broadcast at the nearest socket to the road USER). The 'when' part in this rule contains three clauses (identified here with the "=" operator at the centre of each clause). The clauses are implicitly 'anded' together.

6.6   Most other symbols are operators used to access attribute values. Thus '.EFFECT' refers to the first effect with the event. In the rule, the '.TYPE' operator accesses the TYPE component of the effect and its value is matched (with use of "=") against the quoted value of BARRED. Similarly, the '.POSITION' operator accesses the position on the network where the effect associated with the event is located.

6.7   Boolean operators "NOT" and "OR" may be used within the "WHEN" part of rules. (NOT applies to one clause only). Also, typically the route is given a new value in the "FOLLOW" part of a rule. This may be achieved using functions to calculate portions of a route meeting certain criteria, then using the "JOIN" function to compose a new route from these portions. The two functions currently available for determining routes are MINCOSTROUTE and VIANEARESTLINK. Both invoke a shortest path algorithm; MINCOSTROUTE finds the shortest path between two fixed positions, and VIANEARESTLINK finds the shortest path from a fixed position to a road meeting a certain criteria. Both functions may take parameters specifying junctions to be included or excluded in the path.

6.8   Since bus drivers normally follow fixed routes, the new route is composed by taking the shortest path around the affected road and joining this with the unaffected portion of the fixed route. Roads to be excluded in the calculation are specified as a set enclosed within brackets.

6.9   To operate efficiently, the rules must be evaluated in a short time for all vehicles in the simulation reaching junctions or in range of RTI data. To this end a subsystem, termed the "rule mechanism", compiles the rules into a structure known as a decision tree. In constructing this, the mechanism warns of redundancies (such as one rule being more general than another) and merges identical clauses shared by rules for efficient matching. Advantages of this approach are:
   a) The decision tree can be compiled directly to nested "if..then..else.." code of the implementation computer language, which can be combined with the rest of the simulator system code for maximum efficiency.
   b) Code can be included with the compilation to record the route decisions enacted on behalf of vehicles, to provide a representation of a vehicle's history in the IRTE.

c) A graphical interface enables the modeller preparing a rule set to discern the impact of adding or deleting rules when the decision tree is viewed.

The stages of compilation of rules to efficient code is shown in figure 4.

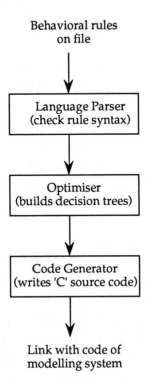

Figure 4: Stages of Rule Compilation

6.10   The rule language offers the benefits of:
   a) *PERSPICUITY* : With little training such rules are readily understood by the model user.
   b) *FLEXIBILITY*. Rules can be added, removed or modified as new behavioural theories are forthcoming from traffic research.
   c) *EXTENSIBILITY*. The language can be made more powerful with addition of new functions.
   d) *PRECISION*. The formality of the language precludes ambiguity.

6.11   Some twenty rules comprising a behavioural "theory" are now in use for the initial test phase of MICSIM. The theory will be modified to take account of empirical and psychological observations of driver behaviour as these emerge from other DRIVE projects.

FURTHER WORK

7.1   Despite the perhaps inevitable bureaucratic irritations, the DRIVE programme has provided a focus for research and development, and will assist the orderly introduction of systems and standards to ease traffic congestion. The DRIVE concepts of RTI and IRTE pose a considerable challenge to traffic modelling research, and SIAS's response has been to introduce a formal framework for representing driver behaviour within traffic modelling systems encompassing the effects of RTI.

7.2   MICSIM will demonstrate the feasibility of the framework, which has also been adopted in the design of PACSIM. Shared rules ensure compatability of traffic behaviour across the different geographical scales modelled by the two systems. The framework is attracting attention from other DRIVE researchers. The language component is seen to provide a general yet unambiguous basis of describing behaviour, allowing the rule mechanism to translate into areas of travel demand and mode choice.

7.3   MICSIM derivatives will stand on their own, and further applications are likely to include the modelling of rural traffic, involving rules to describe complex overtaking behaviour.

CONCLUSIONS

8.1   A certain amount of luck is required to find the right partners if a small company is to benefit from participating in a large EC research programme. In particular, one of the partners must be versed in Euro-bureaucracy and be willing to shoulder a disproportionate burden of administration.

8.2   Elements of a futuristic road traffic information environment were presented, and the emphasis on traffic modelling shown to be concentrated on driver behaviour. This has been tackled by the IMAURO consortium through the introduction of a formal descriptive language to be embedded within a computer system. The formalism has potential for other traffic modelling applications.

8.3   Whether development beyond the prototype stage takes place within the IMAURO consortium, or under the auspices of DRIVE or any other EC funded programme is open to debate. If it does, the first task may be to invent a new acronym.

REFERENCES.

1.   Stergiou B.,Stathopoulos A., "Traffic models and Road Transport Informatics (RTI) systems", Traffic Engineering + Control, December, 1989.

2.   Report Number 1,SECFO Quarterly, Systems Engineering and Consensus Formation Office, Rue de Treves, B-1040, Brussels.

3.   Druitt, S. "Prototype Definition of the MICSIM submodel", SIAS Ltd., 4 Heriot Row, Edinburgh, EH3 6HU.

4.   Dehoux P., Manneback P, Toint P., "PACSIM: A Dynamic Traffic Assignment Model,II Functional Analysis", Traffic Study Group,Department of Mathematics, Facultes Universitaires ND de la Paix,B-5000 Namur, Belgium.

5.   McArthur D.,"Progress with a Rule Mechanism for representing Driver Behaviour within Traffic Simulation Systems", Work Paper EC-3. SIAS Ltd., 4 Heriot Row, Edinburgh, EH3 6HU.

The development of TRAIDS – a traffic impact analysis database

Professor K. W. DICKINSON, Head of Civil Engineering, M. A. MacIVER, Lecturer, and C. L. WAN, Lecturer, Napier Polytechnic of Edinburgh

SYNOPSIS. It is important during the planning and design of a new development that due consideration is given to the traffic impact analysis (TIA) of the proposal on the surrounding community. Currently difficulties arise when preparing TIAs due to a lack of relevant traffic data for different development categories. Therefore over the past two years Napier Polytechnic has, under contract to several Scottish Central and Local Government Departments, produced a trip generation and parking database known as TRAIDS.

INTRODUCTION.

1. Information technology has had a profound influence on the transportation sector of Civil Engineering during the past decade. One area of particular benefit has been the development of methods of data collection, processing and management. Although Highway and Roads Authorities have invested significant time and expense on the collection of appropriate local traffic data the full potential benefits to be derived from this data have yet to realised. There are two major reasons for this, firstly, the data is primarily held and used by a single authority and, secondly, survey results are not held in a readily accessible form. Both of these issues have been addressed during the development of the TRAIDS (which is an acronym for the "traffic impact of developments in Scotland") database described below.

2 In recent years there has been a significant increase in large-scale development planning applications for various land-use categories. As part of a planning application, Local authorities require the submission of a detailed traffic impact analysis (TIA) statement to support the application on traffic grounds. Due to a lack of standardisation in the format of TIAs and the lack of available data, a proliferation of appeals has resulted, leading to lengthy and costly public inquiries.

3 Recognising the above factors a group comprising the Transportation Engineering Research Unit of Napier Polytechnic, seven Scottish Roads

Authorities, the Scottish Development Department and the Scottish Development Agency are investigating aspects of traffic impact analysis. Current TIA practice has been researched and guidelines produced which have standardised the format of TIA methodology throughout Scotland (ref. 1,2). To support these guidelines a nationally agreed trip generation database, TRAIDS, was proposed by the roads authorities. The aims of the system were agreed at the outset of the project and are given below:

    (a) To fully utilise existing and future survey results by pooling data obtained by all members of the consortium and thus provide an agreed dataset for use in the preparation of TIAs and reports to be presented at public inquiries.

    (b) To improve the efficiency of data collection within the consortium by organising a structured series of surveys to supplement existing data and expand the base of information into all those land-use categories which were identified as significant.

    (c) To make appropriate data readily accessible by the development of a micro-computer based system that will be easily operated by traffic engineers and planners.

4   This paper will therefore outline the development of the TRAIDS database which runs on an IBM compatible micro-computer. It was originally developed to run using the dBaseIII software but has now been implemented as a stand alone system. Initially, TRAIDS comprised only retail development data but recent roads authority survey programmes have provided data on other land-uses including industrial, residential, hotel and leisure categories. It is continually being expanded in terms of land-use categories and is being further adapted to include automatic traffic count data. The paper will describe the current stage of development of TRAIDS and finally consider its future development.

BACKGROUND TO TRAFFIC IMPACT ANALYSIS

5   It is important in the planning and design of new developments, that provision is made for adequate traffic access to and egress from the development, and also that adequate car parking is provided at the development. It can be seen that one of the major considerations in the TIA process is the amount of traffic that will be generated by the development. This will give an estimate of the additional traffic that the road network will carry, which will in turn give an indication of, firstly, the need for upgrading parts of the road network and, secondly, the provision of new traffic infrastructure where required. On-street car parking leads to congestion, visibility and road-safety problems, therefore it is essential that adequate off-street car parking is provided to cater for the traffic generated by the development.

6   The current techniques used to estimate the traffic generation of developments are largely based on empirical relationships between certain characteristics of the development and the number of trips having an origin or destination there.   The characteristics used are, for example, floor area for retail centres, number of bedrooms for hotels, number of houses for residential developments and number of employees for offices or industrial premises. Hazel (ref.3) has shown that in the case of retail developments the use of floor area alone is questionable because it is recognised that store characteristics and the catchment area are factors which affect the number of trips made to a store.

7   Many consultants are currently using material such as the traffic generation guidelines produced by the Greater London Council (ref.4) which is based on data collected predominantly in the 1970s. However the significant development changes that have been taking place over the last few years result in traffic survey data becoming outdated relatively quickly. It is clear therefore that such data is inappropriate and the use of more recent local data is necessary.

8   Local authorities have, over the past decade, experienced a significant increase in planning applications for large-scale developments, including retail, industrial, residential and leisure. Recognising this, Local authorities are asking developers to supply comprehensive TIA statements to support the application on traffic grounds. The lack of data that is available is causing difficulties in assessing the impact of these developments on the surrounding road network. This has led to problems arising in respect of the interpretation and format of TIAs and the identification of agreements under Section 52 of the Town and Country Planning Act (Section 50 of the Scottish Act), which cover any necessary improvements to the surrounding road network.

9   The use of a common database has overcome the problems previously experienced with regard to the agreement of data and enables consultants and developers to use data that has been verified by the roads authorities. This may reduced disagreements regarding the trip generation rates of new developments, if rates can be compared with similar local data.   A comprehensive database will provide readily available data which consultants can access in their office without having to go elsewhere, or use outdated trip rates, or carry out major surveys at existing developments.

THE FORMATION OF THE TRAIDS GROUP
10   Overall responsibility for the administration of planning in Scotland rests with the Secretary of State. His responsibilities are discharged. through the Scottish Development Department. The SDD does not impose policies on regional planning authorities but ensures that their policies do not run counter to national policy. Administration of the Town & Country

Planning legislation at a local level is in the hands of regional and district planning authorities.

11   The distribution of planning functions put into effect by the Local Government (Scot) Act 1973 is not uniform over all of Scotland. Planning powers and duties are conferred on only 49 of the 65 district authorities. In Central, Fife, Grampian, Lothian, Strathclyde and Tayside planning functions are divided between the two tiers of local government, the regional councils and district councils. In the three most sparsely populated regions; Borders, Dumfries & Galloway and Highland responsibility for planning lies with the regional council, as is the case with the three all-purpose island authorities.

12   The regional roads authority has responsibility for all roads within their region, excluding trunk roads. The increase in planning applications for new developments have placed additional burdens on the limited number of roads authorities staff who deal with development control. The traffic generation rate of developments was difficult to estimate due to the lack of data available. Each region had carried out a limited number of traffic count surveys at existing developments. Some data exchange took place between regions (ref.5) when new development applications were made, which highlighted the need for all regions to pool their resources in a common database. The original members of the TRAIDS group were Central, Fife, Grampian, Highland, Lothian, Strathclyde and Tayside Regional Councils, the Scottish Development Department and the Scottish Development Agency. Borders and Dumfries & Galloway did not join because of the sparsely populated nature of their particular regions which in their view did not justify the development of a comprehensive database for use in development control.

THE DEVELOPMENT OF TRAIDS
13   The database was originally developed using dBaseIII Plus. This meant that the users required a copy of dBaseIII Plus or its runtime variant to operate TRAIDS. Clearly a stand alone version was considered to be much more attractive and therefore the latest TRAIDS system is stand alone having been developed using Clipper 5.0. The system will now run on any IBM PC compatible with a minimum of 512K system memory. The data files remain compatible with dBase. It is a user friendly, fully interactive system, with a powerful query facility which will filter the database to any user specified condition. For each land-use category you may specify a number of descriptors e.g. LOCATION = "Strathclyde" will result in only records from that region being visible. Although TRAIDS can be operated using the floppy disks as supplied it is preferable to have a 10Mb, or larger, hard disk for ease and speed of operation.

14   It was decided that in order to overcome computer disk formatting problems, traffic survey data would be supplied by the roads authorities in written form and then centrally coded onto computer at Napier Polytechnic, with the accuracy of the data being the responsibility of the source. At the outset, each region sent all their survey data associated with new developments. It was thus possible to plan a programme of additional surveys to be undertaken in the future. It was agreed that initial priority should be given to retail outlets, although eventually the database would cover as many land-uses as possible.

15   Standard data input forms containing the important parameters associated with each land-use category were designed on the basis of the suggestions of regional roads authority engineers. The main parameters considered for each of the categories are listed below.

(a) Retail: development category - food, non-food, mixed use
      location - town centre, out-of-town, suburban
      number of parking spaces
      floor area
      various operational characteristics, e.g. opening hours

(b) Residential: location - town centre, suburban, village, isolated rural
      type - private, public
      number of units
      number of bedrooms
      number of garages and car parking spaces
      gross floor and land area

(c) Industrial: location
      gross floor and land area
      number of units
      number of car parking spaces
      type of activity
      number of employees

(d) Leisure: location
      facilities - swimming pool, games hall, bar, restaurant
      gross floor area

(e) Hotels: location
      number of bedrooms
      number of parking spaces
      facilities - bars, restaurants, for leisure

16   Traffic count data is collected by many roads authorities by manual methods (manual classified counts - MCCs) and using automatic traffic counters (ATCs). Authorities are making increased use of ATCs due to their low operating costs and the vast quantity of data that can be obtained with ease when compared with MCCs. Continuous monitoring is increasingly available at large developments using permanent inductive

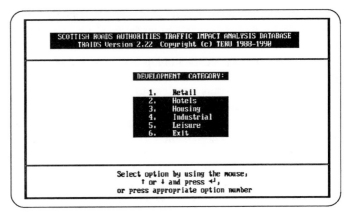

Fig. 1. Development Category Menu

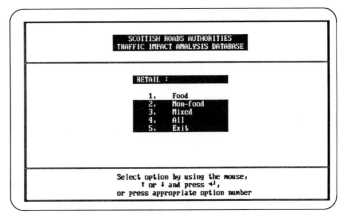

Fig. 2. Retail Sub-menu

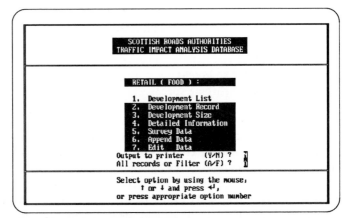

Fig. 3. Retail (Food) Sub-menu

loop detectors at entrances and exits. Temporary counts over short periods are still obtained, using pneumatic tube ATCs. Due to the inordinate volume of this data, in the past, this has seldom been fully analysed. However ATC information in a compressed form is now being introduced into TRAIDS.

SURVEY PROGRAMME

17 Once the initial traffic survey data was received an assessment was made of future survey requirements. It was clear that most of the available data was for retail developments. A survey programme for 1989 was drawn up by TERU and agreed with each roads authority. Every effort was made to accommodate each region's own survey programme, with the inclusion of land-use categories for which little data was available. This survey programme has provided data, in addition to retail, on housing, hotels, industrial, leisure and motorway services.

18 A survey programme is drawn up each year based upon the need to develop specific aspects of the database. The survey programme for 1991 will continue the updating exercise in relation to retail, housing, industrial and leisure categories. Large multi-use developments will also be surveyed to provide data for this expanding area. Over future years the survey programme will fully recognise changing development patterns and the need for associated information. Although the database is constantly being updated and expanded, at the present time there are over 300 individual developments included in TRAIDS.

USE OF THE SYSTEM

19 The database is menu-driven so that users who know nothing about the commands of the language can still operate the program. When TRAIDS is initially accessed, the development category menu appears (Fig. 1), which allows the user to choose the desired development category. If for example **Retail** is chosen a new sub-menu appears (Fig. 2) giving a choice of food, non-food, mixed or all retail developments. The third level sub-menu provides the options shown in (Fig. 3). The database offers the facility of listing all the data or accessing specific data using the Filter option, for example, all Asda stores between 4000sq.m. and 6000sq.m. gross floor area (GFA).

20 The **Development List** option lists the developments alphabetically (Fig. 4) giving the code, development name, category, town, region, date of survey form coding and location. The **Development Record** option also lists the developments alphabetically (Fig. 5) by code giving development name and town. Each individual record is listed with record number, operator, category, day and date of survey, gross floor area(sq.m.), peak hour and trip rate/100sq.m. GFA. The **Development Size** option is similar

CODE	DEVELOPMENT NAME	DEV. CATE- GORY	TOWN	REGION	DATE OF SURVEY FORM CODING	LOCATION
ASDA0000	ASDA	FOOD	DUNFERMLINE	FIFE	01/02/89	OUTER SUBUR
ASDA0001	ASDA	FOOD	DUNDEE	TAYSIDE	15/03/89	OUTER SUBUR
ASDA0003	ASDA	FOOD	GLASGOW	STRATHCLYDE	24/05/89	OUTER SUBUR
ASDA0004	ASDA	FOOD	KIRKCALDY	FIFE	02/06/89	OUTER SUBUR
COOP0000	CO-OP	FOOD	INVERNESS	HIGHLAND	21/11/88	OUTER SUBUR
FINF0000	FINE-FARE	FOOD	MONTROSE	TAYSIDE	09/03/89	TOWN CENTRE
GWAY0000	GATEWAY	FOOD	ABERDEEN	GRAMPIAN	13/03/89	INNER SUBUR
GWAY0001	GATEWAY	FOOD	ABERDEEN	GRAMPIAN	13/03/89	INNER SUBUR
GWAY0002	GATEWAY	FOOD	ABERDEEN	GRAMPIAN	13/03/89	INNER SUBUR
GWAY0003	GATEWAY	FOOD	GLASGOW	STRATHCLYDE	24/05/89	OUTER SUBUR
PRST0000	PRESTO	FOOD	INVERNESS	HIGHLAND	21/11/88	INNER SUBUR
PRST0001	PRESTO	FOOD	EDINBURGH	LOTHIAN	23/12/88	OUTER SUBUR
PRST0002	PRESTO	FOOD	ST. ANDREWS	FIFE	01/02/89	OUTER SUBUR
PRST0003	PRESTO	FOOD	DUNDEE	TAYSIDE	02/03/89	INNER SUBUR
PRST0004	PRESTO	FOOD	PERTH	TAYSIDE	06/03/09	TOWN CENTRE
PRST0005	PRESTO	FOOD	ARBROATH	TAYSIDE	09/03/89	INNER SUBUR
SCMD0000	SCOTMID	FOOD	EDINBURGH	LOTHIAN	23/12/88	OUTER SUBUR
SWAY0000	SAFEWAY	FOOD	EDINBURGH	LOTHIAN	23/12/88	OUTER SUBUR
SWAY0001	SAFEWAY	FOOD	EDINBURGH	LOTHIAN	23/12/88	INNER SUBUR

Press any key to continue...

Fig. 4. Development List

REC NO	OPERATOR			CATE- GORY	DATE		GFA (SQ METRES)	NFA	PEAK HOUR	TRIP RATE
CODE: ASDA0000	DEVELOPMENT: ASDA, DUNFERMLINE									
41	ASDA			FOOD	Thu	28/07/88	4920	2661	1700	13.6
CODE: ASDA0001	DEVELOPMENT: ASDA, DUNDEE									
45	ASDA			FOOD	Thu	04/09/86	5787	3472	1700	8.8
46	ASDA			FOOD	Fri	06/05/88	5787	3472	1600	8.4
CODE: ASDA0003	DEVELOPMENT: ASDA, GLASGOW									
102	ASDA			FOOD	Sun	14/08/88	7200		1400	13.8
103	ASDA			FOOD	Sat	13/08/88	7200		1500	19.6
104	ASDA			FOOD	Fri	12/08/88	7200		1600	15.3
CODE: ASDA0004	DEVELOPMENT: ASDA, KIRKCALDY									
117	ASDA			FOOD	Thu	16/03/89	6500		1430	6.8
118	ASDA			FOOD	Thu	16/03/89	6500		1645	9.7
119	ASDA			FOOD	Fri	17/03/89	6500		1415	9.8
120	ASDA			FOOD	Fri	17/03/89	6500		1630	13.3
CODE: COOP0000	DEVELOPMENT: CO-OP, INVERNESS									
1	CO-OP			FOOD	Thu	25/07/85	4350	2340	1715	13.6
2	CO-OP			FOOD	Thu	21/11/85	4350	2340	1715	12.1
3	CO-OP			FOOD	Fri	22/11/85	4350	2340	1645	13.9
CODE: FINF0000	DEVELOPMENT: FINE-FARE, MONTROSE									
60	FINE FARE			FOOD	Mon	27/10/86	2412	1447	1100	5.6
61	FINE FARE			FOOD	Fri	22/04/88	2412	1447	1400	9.5

Press any key to continue...

Fig. 5. Development Record

Fig. 6. Detailed Information Record

226

to Development Record with the surveys listed in ascending order of GFA.

21   **Detailed Information** of individual development and survey characteristics can be accessed by entering the survey record number. An example is shown for an Asda store in Dunfermline (Fig. 6). The days of opening, petrol station and autobank use the logical operators True or False. The program calculates the peak car park occupation, ratio of peak car park occupation/total number of spaces, the start of the peak hour and the peak hour trip rate, and the ratio of peak hour trips to gross and nett floor area.

22   The **Survey Data** for each record can be accessed by entering the survey record number. The traffic count data (Fig. 7) is listed by time period, arrivals, departures, total number of trips, trip rate per hour and the car park occupation. The trip rate is calculated by taking the total number of one-way trips, which are a combination of arrivals plus departures during a survey period. These are aggregated over 1 hour periods to give the peak hour trip rate. This is then computed and expressed as a trip rate per 100sq.m. of gross and nett floor area.

ANALYSING THE DATA
23   It can be seen from TRAIDS that variations exist within land-use types and also by time. This supports the need to find an alternative method for estimating trip generation rates. For 13 observed food retail sites on Thursdays the range in trip rates, for the peak hour for that day, varies from 7.66 to 21.95 trips per 100sq.m. GFA. For all surveys the peak hour trip rates vary from 5.26 to 30.77 trips per 100sq.m. GFA. For non-food retail a total of 33 surveys range from 0.59 to 16.44 trips per 100sq.m. GFA.

24   TRAIDS is not intended to be used to produce automatic trip rates for various land-use categories. Traffic engineers are required to exercise professsional judgement when using the database. It can be used to compare new developments with existing data of similar characteristics to estimate the trip generation potential of the new development. The Filter option is available for this purpose, which allows the user to search for developments by selecting specific parameter fields, for example, town, region, floor area range. The important characteristics for retail developments are the type of store, floor size, location and operator. TRAIDS provides a range of sites for comparison which will give a more realistic estimate than comparing the new development with data from a limited number of other similar development or by taking an average trip rate of a number of developments. By definition the average trip rates will typically underestimate the trip rates associated with 50% of the developments and this may in turn lead to an underestimation of the detrimental effects of the development on the surrounding road network.

SURVEY FILE:	ASDA0001	DATE:	Thu 20/07/00	WEATHER	:	DULL/SHOWERS	
OPERATOR:	ASDA, DUNFERMLINE			CATEGORY:		FOOD	
RECORD NUMBER	PERIOD BEGINS	ARRIVALS	DEPARTURES	TRIPS	TRIP RATE	CAR PARK OCCUPATION	
1	0900	58	21	79		87	
2	0930	83	56	139	218	114	
3	1000	101	67	168	307	148	
4	1030	139	79	218	386	208	
5	1100	125	142	267	485	191	
6	1130	123	134	257	524	180	
7	1200	116	124	240	497	172	
8	1230	112	112	224	464	172	
9	1300	100	139	239	463	133	
10	1330	104	99	203	442	138	
11	1400	137	110	247	450	165	
12	1430	144	115	259	506	194	
13	1500	75	99	174	433	170	
14	1530	110	95	205	379	185	
15	1600	115	149	264	469	151	
16	1630	159	145	304	560	165	
17	1700	170	164	334	638	171	
18	1730	166	170	336	670	167	
19	1800	153	160	313	649	160	
20	1830	161	148	309	622	173	

Press any key to continue...

Fig. 7. Traffic Survey Record

This problem may be minimised by giving an appreciation of the likely variation in trip rates for a given category of development at any particular location.

25   It is always necessary to consider variations in trip rates when assessing the impact of any development on the adjacent network. The capacity of the road network is normally assessed over time in order to cater for the demand at certain high load periods. There will be variations in the traffic generation of a single development between hours of day, days of the week and months of the year. TIAs are normally based on the traffic flows that will be experienced during the busiest times of the week. To allow for special peaks, such as shopping before Christmas a "highest hour" criteria is used. This may be the 20th or 30th highest hour to avoid the implementation of designs that would remain under-utilised for most of the year. The value of a database in these circumstances lies in the its ability to factor short period counts into peak hour trip rates based on a knowledge of the prevailing trends.

FUTURE DEVELOPMENTS
26   TRAIDS was initially marketed in a dBase version but is now sold in a stand alone form. It is purchased on an annual subscription basis with updates being made available at 6 monthly intervals. Roads authorities are making more use of ATCs for continuous traffic survey purposes. Under the present system however, data is input in individual records for single days or part of a day. Problems were encountered in the data collection process because roads authorities who used ATCs and wish data to be incorporated into TRAIDS have to convert data to written format acceptable to the database. This has highlighted the need to investigate a

more efficient method of incorporating a summary of ATC data into TRAIDS. Such a method is currently being developed and will be useful in allowing ATC data to be used in factoring ad hoc surveys.

27   The database is continually being developed as the needs of roads authorities and consultants become clear.   The area-wide assessment of TIA and an investigation of the trip types to retail developments are currently being undertaken. The areas which will be investigated in the future will include data relating to before and after studies, retail centre competition, catchment area characteristics and trip type classification.

28   Two other database projects, TRICS and GENERATE, are currently operating. TRICS is a collaborative venture between county councils in the south of England to develop a trip generation database. GENERATE is a national dial-up trip generation database developed and managed by county councils in the West Midlands. Discussion has taken place between the three groups to consider the possibility of sharing data. No final decision has been made at this stage.

CONCLUSIONS

29   Although not a sophisticated system the practical benefits of TRAIDS are clearly indicated by its widespread use throughout Scotland. TRAIDS has been installed on computer at the offices of all but two of the Scottish Regional Roads Authorities.   The Scottish Office, several consultants and English Local Authorities also make use of the database. The development of a trip generation database is an on-going process which requires time to develop and considerable input from all the parties involved.   The co-ordination of the survey programme has resulted in benefits to the regions in that the pooling of limited numbers of survey staff provides a more comprehensive coverage of developments at reduced costs.

30   In addition a series of seminars and conferences have been held at Napier Polytechnic which have helped local authorities, consultants and developers to gain a better understanding of the planning and transportation issues, that the current explosion of new developments is creating.

31   The on going aim of the project must be to exploit the full potential of TRAIDS as a tool to aid all the interested parties to process the traffic impact aspects of planning applications. In the future it is possible that the database could be used as an advisory system to assist in the complete TIA process. These areas will require considerable research in order to allow the database to evolve to supply the needs of an effective traffic impact assessment method.

REFERENCES

1. SCOTTISH ROADS AUTHORITIES. Guidelines on Traffic Impact Analysis, Transportation Engineering Research Unit, Napier Polytechnic, Edinburgh, May 1989.

2. DICKINSON K. W. and WOODBURN M. D. Area-Wide Assessment: A Way Forward? Conference on Travel Demand Forecasting, Napier Polytechnic, Edinburgh, April 1991.

3. HAZEL G. M. The Development of a Disaggregate Trip Generation Model for the Strategic Planning Control of Large Foodstores. 1: The problem with current practice and basis of an alternative approach, Traffic Engineering and Control, January 1989, p33 - 39.

4. GREATER LONDON COUNCIL. Traffic Generation : User's guide and review of studies (2nd Edition), Reviews and Studies Series No. 25, GLC, 1985.

5. NICOL R. The Traffic Impact of a Major Retail Development in Central Region, Paper presented for the Institution of Highways and Transportation Premium Paper Award 1988, Central Regional Council, Stirling, November 1987.

Public utility road excavation and reinstatements

D. S. GRAY, Principal Systems Development Officer, Strathclyde
Regional Council

SYNOPSIS. This paper describes the use of Information
Technology in a proposed system for the exchange of
information on Public Utility road excavations and
reinstatements. The technique is to use database software in
conjunction with electronic mail to provide an efficient way
of managing the tens of thousands of messages transmitted
annually.

INTRODUCTION
1. We are familiar with the use of roads for the
transportation of people and goods. An equally important
function is the distribution of underground services. These
include the supply of electricity, gas, water and
telecommunications and the provision of sewerage and
drainage. The Public Utilities which provide these services
have a statutory right to excavate in roads to lay new cables
or pipes or to repair existing ones. Within the 14,000 km of
roads in Strathclyde Region in Scotland there are about
100,000 such openings each year, many in congested areas where
there is a risk of damage to other services, a risk of danger
to workers from gas or electricity, and inconvenience to the
public.
2. The Public Utilities Street Works Act of 1950 requires
Public Utilities to exchange information on any proposed
opening between themselves and the Roads Authority. The
better the communication between these parties the better the
chance of alleviating the effects and dangers of these
excavations! For the past ten years the Public Utilities and
Roads Authorities in Strathclyde and the adjacent Lothian
Region have been collaborating in a voluntary scheme to
transmit opening notices electronically. This initiative is
known as SUSIE (Scottish Utilities Services Information for
Excavators). As Information Technology has developed, better
and better techniques have been adopted for the transmission
and receipt of messages and in consequence the system has
gained credibility with the Roads Authorities, Public
Utilities and private excavators alike.
3. Good communications is, however, only part of good

management. There is also a need for automatic validation and manipulation of the data transmitted. This paper describes the use of current Information Technology techniques to prepare a prototype system for the next version of SUSIE.

RESOURCES

4. The prototype system was developed on Strathclyde Roads' DEC VAX minicomputer cluster utilizing the VMS operating system, VMS electronic mail and the Ingres database package. A private wide area network provides high speed datacommunications to all Roads offices within the Region. Outside bodies can access the machines through low speed dial up modems although for frequent use the rental of private circuits is recommended.

EXISTING SYSTEM

5. Previous developments have resulted in the adoption of a standard set of forms for communicating information about excavations. These include

(a) Application/Opening Notice as shown in Fig. 1 which is sent by a Utility to the Roads Authority and to all other Utilities

(b) Approval/Refusal of Major Planned Works which is used by the Roads Authority to reply to the Utility making an application

(c) Confirmation of Opening Notice which is used by Utilities to confirm a start date for major planned works once approval is given

(d) Emergency Reinstatement Notice which combines an application notice and a completion notice and is used in emergency situations only

(e) Completion/Permanent Reinstatement Notice which is sent by the Utilities to the Roads Authority on completion of permanent reinstatement work

(f) Defect Notice which is sent by the Roads Authority to notify Utilities of defects found in reinstatements

(g) Reply to Enquiry which is used by Utilities, having received an application/opening notice, to advise on the location of their existing plant

(h) Notification of Damages Sustained which is sent to the SUSIE Information Officer by a Utility whose plant has been damaged by another Utility.

These forms are currently transmitted using messaging terminals but these suffer from a lack of facilities for data validation and data management. Hence the need for a new system.

ORGANISATION OF DATA

6. An intuitive approach to Public Utility openings might be to think first of the physical excavations and then of the

```
                SUSIEPHONE / P.U.S.W.A. SYSTEM
                APPLICATION / OPENING NOTICE          P301
Sent to: {    }
                Application for Major Planned Works: { }
                Notification of Minor Planned Works: { }
                Notification of Emergency Works:     { }
                Application for Minor Planned Works: { }
Utility Code: {G51}              Works Reference: {           }
Date of this Appl / Notif: {today }   Date of Works (Prop / Act): {     }
            Location: {                        }
            In Street: {                      }
              Town: {                        }
        Nature of Work: {                          }
Type of Works: { }       Plan Number / Grid Ref. (optional): {       }
Street Code:  {    }     Patching Area Code:        {   }
Work carried out by DLO (1) or Contractor (2): { }
Contractor's Name: {                        }
   "    Address: {                      }
   "    Tel No.: {         } Ext: {   }
No. of Excavations: {   }
Additional Inf / Req: {                      }
              {                    }
Reply Required (Y / N): {Y}

  ....(F11) ....(F12) SEND(F13) ....(F14) QUIT(F17)
```

Fig. 1.   Application/Opening Notice

various administrative stages from application notice through permanent reinstatement to possible defect notice. In Information Technology terms this means setting up a database table for Openings where a row would contain sufficient fields to flag every type of event that might occur during the life of that excavation. Such an approach is difficult to develop since it requires that all possible life histories must be anticipated before tables can be defined.

7. A simpler approach is to treat the forms themselves as the primary entities of the system. The definition of the Application/Opening Notice entity is shown in Table 1.

DATA FLOW

8. The flow of data through the system when an Application/Opening notice is used is shown in Fig. 2. When the SEND function is invoked, data is transferred from the screen to the database table for applications/openings and a copy of the screen is sent to a mailing list of users.

9. The situation where the Roads Authority replies in respect of major planned works is shown in Fig. 3. Here, a SELECT function populates the screen from an entry in the Application/Opening table. The user then records his approval or reasons for refusal and invokes the REPLY function to

transfer the data to the Approval/Refusal table and send a copy of the screen back to the Utility which initiated the Application/Opening notice.

10. In selecting records from the Application/Opening table it is necessary to ensure that a reply has not already been sent. One way of doing this would be to put flags into the table to indicate where such operations had been carried out on the data. This approach requires that all possible operations are known when the table is defined. It is also inflexible because it builds in dependencies between database tables at the table definition stage of system development rather than at the programming stage. A better solution is to

Table 1. Application/Opening Notice entity description

ENTITY DESCRIPTIONS	PAGE 1 OF 19
APPLICATION: SUSIEPHONE/P.U.S.W.A.	
VERSION : 4.0	DATE: 18.06.90

ENTITY NAME: s301
ENTITY DESCRIPTION: Application/Opening Notice
HOST LANGUAGE: 'C'   DBMS: Ingres

DATA ITEMS

KEY	NAME	DESCRIPTION	HOST TYPE	DBMS TYPE
	field1	Sent to	char[6]	varchar(5)
1	field7	Utility Code	char[4]	varchar(3)
2	field8	Works Reference	char[16]	varchar(15
	field9	Date of this Appl/Notif	char[26]	date
	field10	Date of Works(Prop/Act)	char[26]	date
	field12	Location	char[41]	varchar(40)
	field5	In Street	char[41]	varchar(40)
	field6	Town	char[41]	varchar(40)
	field26	Nature of Work	char[41]	varchar(40)
	field11	Type of Works	int	integer
	field13	Plan Number/Grid Ref (optional)	char[11]	varchar(10)
	field14	Street Code	char[8]	varchar(7)
	field15	Patching Area Code	char[5]	varchar(4)
	field16	Work carried out by DLO(1) or Contractor(2)	char[2]	varchar(1)
	field17	Contractor's Name	char[41]	varchar(40)
	field18	Contractor's Address	char[41]	varchar(40)
	field19	Contractor's Tel No.	char[13]	varchar(12)
	field20	Ext	char[5]	varchar(4)
	field21	No. of Excavations	char[4]	varchar(3)
	field22	Additional Inf/Req	char[41]	varchar(40)
	field23	Additional Inf/Req	char[41]	varchar(40)
	field24	Reply Required (Y/N)	char[2]	varchar(1)

SYSTEMS DEVELOPMENT DOCUMENTATION	FORM NO 9

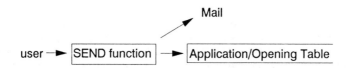

Fig. 2. Application/Opening Notice data flow diagram

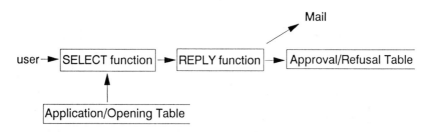

Fig. 3. Approval/Refusal of Major Planned Works data flow diagram

include in the selection criteria the condition that a matching record should not exist in the Approval/Refusal table.

PROGRAM STRUCTURE
11. Following table definition, the next stage in the development process was to create screen forms for the input and display of data. This is done using a forms editor. To reduce the scope for human error during input the fields on the form are given various attributes such as "mandatory", "optional" or "display only". Validations can be carried out on the data entered either by comparison against a fixed list of options or against values in a database table.
12. The programming technique was to write the framework in the 'C' language. Within this were embedded FRS (Forms Run-time System) commands to control the display of the forms and to exchange data between the fields in the forms and 'C' variables. Also inserted were SQL (Structured Query Language) statements to transfer data between the 'C' variables and the database tables. The SQL language includes statements for issuing commands to the computer's operating system and these were used to interface with electronic mail.

ELECTRONIC MAIL
13. Using electronic mail to send notices in addition to recording these in database tables is a convenient way of giving the user positive notification that a message has been

235

received. When a user logs in to the system he or she is automatically notified of any new mail waiting to be read.

14. Incorporating electronic mail requires some thought since here we are dealing with a multi user system where a single user might be running several processes. The problem is in uniquely referencing the various operating system files used.

15. The first step in sending a copy of the screen via electronic mail is to print the screen to a file. To make this file unique to the user, the computer's node name and user's logical terminal name are incorporated in it's specification. The next step is to issue an operating system command through SQL to mail the file to a mailing list of users. It was found, however, that this technique was inefficient since the operating system would take several seconds to transmit the messages before allowing the user to continue with the screen dialogue.

16. The solution was to arrange for a batch process to send the mail. This raises new problems since every invocation of a SEND or REPLY submits a separate batch job to a queue for processing and these jobs and the files to which they refer must be kept unique. Fortunately, the VMS operating system automatically supplies a version number to a file when it is created and increments it every time the file is opened. Thus a command file for mail commands can be opened with the computer's node name, the user's logical terminal name and a version number within it's specification. Within this command file the screen image files are similarly referenced. In this way any number of batch jobs can be submitted by any number of users without conflict.

DISTRIBUTED SYSTEMS

17. The system described here is fully operational and has been shown to be a practical method of exchanging Public Utility notices. However, not all Utilities want to access another authority's machine to operate such a system particularly if they already have their source data within their own computerised management systems. Also, Public Utility and Roads Authority boundaries are not always conterminous. This means that Utilities would have to log in to different machines according to the Roads Authority region within which they were planning to work.

18. The answer to these problems may lie in Distributed Database systems and X400 messaging. The use of X400 techniques to send mail between differing computers is possible although, at present, it is expensive to buy the software and there are still incompatibilities between some makes of computer. A database system will still be required for the validation and automatic population of forms and although Distributed Database systems are available there will be management difficulties in setting up a system to span different organisations.

CURRENT LEGISLATION

19. The Street Works Bill currently before the United Kingdom Parliament contains a requirement for highway authorities to keep a register of works. In anticipation of this the Department of Transport is commissioning a contract for a logical design for a Computerised Street Works Register. Existing working practices will influence the design and it is hoped that the experiences in Lothian and Strathclyde will contribute to the development of a suitable national system.

ACKNOWLEDGEMENTS

20. Thanks are due to Mr D. Carruthers, Director of Roads, Strathclyde Regional Council, for permission to publish this paper and to those of my colleagues who assisted in it's preparation.

TRADEMARKS
1. DEC, VAX and VMS are registered trademarks of Digital Equipment Corporation.
2. Ingres is a registered trademark of Ingres Ltd.

Information technology in Lloyd's register 1991

J. R. MAGUIRE, Project Manager, and G. ORME, Manager,
Lloyds Register Industrial Division

SYNOPSIS. An overview of information technology use
within a modern specialist Civil & Structural engineering
department is given. On the technical side IBM, SUN, and
VAX hardware systems are described, together with
supported software package such as NASTRAN, PATRAN and
ADINA. On the business side PC platforms are outlined, as
well as current philosophy regarding software for word
processing, spreadsheet analysis, databases, etc.

INTRODUCTION
1. Lloyd's Register is a long established
organisation of over 1500 experienced technical staff
operating worldwide from more than 240 offices serving
over 100 countries. Our UK headquarters is located in
London, and is made up of four main groups. Fenchurch
Street is the base of our Ship and Offshore Divisions,
whereas Croydon is the home of the Industrial Division
and Engineering Services Group. This paper addresses
mainly computing at the UK headquarters but also refers
to worldwide networks and links. A view is given of the
facilities used by the Civil & Structural Department
(part of the Industrial Division).

MAIN THEMES
2. The rest of the paper will provide a "snapshot"
picture of information technology in Lloyd's Register as
it is in 1991. In turn, the main themes addressed are
networks, hardware, software, links and support.

NETWORKS

3.1 <u>General.</u> There are four main classes of network at Lloyd's Register. The first supports our world-wide on-line maritime information services such as SEADATA and CLASSDATA (shipping information and classification). These databases form the largest source of maritime information available in the world. These are accessed over a public domain network based on an IBM mainframe. The second network is the world-wide minicomputer (PRIME) network which Lloyd's Register uses for reporting and control of surveys as well as for internal administrative purposes. The third network is an engineering workstation network, which is described in more detail below (see 3.2), as is the fourth - the office system network (see 3.3).

3.2 <u>Engineering Networks.</u> The engineering network in our Croydon offices comprises SUN 3 & 4 workstations interconnected by a Ethernet network, and linked to the VAX based engineering network in Fenchurch Street and to the IBM mainframe at Fenchurch Street. The main functions of the network are to perform finite element analysis as run artificial intelligence tests. The nature of the link and the analysis is described later (see 4.3 and 5.3).

3.3 <u>Office System Network.</u> Office systems comprise IBM PS/2 computers interconnected by a Novell network for word processing, and Datapoint 8800 computers interconnected by an Arcnet for contract control. The links are described in more detail later (see 5.5).

HARDWARE/SOFTWARE

4.1 <u>General.</u> As software appears on a number of different hardware platforms (due to different departmental requirements) it is easiest to describe hardware/software by reference to hardware. The main platforms are the IBM mainframe, SUN workstations, the VAX systems, Datapoint & Prime, PC's, Wang and Hewlett Packard (HP). Desktop Publishing is also described (see 4.8).

4.2 <u>IBM Mainframe.</u> The central IBM 3084Q mainframe computer is located at Fenchurch Street, and linked to Croydon via a Megastream link to a number of IBM 3278 terminals and 3268 printers. This mainframe was chosen for its large data storage potential as well as processing power for large finite element analyses. It also acts as the network hub for all other systems (files can be transferred between networks via the mainframe as most systems link to it). Installed software includes MSC/NASTRAN version 65 (general finite element analysis), ADINA version 86 (non-linear finite element analysis), LR-EMAIL (electronic mail system), ORACLE version 5.1 (relational database management system) and others.

240

4.3 <u>SUN Workstations.</u> At Croydon a number of SUN 3/60C's are connected to the SUN 3/180 file server. Each has its own local printer, an OKI 292, as well as links to Dataproducts IM615 high speed printer and a HP 7550 plotter. There are local and high-speed print facilities as well as access to thermal image and plotting devices. The workstations were chosen primarily for their good performance in finite element pre-and post-processing. Software installed, running under SUNOS 3 (UNIX 4.2 BSD), includes PATRAN version 2.3 (finite element pre-and post-processor), SUN-FORTRAN and others.

4.4 <u>VAX System</u>. A number of VAX station 3100 and Micro VAX 3400 machines (attached to an Ethernet IAN used for finite element pre/post-processing) are located at Fenchurch Street and are accessed from Croydon via the Megastream link using Pericom terminals or SUN workstations. Hewlett Packard HP 7550 plotters are also attached. Installed software, running under VMS includes PATRAN version 2.4, ABAQUS, BOSOR version 84 (non-linear analysis code), and others.

4.5 <u>Datapoint and PRIME</u>. The Datapoint 8800 is used for contract control and co-ordination. The PRIME 2250 (and 5500) is used in connection with LR's Fuel Oil Bunker Assessment Services (FOBAS).

4.6 <u>IBM PC's</u>. IBM PS/2 personal computers are used for both word processing and technical work, although this is an area where rapid changes are taking place. For word processing models 30 and 50 (1 MB RAM, 21-60 MB hard disc) are used together with HP Laserjet printers. Word processing software is mainly Multimate Advantage II (network version), and WORDPERFECT Version 5, running under PC DOS 3.30. For technical work models 70 and 80 (2MB RAM, 60 and above MB hard disc, 80387 co-processor) are used. Technical software includes, engineering packages, graphics (e.g. Microsoft DRAW), spreadsheets (e.g. LOTUS 1-2-3), and databases (various). It is now planned to increase the range of technical software on PC's to include NISA II (finite element package).

4.7 <u>Wang and HP</u>. A WANG system for word processing (OIS 70) is in existence but is gradually being replaced by the IBM PC's. Hewlett Packard desktop machines (9286, 9836, 9845) are used in standalone mode for plan appraisal work, running small structural analysis programmes.

4.8 <u>Desktop Publishing</u>. Although corporately Lloyd's Register has an advanced DTP facility at Fenchurch Street using Apple Macintosh workstations able to produce print quality documentation, a basic facility also exists locally at Croydon, namely Aldus Pagemaker software running on an IBM PC under Microsoft Windows (with a mouse), hard copy being generated on an IBM 4216 postscript printer. A DATACOPY Model 230M Scanner is also attached to this system.

4.9 <u>Electronic Mail</u>. An electronic mail system mounted on the mainframe enables any user of a PC on the Office Network, IBM terminal or any of the PRIME terminals on the world-wide network to send and receive messages to/from any part of the World. This network incorporates store and forward facilities.

LINKS/SUPPORT

5.1 <u>General</u>. There are four main links connecting hardware at Fenchurch Street and Croydon, and these are described below.

5.2 <u>The IBM Link</u>. IBM terminals at Croydon are linked via the Megastream to the IBM mainframe at Fenchurch Street.

5.3 <u>The SUN Link</u>. The Ethernet networks in Croydon and Fenchurch Street are connected via a dedicated SUN – SUN Megastream link by using a SUN workstation in Fenchurch as a gateway server. In terms of finite element analysis this means that model preparation can be is carried out using PATRAN on the SUN, transferred via the Megastream and Ethernet link and the analysis carried out using NASTRAN on the IBM. Once complete, analysis results pass back to the SUN where post-processing is carried out using PATRAN.

5.4 <u>The VAX Link</u>. Networked access to the VAX Computers at Fenchurch Street is made from the terminals at Croydon via the Ethernet link over the Megastream..

5.5 <u>The PC Link</u>. The IBM PC's, on their Novell network, link through a gateway server onto the Megastream and thence on to the IBM mainframe.

5.6 <u>Other Links</u>. The high speed Megastream link between Fenchurch Street and Croydon is duplicated for reliability. Besides high and low speed data traffic it also carries a number of voice channels.

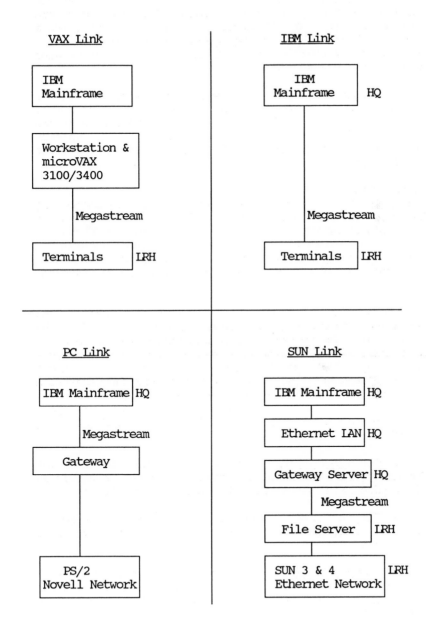

5.7 <u>Support</u>.   Installation, maintenance, training and software support is a significant task in such a large organisation.   Computer Services is responsible for establishing these powerful facilities and as a result is able to provide advice and guidance on an extremely wide variety of computing issues.

SUMMARY AND THE FUTURE
6.   This paper has provided a "snapshot" picture of information technology in Lloyd's Register in the Civil & Structural Department. A major point to note is that the IBM mainframe forms a hub to which a number of networks are linked.   This allows for a high degree of interconnectivity and future enhancements.   Lloyd's Register has made itself adaptable to the rapid changes taking place in the world of computing in order to take advantage of the opportunities that information technology changes bring.

ACKNOWLEDGEMENTS
7. The authors are by no means "computer buffs" – much of the background to this paper was supplied by Lloyd's Register Computer Services, namely Jason Beart, the Manager, Computer Services, and colleagues Keith Hosken, Justin Newland and Peter Hawkins. Their assistance, both verbal and written, is gratefully acknowledged.

REFERENCES (Internal publications)
1. "Information Technology in Lloyd's Register, 1988" C.J.J. Beart, LRTA Paper No. 1988/9.

2. "Overview of Software and Hardware at LRH" J. Newland, Sept. 1989.

Database application for structural systems in high-rise commercial buildings

S. SINGH, Associate Professor, National University of Singapore

SYNOPSIS. The author developed computer based cost data-base incorporating the results of charts established to investigate the effects of column grid size, number of storeys, location of structural components, grades of concrete etc. using traditional structural systems viz. reinforced concrete beam and slab system, reinforced concrete flat slab and waffle slab systems, and prestressed beam and reinforced concrete slab system. The database developed can be used for the selection of appropriate structural system/scheme for cost optimisation at the design stage.

INTRODUCTION.

1. At the initial stages of architectural design for any project, the architect is to consider various conflicting requirements while making the choice for a suitable structural system/scheme. Thus the structural system/scheme finally selected may not be with a minimum cost. While considering different aspects of the problem he thus needs to consider the comparative cost of different systems/schemes for cost optimisation.

2. Cost estimates for structural works are often made by assuming approximate quantities of concrete, reinforcement and formwork. In the absence of realistic information relating to variations in quantities of materials with changes in design parameters, the quantities assumed tend to be very approximate and the percentage error could be large. Where more realistic estimates are required engineer works out alternative structural schemes for computing the quantities and costs for the various schemes. It is extremely unsystematic and wasteful if structural schemes are to be worked out and cost estimated every time a new building project comes up. With this in view, an effort was made by the author to develop an interactive computer based cost data base for cost estimation of structural systems in high rise commercial buildings, up to 50 storeys high, using different structural systems. The structural systems

considered were reinforced concrete beam and slab system,
reinforced concrete flat slab and waffle slab systems and
prestressed concrete beam and R.C. slab system.

3. Singh (ref. 1) described the interactive computer
model for approximate cost estimation of reinforced
concrete beam and slab structural system in high rise
commercial buildings, but, in this database three more
structural systems have been incorporated so as to make it
comprehensive and more useful.

4. This paper outlines the computer based cost
database, choice of methods and approach adopted, and
illustrates its important applications. Further, the
sensitivity of results is discussed based on a number of
case studies in the local construction industry.

APPROACH OR CHOICE OF METHODS

5. A cost database can either be developed based on the
cost information of completed building projects or
alternatively based on the first principles of analysis,
design, computation of quantities and costing. The
accuracy in the case of first method depends on whether
the various structural components of completed buildings
were designed using the methods being adopted at present.
Murthy (ref. 2) investigated results based on this
approach and found substantial differences in quantities
considering similar buildings, structural schemes and
design parameters. Further, a comparison of cost
estimating accuracy of different estimation methods has
indicated that percentage mean deviation of estimates from
tenders and percentage coefficient of variation of errors
are lowest in estimates which are resource use based as
compared to those based on historical cost information
(ref. 3). In view of the above, the latter approach was
adopted for developing the cost database.

STRUCTURAL SYSTEMS, SCHEMES, ANALYSIS AND DESIGN

6. The structural schemes considered for reinforced
concrete beam and slab construction and prestressed beam
and R.C. slab construction are given in Figs. 1 and 2
respectively. The sizes of the square column grids ranged
from 6 to 10 metres for the first type .of construction
while for the second the range was from 10 to 14 metres.
The analysis and design were in accordance with the limit
state design proposed in the British Code of Practice
CP8110: Part 1: 1986, the service loads being taken from
the British Code of Practice CP3: Chapter V: Parts I and
II: 1972. Frame-shear wall interaction was considered in
the analysis for lateral loads, sub-frame, grid beam and
continuous beam analysis being carried out for gravity
load analysis depending on the appropriateness.

7. For the analysis of structural schemes using flat
and waffle slab systems empirical method as codified in

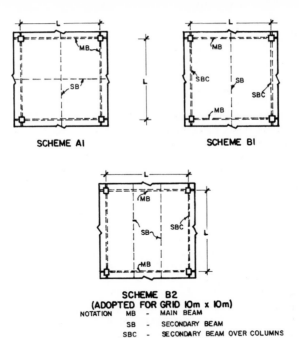

Fig. 1. Designation of structural schemes and components (Reinforced concrete beam and slab system)

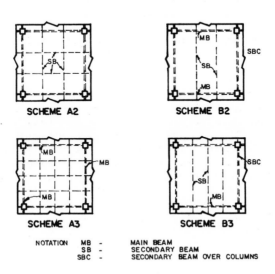

Fig. 2. Designation of structural schemes and components (Prestressed concrete beam and R.C. slab system)

247

the British Code of Practice CP8110: 1986 has been used. Square grids with sides of 6.4, 8 and 10.4 metres for those with waffle slabs were considered. The grid size in the latter case were varied so as to accommodate the standard moulds available locally.

COMPUTER BASED COST DATABASE

8. Computer based cost models (Programs) were developed using the results of charts and statistical relationships (refs. 4-8). These programs have been linked together to form the cost data base. The data base elements for which quantities and costs can be computed are slab, beams (if applicable), columns, shear walls and total structure. The database is perfected to run on IBM 3081 mainframe computer and a micro-computer version of the same was also made. Flow charts developed to write the programs incorporated in the database are illustrated elsewhere (refs. 1,7).

APPLICATIONS

9. For clarity, in each case, the design problem has been defined first and based on the data given, a solution using the computer based cost database has been obtained.

Comparative Cost Estimation

10. The database developed is capable of supplying the comparative cost information for the effects of different design parameters on structural cost which is needed at the architectural design stage for cost optimisation. Such an application is illustrated in Problem 1 - below.

Problem 1 - Structural Systems/Schemes

A design team is involved in the planning of 40 storey commercial high rise building and the work is at the very initial stages. It is required to present the comparative unit costs for the following structural systems/schemes using the given data:

Structural Systems/Schemes	Grid Size (m)
R.C. beam and slab with one secondary beam (Scheme B1, Fig. 1)	10.0 x 10.0
R.C. beam and slab with two secondary beams (Scheme B2, Fig. 2)	10.0 x 10.0
Prestressed beam and R.C. slab with two secondary (Scheme B2, Fig. 2)	10.0 x 10.0 12.0 x 12.0
Prestressed beam and R.C. slab with three secondary beams, (Scheme B3, Fig. 2)	14.0 x 14.0

Prevailing rates of materials:
Concrete ($/cum) grade 25N/sq mm	100.00
30N/sq mm	115.00
Reinforcements ($/kg) High yield steel	1.10
Prestressing strands ($/kg)	4.00
Formwork ($/sq m)	18.00

Solution obtained using the computer based cost database is given in Table 1 which can be considered along with other conflicting factors to select an appropriate scheme for cost optimisation.

Table 1. Reinforced Concrete Beam and Slab Construction (Quantities/Cost per sq m of floor area)

PROJECT TITLE: BEAUTY PLAZA

SALIENT FEATURES

GRID SIZE: 10.0 10.0   GRID LOCATION: 1**

NUMBER OF STOREYS: 40   SCHEME: 2*

ELEMENT	CONCRETE GRADE (N/SQ MM)	CONCRETE (CU M)	STEEL (KG)	FORMWORK (SQ M)	COST (\$) +
SLAB	25	0.1757	8.3	0.86	42.2
MAIN BEAM	25	0.0193	7.6	0.12	12.5
SECONDARY BEAMS	25	0.0158	4.4	0.13	8.8
SECONDARY BEAMS OVER COLUMNS	25	0.0144	3.2	0.11	7.0
COLUMNS	30	0.0590	17.1	0.17	28.8
SHEAR WALLS	30	0.0721	7.8	0.40	24.2
TOTAL STRUCTURE					123.4

NUMBER OF STOREYS: 40   SCHEME: 3

ELEMENT	CONCRETE GRADE (N/SQ MM)	CONCRETE (CU M)	STEEL (KG)	FORMWORK (SQ M)	COST (\$) +
SLAB	25	0.1206	5.3	0.83	32.9
MAIN BEAM	25	0.0215	6.1	0.14	11.3
SECONDARY BEAMS	25	0.0351	5.4	0.29	14.6
SECONDARY BEAMS OVER COLUMNS	25	0.0160	2.0	0.13	6.1
COLUMNS	30	0.0549	15.6	0.17	26.5
SHEAR WALLS	30	0.0721	7.7	0.40	24.0
TOTAL STRUCTURE					115.4

*1 INDICATES   SCHEME A1   **1 INDICATES   INTERIOR GRID
 2   SCHEME B1   2   FIRST INTERIOR GRID
 3   SCHEME B2   3   EXTERIOR GRID
                                   4   CORNER GRID

+UNIT RATES FOR CONSTITUENTS:

ELEMENT	CONCRETE (\$/CU M)	STEEL (\$/KG)	FORMWORK (\$/SQ M)
SLAB	100.00	1.10	18.00
BEAMS	100.00	1.10	18.00
COLUMNS	115.00	1.10	18.00
SHEAR WALLS	115.00	1.10	18.00

Table 1. Prestressed Beam and R.C. Slab Construction (Quantities/Cost per sq m of floor area)

(Cont'd)

GRID SIZE: 10.0*10.0   GRID LOCATION: 1

NUMBER OF STOREYS: 40   SCHEME: 2

ELEMENT	CONCRETE GRADE (N/SQ MM)	CONCRETE (CU M)	STEEL (KG)	STRANDS (KG)	FORMWORK (SQ M)	COST ($)
SLAB	30	0.1206	5.3	-	0.83	34.58
MAIN BEAMS	30	0.0160	5.5	0.7	0.11	12.56
SECONDARY BEAMS	30	0.0268	4.8	0.9	0.24	16.27
SECONDARY BEAMS OVER COLUMNS	30	0.0121	1.8	0.3	0.11	6.79
COLUMNS	30	0.0538	14.7	-	0.17	25.33
SHEAR WALLS	30	0.0616	7.2	-	0.36	21.49
TOTAL STRUCTURE						117.03

GRID SIZE: 12.0*12.0   SCHEME 2

ELEMENT	CONCRETE GRADE (N/SQ MM)	CONCRETE (CU M)	STEEL (KG)	STRANDS (KG)	FORMWORK (SQ M)	COST ($)
SLAB	30	0.1456	7.7	-	0.84	40.29
MAIN BEAMS	30	0.0192	6.8	1.0	0.11	15.52
SECONDARY BEAMS	30	0.0320	6.5	1.3	0.23	20.15
SECONDARY BEAMS OVER COLUMNS	30	0.0144	2.4	0.5	0.11	8.36
COLUMNS	30	0.0582	17.8	-	0.15	29.06
SHEAR WALLS	30	0.0505	6.1	-	0.29	17.80
TOTAL STRUCTURE						131.18

Table 1. Prestressed Beam and R.C. Slab Construction (Quantities/Cost per sq m of floor area)

(Cont'd)

GRID SIZE: 14.0*14.0   SCHEME: 4

ELEMENT	CONCRETE GRADE (N/SQ MM)	CONCRETE (CU M)	STEEL (KG)	STRANDS (KG)	FORMWORK (SQ M)	COST ($)
SLAB	30	0.1256	6.7	0	0.79	35.99
MAIN BEAMS	30	0.0250	8.8	1.3	0.12	19.75
SECONDARY BEAMS	30	0.0635	6.4	1.0	0.37	25.06
SECONDARY BEAMS OVER COLUMNS	30	0.0191	1.7	0.5	0.12	8.18
COLUMNS	30	0.0630	18.8	-	0.14	30.39
SHEAR WALLS	30	0.0423	5.2	-	0.24	14.94
TOTAL STRUCTURE						134.32

Approximate Structural Cost Estimation of an Overall Project

11.   Given the salient design features of a commercial building project, the data base developed is capable of computing the structural cost of an overall project. This is illustrated in Problem 2.

Problem 2 - Total Structural Quantities/Cost

Determine the total structural quantities for a 25 storey commercial building project (Fig. 3) using prestressed beams and R.C. slab construction (Scheme B2, Fig. 2) given the following design features:

i)   Details of grid sizes, grid locations and their numbers

Grid Size	Grid location	No. of grids
12.7 x 12.0	Corner	4 x 25
12.7 x 12.0	Exterior	8 x 25
12.0 x 11.5	Exterior	6 x 25
12.0 x 11.5	First interior	8 x 25
12.0 x 11.5	Interior	4 x 25

ii)   Shear Core area 553.92 m^2/floor

iii)   Unit rates of different constituents:

Concrete ($/cu m)	115.00
High Yield Steel ($/kg)	1.10
Prestressing strands ($/kg)	4.00
Formwork ($/sq m) in solid slab	18.00
beams	16.00
Shear walls & columns	14.00

Concrete grade of 30 N/sq mm is to be used in all components.

Solution obtained using the computer based cost database is given in Table 2.

The cost database has various other applications such as for checking of estimates for structural works, calculation of quantity index for structural works, establishing cost index for structural works, budgeting of materials and for various other building economic studies. However, due to limitation of space, the above are not being fully illustrated here.

SENSITIVITY OF RESULTS

12.   Case studies of six completed projects were made with the object of comparing actual quantity of constituents taken from their bills of quantities with the ones obtained by using the database developed. The comparison indicated that the actual quantities consumed in different projects were always more than those computed using the data base. ,The difference varies from project to project, the overall range being 4.76 per cent to 18.28 per cent. This suggests that an allowance of about 5-20 per cent should be added to the quantities/cost, obtained by using the cost data base. The comparison of actual and database quantities of constituents in different components for a typical project are given in Table 3 and its salient features in Table 4.

CONCLUSIONS

13.   Appropriateness of a structural system for a building from the point of view of cost depends on the relative prices of materials of construction which vary disproportionately from time to time. The database developed form a convenient tool in estimating structural costs for different systems/schemes for cost optimisation at the initial stages of design.

14.   The computer based cost database developed is also of great utility for approximate structural cost estimation of an overall project given its design features, for checking the design and cost estimates for structural works, for calculation of quantity index for

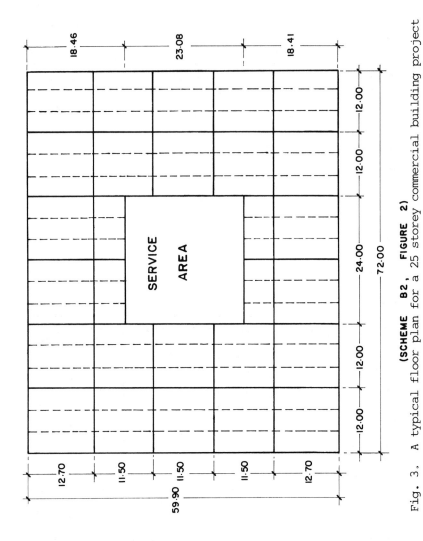

Fig. 3. A typical floor plan for a 25 storey commercial building project

(SCHEME B2, FIGURE 2)

structural works and for various other building economics studies in the building industry.

15. The cost database created do not include all building configurations, structural systems and structural materials. However, the database created can be continuously modified and enlarged to encompass more configurations, systems and materials with continued research in this field. The database created can also be incorporated as a part of an expert system for buildings.

Table 2. Prestressed beams and R.C. slab construction (Quantities/Cost for the overall structure)

```
PROJECT TITLE:          COMMERCIAL BUILDING
FLOOR AREA (SQ M):      107820.00
SHEAR WALL AREA (SQ M):  13848.00
```

SALIENT FEATURES

                          ++
GRID SIZE (M)	GRID LOCATION	NUMBERS
12.7 x 12.0	4	100
12.7 x 12.0	3	200
12.0 x 11.5	3	150
12.0 x 11.5	2	200
12.0 x 11.5	1	100

NUMBER OF STOREYS: 25   SCHEME: 2*

ELEMENT	CONCRETE GRADE (N/SQ MM)	CONCRETE (CU.M)	STEEL (TON)	STRANDS (TON)	FORMWORK (SQ M)	COST+ ($ M)
SLAB	30	15665.2	820.33	-	90820.	4.34
MAIN BEAMS	30	2152.9	696.84	120.16	12504.	1.69
SECONDARY BEAMS	30	3467.2	724.09	156.00	25167.	2.22
SECONDARY BEAMS OVER COLUMNS	30	1618.2	272.15	59.85	12504.	0.92
COLUMNS	30	3990.6	1118.32	-	13528.	1.88
SHEAR WALLS	30	3040.7	308.49	-	23549.	1.02
						12.08

```
*1 INDICATES   SCHEME A1     ++1 INDICATES   INTERIOR GRID
 2             SCHEME B2       2             FIRST INTERIOR GRID
 3             SCHEME A3       3             EXTERIOR GRID
 4             SCHEME B3       4             CORNER GRID
```

+UNIT RATES FOR CONSTITUENTS:

ELEMENT	CONCRETE ($/CU M)	STEEL ($/KG)	STRANDS ($/KG)	FORMWORK ($/SQ M)
SLAB	115.00	1.10	-	18.00
BEAMS	115.00	1.10	4.00	16.00
COLUMNS	115.00	1.10	-	14.00
SHEAR WALLS	115.00	1.10	-	14.00

Table 3. Comparison of actual and computer based database quantities of constituents in different components

Components/ Constituents	QUANTITIES Actual	Database	Percentage of difference compared to (2)
(1)	(2)	(3)	(4)
Slab			
Concrete (Cu m)	3252.93	3048.00	+ 6.3
Reinforcement (Ton)	172.72	153.89	+ 10.9
Formwork (Sq m)	21032.36	19497.00	+ 7.3
Beam			
Concrete (Cu m)	1672.39	1441.60	+ 13.8
Reinforcement (Ton)	450.45	396.85	+ 11.9
Prestressing			
Strands (Ton)	80.28	68.96	+ 14.1
Formwork (Sq m)	12187.56	11176.00	+ 8.3
Columns			
Concrete (Cu m)	606.37	514.10	+ 15.2
Reinforcement (Ton)	104.51	92.07	+ 11.9
Formwork (Sq m)	2867.65	2535.00	+ 11.6
Shear Walls			
Concrete (Cu m)	620.91	558.20	+ 10.1
Reinforcement (Ton)	50.77	44.73	+ 11.9
Formwork (Sq m)	8193.33	7120.00	+ 13.1

Table 4. Salient Features of Project

Structural System/ Scheme	No. of storeys Podium Block	Tower Block	Floor area (m²)	Shear wall area (m²)	Grid size range (m)	Cont- inuity
Prestressed beam and slab, Scheme B1 (Figure 2)	5	11	23487.08	3901.00	7.22*13.00 to 7.93*13.83	4

* Number of continuous spans

REFERENCES

1. SINGH, S., and MURTHY, C.K., Computer model for approximate cost estimate of structural system in high rise commercial buildings, Proceedings of the 4th International CIB W-55 Symposium on Building Economics. Copenhagen (Denmark), September 1987.

2. MURTHY, C.K., A comparison of prestressed, partially prestressed and reinforced concrete structures and comparison of costs and structural systems for some commercial buildings in Singapore. Proceedings of Concrete Institute Conference on Our World in Concrete and Structures, 1977.

3. BENNETT, J., Cost Planning and Computers. Building Cost Techniques: New Directions, edited by Brandon, P.S., E & F.N. Spon Ltd., England, pp.17-26, 1982.

4. SINGH, S., and MURTHY, C.K., Charts for quantities of materials in reinforced concrete structures for buildings, Proceedings of 5th Our World in Concrete and Structures, Singapore, August 1980, pp. F1/01-19.

5. SINGH, S. and MURTHY, C.K., Charts for quantities of materials - flat and waffle slab construction, Proceedings of 6th Conference on Our World in Concrete and Structures, Singapore August 1981, pp. E3/01-19.

6. SINGH, S. and MURTHY, C.K., Economics of structural floor systems, Proceedings of Seminar on Structural Systems for high rise buildings, Singapore, August 1983, pp. 1-40.

7. SINGH, S. and MURTHY, C.K., Economics evaluation of structural systems in high rise commercial buildings, Proceedings of the 10th Triennial CIB Congress on Advancing Building Technology, Washington, D.C., September 1986, pp. 2619-2627.

8. SINGH, S. Cost Models for approximate cost estimation of structural systems in commercial high rise buildings, National University of Singapore. Ph.D. Thesis 1986.

Informatics and strategic management in the building business

P. A. CETICA and A. R. PII, Univesita di Firenze

SYNOPSIS. The research is carried out on the strategic management of the initiative in the construction area.

The object is to define the methodology for the strategic management which contains the economical aspects as well as the ambiental, political, cultural, commercial and technological points of view in the construction. A rather complex object we can realize through the preparation of decision support systems, modular and compatible.

1. THE STRATEGIC MANAGEMENT OF THE INITIATIVE

Looking at the obvious and relentless diffusion of an industrial profile through the building business, it becomes more important and urgent every day to frame the complex economical problems, the planning and the management, production and marketing, the legal aspects and the design inside the proceedings and proper means of planning and strategic management.

Looking at other industrial fields than the building business the strategic analysis is interesting only inside the sphere of the enterprise, whereas in the buidling business this theme implicates two ambits different between them but interacting: the ambit of the enterprise and the ambit of the initiative.

Regarding the ambit of the enterprise we dispose of methods and instruments already known and confirmed in other industrial segments, which do permit today also to plan and manage the stra-

tegy of the building enterprise already well defined inside the current of the industrial logic.
But looking at the ambit of the initiative it is
impossible to adopt these known methods directly due to the precise characteristics of the
building product, different from the products
of other industrial fields: needed are methods
and means specially elaborated for the buiding
business; without them it is now practically
impossible to achieve the undertaken initiative
There is another big difference to consider:
in other industrial fields the production is
organized to reach the target already well
defined to maximise the actual value of the future profits; other corporation targets may be
found, even of sociologic-cultural character
but always directed to the idea of profit.
But in the initiative sphere the strictly economical aspect remain as corporation target, but
where urban and territorial interventions are
involved the serious consideration of the initiative target is highly important.
This means the target of all those who are involved and are external to the profit-target
but dedicated for the greater part to the ambit
of expectations further on than simple productivistic motivations.
In the strategic planning of the initiative
interesting and determinant is the transition in
the idea as in the common routine from the strategic planning to the strategic management.
The strategic planning, rigid and red-tape unable to indicate opportunely the necessary adjustments to follow the becoming of the ambience,
is choosen (more or less unconsciously) as
pattern for different kinds of planning: the
territorial planning for instance which has shown
the incapacity to follow the times and the
thoughts and very often has become an hindrance
for a real harmonic development of the territory.
False anticipations, incapacity to immagine the
future, subjective valuations sometimes fortunately ingenious, but very often rather poor.
This kind of planning has often been surprised

by the becoming of life and suggest today new
urbanistics, mainly refering to a strategic management rather than to a strategic planning.
It is really the idea of management which inspi-
red, among others, the new provisions permittin
modifications of building units even outside of
a direct control or authorizing variations in
course of work without interupting the production,
or in front of the territorial problems propose
organisms to manage the becoming rather than to
materialize the rigid design defined once and
forever.
2. THE MULTIMEDIAL MODULAR INFORMATIC SYSTEM(DSS)
The dynamic management of the strategic project
(territorial, urban or facilities) has become
possible through the introduction and operative
diffusion of "multimedial" informatic systems
permitting to modell a decisional process through
which we can control immediatly the effects of
every decision inside the initiative.
Among these systems we find obviously the well
known CAAD which allows paratridimensional simulations through which we can estimate the effects
each single formal choice has upon the physical
characteristics of the building elements in which
the initiative is accomplished.
But even the CAAD is not enough to control the
whole scale of necessary decisions, even if many
of them have already an integrated module to
control the costs of the building elements which
are in project.
But even so, the CAAD offers no help whatsoever
regarding for example the decisions relative
- to the economic-financial ambit,
- to the planning and the management of the
     initiative
- to the organization of production, in function
     to optimize the time of realization
- to the definition and realization of the marke-
     ting program
- to the legal aspects and
- to assist the relation with the authorities
     of control.
Ambits in which specific decisions have to be
made and therefore, together with all the other

aspects which each specific initiative contains
have to be looked upon carefully, one by one
and together in their interacting.
Therefore the CAAD covers only a part of all the
problems linked to the initiative, thereof is
only a part of the necessary instruments to manage strategicly the initiative, to take all
necessary decisions: they are components, modules
of an operative, multimedial array, a decision
support system (DSS).
The system must be multimedial because it has to
be a support for decisions belonging to different
subjects of study: the CAAD and the module for
cost-calculation need different medias therefore
the combination "CAAD-cost-calculation" is a
multimedial combination.
Obviously all modules of the informatic system
have to be compatible and combinable among them.
Therefore we have at disposal for all necessary
initiativ decisions a multimedial DSS with modular structure.
The considerable articulation of all targets in
relation to the expectative dedicated to the initiative and the, therefore resulting numerous
interacting decisions to take to be able to reach
these targets, brings about a high level of
complexity.
The modular and multimedial DSS permits the strategic management of the initiative at a high level
of complexity and offers a modular system therefore adjustable to every dimension of intervention.
With this DSS it is possible to create a relationship between the single decision necessary to define, plan and realize the initiative and the
complex series of targets who give the meaning
to the same initiative.
Therefore we are not dealing with automatisms of
an artificial intelligence but with tools of
computerized help which, giving complete libert
of decision, allow to value the effects every
single decision has upon the complete frame of
the initiative and upon every single element.

3. STRUCTURE OF THE MULTIMEDIAL MODULAR DSS
The articulation of a multimedial modular DSS
must meet the structure of the decisional process
which understands:
a- organization of the target-system that all
   involved intend to reach,
b- ascertainment of the active or potential
   resources which can be possibly used inside
   the frame and bonds of the ambiental opportunities where the initiative will affect and
   take place;
c- definition of the optimal utilisation and sy-
   nergy of the ascertained resources, to be able
   to reach the system of prefixed targets;
d- planning of an operative program including all
   necessary inputs for all operators who must
   process the necessary documents for the executive phase and have than to carry on the
   initiative.
It is possible to individualize a DSS structure
parallel to the articulation cited above.
First of all the structure of the problem related
to the initiative must be defined, the components
and the interacting factors, to be able to prepare the informatic system.
Immediatly, at the first approach, must be prepared a "PILOT-MODULE" allowing a first survey of
the problem, to evaluate the characteristics, the
consistence and the first possibilities of solution.
This module, more precise later on, will supply
the possibility of immediate operating, even if
only in a preliminary way.
Whilst the problem acquires structure and consistence, we shall prepare various modules and
submodules on the base of the suggested structure
by the "PILOT-MODULE".
A first, coordinated whole, shall be the "TARGET-
MODULE", arranged to organize and classify the
targets in accordance with the different operators
involved, gravitating around the initiative and
characterizing the same.
This module permits also to evaluate the degree
of expected utility, therefore the mesure of the

degree of fulfillment which will be expected to obtain for the single target in the general pro - cess of suboptimazion.

Another, coordinated ensemble of "VARIABLE-MODULES" will permit the classification and the aggregation of the resources, of the bonds and opportunities on which we think we must proceed to realize the identified targets.

The multimedial DSS is realized especially in these "variable modules" which must be exactly of the multimedial type to treat conveniently different facts of different structure and nature: for example the economical aspects, the ambiental or landscape considerations, or the politics of the concerned administration.

Particular attention and care shall be given to the componibility and the compatibility of these multimedial modules.

Finally, the "STRATEGIC MANAGEMENT OF UTILITY-MODULE" dedicated to the optimation of the degree of achievement of all targets, putting in relation the facts on which we'll act with the same targets, allowing therefore a strategic, dynamic manage- ment of the choices relative to the initiative.

This last module represents the heart of the operative system, granting the possibility of a strategic, dynamic management of the resources in function to the proposed targets and their becoming, allowing an immediate estimation of the effects, the necessary adjustments and the proceedings of their application to follow the becoming of the ambience, they have upon the final mesure of utility.

4. THE CATASTROPHE

We must say, that in this determinant introduction of informatics in the process of definition and planning of urban and territorial interventions through which an initiative is realized, is still looked at with a certain suspicion.

For too many, infact, appears still too tight the relation between informatics and quantity; this hindrance is not easy to overcome when we look for an approach of the same informatics to plan and build, connected more often to qualities not to be quantified.

Trying to overcome this hindrance means really
to make to meet project and informatics, over-
coming the banality of the automatized design,
looking to really understand the new industrial
dimension of the building.
A dimension which is still unknown, accustomed
as we are to move on building-yard concepts,
perhaps a bit more mature, but still imbued of
the "MASTER'S" idea, monumental and speculative
productivistic in the building as even in the
planning.
The transit of the quality of the project and the
building, to the quantity of informatics is
effectively a CATASTROPHE as THOM said.
A necessary, expected and desired catastrophe,
but bringing problems not easy to resolve:
we think that the operative answer to these problems lies inside of the strategic dimension;
in a dimension therefore characterised by proceedings developed through the target definition
and the following choice of resources to employ
for to reach them.
The choosing in fact implies the presence of a
value-system-guide, which shall be the system
of quality, controling the definition of the
planning and building targets.
But the resources and their strategic organization
must be expressed in quantity-terms, because it
is through them, that we determine, describe and
realize the physical characteristics, mesurable
of the final planning and building product.
It is in the transition from the quality-system,
particular to the targets, to the quantity-system,
particular to the resources, therefore in the
strategic dimension, where a whole value-system
belonging to the quality-area, is translated in
quantity-terms.
The informatic must therefore be considerated
in its multimedial appearence, as an essential
support-system for the entire decisional process,
therefor as partecipant in the catastrophe.
Through the catastrophe, the planning and the
building translate the quality of values in
quantity, permitting them to partecipate effectively in the becoming of Men's life in the world

This informatic creates the possibility for the catastrophe, through which the great themes of architecture become architecture.

This way of being of the informatics, not much known, neither much used, but of extreme power, natural, full of suggestions and disponibilities, easy to manage and adjustable to all circumstances, not deterministic and completely open to subjectiveness.

These means must be studied and explored with new and unencumbered attentions; the dimension "strategic-informatics" which offers the opportunity to overcome the catastrophe welding qualit and quantity in one unique operation in which the project is able to show all the creative dignity, which the quantitative, manneristic productivisme has made to forget, but not to die.

5. CONCLUSIONS

The state of the contemporary building and the operative possibility of the strategic management of the initiative, relying upon the multimedial informatic system opens a set of new opportunities for the project and the building, which needs to be carefully analysed.

The research in course at the university of Florence aims to construct a theoretic system and a set of applyable proceedings fitted to the new construction conditions.

The verifications, even on international level, which are done on the approach of this research, have the purpose to rouse the attention on the treated themes, creating around them an organic line of coordinated research, bringing first about explanation and specification on the same themes, then individualization and experimentation of the applicated proceedings.

The role of informatics, in this ambit, seems every day more determinant and needs deep examination to be able to single out and prepare all necessary instruments for the development of the strategic management of the whole field of construction.

The development of an intelligent knowledge-based system for the diagnosis of the causes of cracking in buildings

I. M. MAY, Senior Lecturer, M. M. ALWANI, Research Assistant, and W. M. K. TIZANI, Research Assistant, Department of Civil Engineering, University of Bradford

SYNOPSIS

The development of an intelligent knowledge based system for the diagnosis of causes of cracking in buildings is described. Particular reference is made to the acquisition of the knowledge, the uncertainty inherent in the knowledge, and the two stage verification system for the knowledge. An example run of the system is given to demonstrate its use.

INTRODUCTION

1. The increase in interest in intelligent knowledge based systems, IKBS, is evident by the increasing number of published research papers and applications in this area (ref 1). Knowledge based system techniques are being applied to a wide variety of domains within many disciplines, not least in the civil engineering profession, where a tremendous interest has been generated (ref 2).

2. Before the advent of knowledge based systems, computer programmes were applied only to a limited class of civil engineering problems which could be solved using algorithms based on mathematical models (ref 3). However, many problems, for example fault or defect diagnosis, cannot be solved using algorithmic methods, instead heuristic knowledge or "rules of thumb" are used. Currently, knowledge based system techniques can offer a solution for such problems.

3. The current state of the technology is such that knowledge based systems can deal with practical problems resulting in real benefits to industry (ref 3).

4. This paper describes an IKBS for the diagnosis of cracking in buildings, particularly in masonry. The description is similar but briefer than that given by the Author's elsewhere (ref 5).

5. Three aspects of IKBS technology in which problems are still believed to exist, namely, acquisition of knowledge, the inclusion of uncertainty in an IKBS and the validation of such systems, are then discussed.

6. It is presently considered, for example (ref 4), that knowledge based systems are aids to the engineer who is ultimately responsible for the advice given to a client. Therefore it is envisaged that the system described in this paper would be used by someone knowledgable about cracking. It is not intended to replace such a person.

DESCRIPTION OF DOMAIN

7. Cracking, which occurs in many structures, may be due to a variety of

causes and may or may not be of any structural significance. For example, cracks due to drying out will only require filling and redecoration whilst those due to settlement could require expensive remedial works. If the cause of cracking in not diagnosed correctly then this can lead to unnecessary expensive repairs being carried out, or necessary repairs being omitted, leading to higher costs later on.

8. One further problem is that any expert may have met and had experience of only a limited range of cracking problems. When encountering an undiagnosed case of cracking, the expert may diagnose incorrectly the problem as being due to a cause that he/she has experience of. Thus it is possible for two experts to disagree on the diagnosis of the cause of a particular problem of cracking. The IKBS may help solve disputes because having arrived at a diagnosis, the reasoning is then given. In some cases, however, the cause of cracking may not be due to a single effect but can be the result of two or more simultaneous causes. In order to embody this within the IKBS, a number of causes are likely to be investigated. These are then ranked in likelihood of occurrence and the engineer will then need to confirm which cause or causes are responsible for the damage to the structure under investigation.

9. The domain is considered to be suitable for IKBS because the knowledge is mainly heuristic. This can be seen, for example, in the PSA Defects In Buildings Manual (ref 6) which contains a large body of knowledge. This has been used extensively in developing the knowledge base for the system.

DESCRIPTION OF THE SYSTEM

10. The general outline of the system is given in Fig 1.

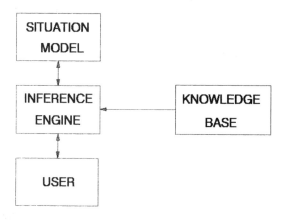

Fig 1. General outline of the system

11. The system is written using PROLOG (ref 7) and runs on an IBM AT type microcomputer, with 640K RAM and a hard disc, using DOS. The system basically comprises three parts, namely, the inference engine, the knowledge base and the situation model.

12. The knowledge base contains the knowledge about the domain of cracking. The acquisition and representation of the knowledge, together with

the modelling of uncertainty, is discussed later on.

13. The situation model contains the information about the current state of the case under investigation and is continuously updated and enlarged as a consultation proceeds.

14. The inference engine acts as the interface between the user, the knowledge base and the situation model. It controls any consultation with the system by asking for information from the user and the knowledge base, carrying out logical manipulation of such information and responding to the user's requests. A fuller description of the inference engine is given elsewhere (ref 8).

KNOWLEDGE REPRESENTATION AND ACQUISITION

15. In order that the system can make meaningful diagnoses, the knowledge about the domain has to be collected and represented correctly, accurately and comprehensively.

16. It was determined that the knowledge could be represented using Production Rules of the form

> If
> cond 1 *
> cond 2 *
> cond n *
> then
> Goal,

where cond 1 to cond n are conditions which are necessary to establish the goal and "*" represents the logical connection between the conditions i.e. "and" or "or". An example of a rule for cracking is:

> rule 12:
> if
> 'horizontal cracks in mortar bed joints' which is necessary and
> 'evenly spaced cracks' which is ext_supplementary and
> 'lowest crack 4 courses above dpc' which is supportive and
> 'ferrous wall ties used' which is necessary and
> 'black ash mortar used' which is ext_supportive and
> 'air salt content high' which is ext_supportive and
> 'wall bulge at eaves' which is supportive and
> 'cracking internal plaster' which is supportive
> then
> 'horizontal cracks in external cavity walls due to ferrous wall tie corrosion'

The purpose of the statements "which_is necessary" etc are explained later on in the paper.

17. The goal for one rule can be a condition for another rule, thus investigating a particular cause of cracking can involve a number of rules, as shown in Fig 2. The top goal which would be a particular cause of cracking is shown as Goal A. The Goals B, C and G are known as SUBGOALS, and the rules which are used to obtain them are known as SUBRULES. The entire rule including all the SUBRULES is known as a RULE. Any SUBRULE can be used in a number of different RULES.

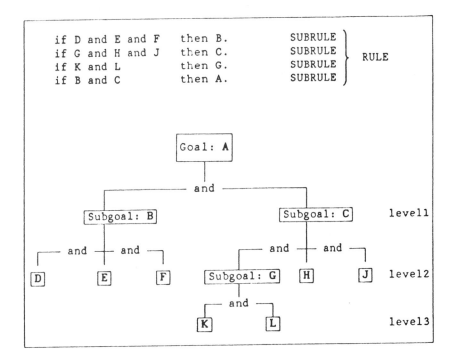

```
    if D and E and F    then B.       SUBRULE ⎞
    if G and H and J    then C.       SUBRULE ⎟ RULE
    if K and L          then G.       SUBRULE ⎟
    if B and C          then A.       SUBRULE ⎠
```

Fig 2. An example of a RULE hierarchy

METARULES

18. Because the knowledge base contains a large number of causes of cracking, it is necessary to initially eliminate those causes which can not be responsible for the cracking under investigation. This is carried out using a series of parameters, the values of which are determined from questions asked at the beginning of a consultation. The name given to these parameters is RULE BASIC PARAMETERS.

19. Each of the causes of cracking has the values of these parameters preset. After the preliminary consultation, where the user inputs values for these parameters, all those rules, whose preset parameter values match the values input by the user, are selected for further investigation.

20. The parameters currently used in the knowledge base are shown in Table 1.

Table 1.

	Parameter Name	Question Asked
1.	struct_type	Select the type of structure?
2.	distress_member	Select the distress member?
3.	cavity_wall	Is the member of cavity construction?
4.	inner_material	What kind of inner leaf material has been used?
5.	outer_material	What kind of facing material has been used?
6.	vert_crack	Is the cracking predominantly vertical?
7.	horiz_crack	Is the cracking predominantly horizontal?
8.	comb_crack	Is there a combination of vertical and/or horizontal and/or diagonal cracking?

21. When one of the questions shown in Table 1 is asked, a set of options are given to the user, from which one is chosen. As an example, when question 2 is asked, the options are:-

cladding
parapet
spandrel
load_bearing wall
and free_standing wall

22. During a consultation, not all of the questions will necessarily be asked. For example, if the answer to question 3 is 'No', then no enquiry about the inner leaf material is made (question 4). Details of a typical consultation are given later. After the preliminary questions have been asked, up to about 8 different RULES are likely to be selected for further investigation, for the particular case of cracking under consideration.

23. The main advantages of this approach are that:-

(a)   the consultation is speeded up by avoiding unlikely causes

and   (b)   because the system does not ask questions about irrelevant causes, it appears to behave more like an expert.

ACQUISITION OF KNOWLEDGE

24. One of the major problems in the development of any knowledge based system is the collection, coding and subsequent checking of the knowledge. For the system described, two routes were adopted for knowledge acquisition. The first was to use available literature, in particular reference 6, together with other papers and reports (ref 9, 10).

25. The knowledge was converted into RULES, and the values of the parameters required by the METARULES determined as described above.

These rules were then used to form a prototype system.

26. The prototype system was then shown to an expert in order that the knowledge could be checked. This was achieved by the following process. Values of the RULE BASIC PARARMETERS were selected such that each RULE was accessed in turn, so that the knowledge it contained about a particular cause of cracking could be investigated. The expert could then check on the validity of the RULE. This process was also found to cause the expert to add further knowledge about the cause of cracking represented in the particular RULE, and, often to comment on associated causes thus leading to an increase in both the total number of RULES and the knowledge in other RULES.

27. One concern that the Authors still have is that there is no way to ensure that all possible causes are included in the knowledge base. It is hoped, however, that as more engineers use the system, any omissions will be noted and relevant RULES added.

28. The check on the system described above is obviously not exhaustive. The Authors consider this to be both knowledge acquisition and the first stage of a two stage validation process.

29. The second stage of validation will be the use of the system for a number of "site" investigations. The engineers involved will, generally, not have been involved with the development of the system. They will use the system in "real life" situations and comment on:-

      (a)   the validity of the particular RULES "fired" during the consultations,

      (b)   the possible causes chosen by the system,

and   (c)   the ranking of the causes chosen by the system.

30. This will allow the Authors to build up a library of trial investigations for which the system has been used, and to arrive at an estimate of the accuracy of the system.

31. One further point about the current knowledge base is that only one line of reasoning for any cause has been included. When knowledge for any particular cause includes contradictory evidence, then the Authors have attempted to choose that which gives a worse scenario. Fortunately, to date, the conflicts have only been of a minor nature. It could be necessary at a future date, if a strong conflict existed, for both sets of evidence to be included in the knowledge base and the user would then have to make the final decision as to which knowledge to use.

32. Martin (ref 11) has adopted an approach where the knowledge given by a number of authorities about the same topic can exist in parallel. The user of the system then determines which knowledge to use.

ORDERING OF CAUSES

33. Often in practice, it is not possible to give any one cause complete certainty of being the reason for the observed distress. In the IKBS, each of the causes investigated is given a numerical estimate of the likelihood of it having been the actual cause.

34. In the system described, uncertainty is assumed to derive from 3 areas, those being:-

      (a)   the certainty of the rule

      (b)   the relevance of the conditions

and   (c)   the certainty of the input.

The uncertainties are represented by the use of certainty factors, CFs, on the scale of -5 to 5. For the user's input, a CF of 5 means definitely yes, a CF of -5 means definitely not, a CF of 0 means not known and the intermediate values represent varying degrees of certainty.

35. For the system's output, the certainty factors are calculated for the conclusions, a CF of 5 means MOST LIKELY , a CF of -5 means MOST UNLIKELY, a CF of 0 is indicated as POSSIBLE and the intermediate values represent varying degrees of certainty reflected by the use of appropriate wording. A CF of 0 means equally likely as unlikely, the wording POSSIBLE is used here, however, to indicate to the user that such a conclusion should not be discarded. The certainties given for each cause of cracking allows a ranking to be obtained which will assist in determining the precise cause, or combination of causes, by the user of the system.

36. The certainty of the RULE is determined when the RULE is first written by questioning experts at the knowledge acquisition stage. Up to the present time, all rules have been given a certainty of 5 which implies that the RULES are considered correct.

37. The relevance of the conditions is expressed using certainty directives and allows crisp logical statements to become fuzzy. As an example, consider the RULE,

IF a and b THEN c.

In this case, c is true only if a and b are true. In practice, however, it may only be absolutely necessary for a to be true, for c to possibly occur, with b only giving further support to the occurrence of c.

This could be written,

IF a THEN (c is possible).

IF a and b THEN (c is more likely).

38. In order to obtain this facility, certainty directives are used in this form,

Condition which_ is Certainty Directive

There are 6 certainty directives which are NECESSARY,

EXT_SUPPLEMENTARY, SUPPLEMENTARY, SUPPORTIVE, CONTRADIC-
TIVE and PARAMETER.

39. The use of the certainty directives together with the associated formulae allow the certainty factors to be updated.

CERTAINTY DIRECTIVE FUNCTIONS

1. The Necessary Directive.

40. The necessary directive is used for conditions in rules in which the conclusions depend strongly on these conditions. When the directive "necessary" is attached to a condition in the premise of a SUBRULE, the updated certainty factor of the conclusion of this SUBRULE is calculated as follows. If the condition is satisfied with certainty A and the conclusion has a prior certainty B, then the updated certainty factor of the conclusion C, is given by:-

$C = $ minimum (A,B).

The remaining of the CERTAINTY DIRECTIVES are listed in the order of strength.

2. The Ext-Supplementary Directive.

41. The ext_supplementary directive is used for those conditions which support or contradict the conclusion, and is the strongest of the five remaining directives:-

$$C = B + 2^* A/5, \text{ and}$$
$$C < 5, \text{ and}$$
$$C > -5.$$

3. The Supplementary Directive.

42. The supplementary directive is used for conditions which support or contradict the certainty of the conclusion less strongly than the "ext_supplementary" directive. C is calculated as follows:-

$$C = B + A/5, \text{ and}$$
$$C < 5, \text{ and}$$
$$C > -5.$$

4. The Supportive Directive

43. The supportive directive is used for those conditions which only support positively the conclusion. C is calculated as follows:-

If $A < 0$ then $C = B$.
If $A > 0$ then:
$$C = B - A/5, \text{ and}$$
$$C < 5, \text{ and}$$
$$C > -5.$$

5. The Contradictive Directive.

44. The contradictive directive is the opposite of the supportive directive C is calculated as follows:

If $A < 0$, then $C = B$
If $A > 0$, then:
$$C = B - A/5, \text{ and}$$
$$C < 5 \text{ and}$$
$$C > -5.$$

6. The Parameter Directive.

45. The parameter directive is used for those conditions which do not affect the certainty of the conclusion and for which,

$$C = B.$$

46. The certainty factors of the conclusions are updated as follows:

1. Every condition in the PREMISE of a SUBRULE is given a CF depending on the user responses to questions about it.
2. The CF of a condition preceded by the operator "not" is multiplied by -1.
3. The CF of the conclusions are updated everytime a condition in the PREMISE of their SUBRULE is established with a certainty factor. The updated figure is calculated using the function for the CERTAINTY DIRECTIVE attached to that condition and its CF.
4. If a condition is a subgoal, the CF of the condition is that of the subgoal.
5. The final certainty factor of the RULE is that of the goal reduced by the certainty factor for the RULE.

47. This method thus allows the relevance of data to be included in the results of the consultation. It also allows the user to input an answer of "don't know" without invalidating the entire consultation.

USING THE SYSTEM

48. The user of the system is expected to be familiar with the problem of cracking in buildings. Even experts with a very wide experience of cracking should find the system useful.

49. It is essential, that the user is knowledgeable about the terminology used in the domain of cracking. Also, the user should be aware of the different stages of the problem solving strategy used by the system. This is important so that there is no confusion as to what the system is trying to do at any particular stage.

RUNNING THE SYSTEM

50. At the start of a consultation, the system displays a message explaining what the system does and what the user is expected to know in order to run it. The stages in the operation of the system are given below:-

1. Preliminary Questionnaire.

51. A series of preliminary questions is posed. Based on the answers to the questions, a number of causes are selected as applicable for this particular consultation. The user is then given the option of choosing which of those applicable causes is to be investigated first. Otherwise, the causes are investigated in the given order.

2. Investigation Of The Causes Of Cracking.

52. The likelihood of the chosen cause is established by investigating the evidence. This is accomplished by the use of interactive questioning. The user is able to use the HELP and WHY facilities with any question posed by the system. An explanation of these facilities is given later on. When all the items of evidence have been exhausted, the likelihood of the cause is indicated by certainty factor. The conclusion of the investigation is then displayed, this includes the cause with its certainty factor accompanied by a qualitative description of the likelihood (LIKELY, VERY LIKELY, etc) and a brief text describing the cause. The user can request to see HOW the system arrived at the conclusion, and the Authors would suggest that any user should always do so in order that they confirm the cause. The user can also select the WHAT_IF facility.

53. The user should investigate all the applicable causes which have been selected in (1).

3. Results.

54. The results and summary of the consultation is then output. The results comprise all the causes which have been investigated, each with its certainty factor.

4. End Of a Consultation.

55. A consultation ends when either all the causes which have been selected as applicable have been investigated or the user ends the consultation. Before exiting, the user is given the option of starting another consultation.

THE EXPLANATION FACILITIES.

1. The HELP Facility.

56. A HELP facility has been developed to give explanations, about the questions posed by the system in order to establish values of parameters, which help the user to give the correct values. The HELP data can be requested by the user at any stage of questioning.

2. The WHY Facility.

57. The function of the WHY facility is to explain what a specific question is trying to establish and operates as follows. When information is requested, the user is able to ask WHY. An explanation is then produced by the system consisting of the following:-

        (a)   what the question is trying to establish, and

        (b)   what each of the subgoals up to the goal, which is the cause of cracking, is trying to establish.

3. The HOW Facility.

58. The function of the HOW facility is to show how the system has arrived at a conclusion. Once the system has established a conclusion, the user can then request to be supplied with all the information and the logical path that the system has used in order to arrive at this conclusion.

4. The WHAT IF Facility.

59. The user can use the WHAT_IF facility to change one or more of the inputs given earlier and the effects of these changes on the cause can then be re-investigated. The user is then given the option of allowing these changes to become permanent or to revert to the original data. One use of this facility is to allow checks on the sensitivity of the outcome due to changes in a particular item of data.

EXAMPLE RUN

60. A typical run of the system is given below together with explanations. In the description below:-

        _   indicates system questions,

        *   indicates user answers and

        * *   indicates comments.

** The defect under consideration is caused by the corrosion of ferrous wall ties, particularly in black ash mortar or where there is a high salt content in the air.

_ Select the type of structure

* brickwork

** This and subsequent non-numeric answers would be selected from a menu, which in this case contains the options concrete_frame, steel_frame, brickwork, timber_frame and dont know

_ Select the distressed member

* cladding

_ Is the member of cavity construction?

* yes

_ What kind of inner_leaf material has been used?

* dont know

_ What kind of facing material has been used?

* clay brick

** The question enquiring about the type of inner_leaf material used is only asked if the answer to 'Is the member a cavity wall?' is given as Yes. If it had been No, then the next question would have enquired about the type of facing material that has been used.

_ Is the cracking predominantly vertical?

* no

_ Is the cracking predominantly horizontal?

* yes
_ Is the cracking either predominantly diagonal or a combination of vertical and horizontal cracking?
* no
** As with the question enquiring about the type of inner_leaf material used, the question enquiring whether the cracking is predominantly horizontal is related to a conditional parameter. It is only asked if the answer to the previous question, 'Is the cracking predominantly vertical?', is given as No or Dont Know.
** Based on these values, set for the RULE_BASIC PARAMETERS, a number of causes, or RULEs, are selected. In this instance, 6 different causes are selected for further investigation:
_ RULE 12 horizontal cracking in external cavity walls due to wall tie corrosion,
_ RULE 14 horizontal cracking in external masonry walls near pitched roof eaves level due to roof spreading
_ RULE etc
** The user can control the order in which the causes are to be investigated. Alternatively, the selected causes will be investigated one at a time in the above order. The system always displays the cause it is investigating at anytime. RULE 12 is selected for an example run. The first output screen will be:-
_ This defect is caused by the corrosion of ferrous wall ties particularly in black ash mortar or where there is a high salt content in the air. The corrosion expands the ties and opens up horizontal cracks in the wall.
** The system displays 'Press Return to Continue'. Further investigation now begins.
_ Does the cracking occur in horizontal mortar bed joints?
* yes
_ Are the cracks generally a consistent number of courses apart?
* why
** the system outputs the WHY display
_ I am asking this question in order to establish whether the cracks are, generally speaking, evenly spaced. Since these cracks are due to wall tie corrosion, and wall ties should be evenly spaced, then the cracks should also be evenly spaced
** the previous question is then repeated
_ Are the cracks generally a consistent number of courses apart?
* yes
_ Is the lowest crack 4 courses above the dpc?
* yes
_ Have ferrous wall ties been used in the cracked cavity wall?
* yes
_ Had black ash mortar been used in building the cracked cavity wall?
* Help
** The system outputs the HELP display
_ To find out what type of mortar has been used, a mortar sample taken from the centre rather than the face of the wall, should be sent away for analysis.
** The previous question is then repeated
_ Had black ash mortar been used in building the cracked cavity wall?
* yes

_ Is there a high salt content in the air?

* no

- Is the cavity wall seen to bulge or the outer leaf push up at eaves level and disrupt the roof finish?

* yes

_ Is there similar cracking internally as there is externally?

* no

** the following conclusion is then displayed.

_ it is MOST LIKELY with a certainty factor of 5.0 that the cause of damage is: the corrosion of ferrous wall ties particularly in black ash mortar or where there is a high salt content in the air. The corrosion expands the ties and opens up horizontal cracks in the wall.

Derived by RULE 12

Would you like to see how?

* yes

** The HOW facility displays the RULE hierarchy with a qualitative estimate of certainty for each part of the RULE

* yes

_ horizontal cracking in external cavity walls due to wall tie corrosion is MOST LIKELY was derived by RULE 12 from:-

1. horizontal cracks in mortar bed joints is DEFINITE and
2. evenly spaced cracks is DEFINITE and
3. lowest crack 4 courses above dpc is DEFINITE and
4. ferrous wall ties used is DEFINITE and
5. black ash mortar used is DEFINITE and
6. air salt content high is DEFINITELY IMPOSSIBLE and
7. wall bulge at eaves is DEFINITELY and
8. cracking internal plaster is DEFINITELY IMPOSSIBLE

** At this stage, the user can either investigate another cause, exit or use WHAT_IF. If the WHAT_IF facility was selected, the option of "changing" or "checking" a parameter value or "exiting" WHAT_IF is given. If the value of the above parameter "horizontal cracks in mortar bed joints" is changed from 'yes' to 'no', then after re_running the diagnosis, the conclusion will be:-

_ It is IMPOSSIBLE with a certainty factor of -5 that the cause of damage is due to:

the corrosion of ferrous wall ties etc

** Again the user is asked if they would like to see HOW

_ Would you like to see HOW

* yes

_ Horizontal cracking in external cavity walls due to wall tie corrosion is IMPOSSIBLE was derived by RULE 12 from

1. crack in mortar bed joints is DEFINITELY IMPOSSIBLE and
2. evenlyspaced cracks is DEFINITE and
3. etc

** The user can now either "change" or "check" another parameter value or "exit_ WHAT_IF". If "exit WHAT_IF" is selected,the user will be given the option of retaining either the original values of the parameters or the new values input. This will determine which results will be given as the conclusion to the consultation with that particular RULE in the final output screen. The diagnosis continues as below.

_ Would you like to investigate more solutions?

* yes
** If 'no' then the user can exit, but in order to carry out a meaningful investigation, then 'yes' should be selected. The next cause is now investigated and the result is given. The investigation of the likely causes will continue until all the selected likely causes have been investigated unless the user has answered 'no' to the previous question.
** Finally, a summary of all the likely causes which have been investigated is given, together with the likelihood of each cause having been the actual cause.
_ horizontal cracking in external cavity walls due to wall tie corrosion is MOST LIKELY with a certainty factor of 5.0,
horizontal cracking in external masonry walls near pitched roof eaves level due to roof spreading is DEFINITELY IMPOSSIBLE with a certainty factor of -5.0,
etc.

CONCLUSIONS

61. An intelligent knowledge based system for the diagnosis of causes of cracking in buildings has been described and a number of facilities which make the system particularly suitable for use in practice discussed.

62. These facilities include HOW, which describes the line of reasoning to obtain the cause of cracking. This is considered to be essential for the user to be able to confirm the system's diagnosis. Also included is WHAT_IF, which allows the user to investigate the sensitivity of the choice of any parameter.

63. It has been found, in common with other investigations, that the acquisition of knowledge and the checking of the knowledge base are areas in which major problems can arise. It is concluded that the development of an extensive prototype system and the subsequent checking of the system by an expert has proved to be successful. The IKBS will undergo further checks in the future, when it is used for site investigations.

64. In many cases of cracking, it may not be possible to determine an individual cause of cracking either because of incomplete evidence or because the cracking is due to a combination of two or more causes. It is therefore necessary to consider a number of possible causes and to be able to rank them. A system capable of doing this has been described.

ACKNOWLEDGEMENTS

The Authors would like to thank Mr Stuart Bell and Mr Mike Backhouse of Armitage Brick Limited for their valuable assistance with the development of the system, and the Science and Engineering Research Council for providing funding for the work.

REFERENCES
1.   TOPPING B.H.V. ed. Artificial intelligence techniques and applications for civil and structural engineers, Proc. Artificial intelligence civ-comp 89, Civil-Comp Press, Edinburgh, 1989.
2.   MAHER M.L. Problem solving using expert system techniques, in Expert systems in civil engineering, eds. Kostern C.N. and Maher M.L., Amer. Soc. Civ Engrs, New York, 1986.
3.   SHAW M.R. Expert systems in the construction industry, Building Research Establishment, Watford, 1989, Report IF4/89.
4.   BLOCKLEY D.I. and HENDERSON J.R. Knowledge base for risk and cost benefit analysis of limestone mines in the West Midlands, Proc. Instn. Civ Engr, Part 1, 1988, 84, June, 539-564.
5.   MAY I.M. and TIZANI W.M.K. A knowledge based system for the diagnosis of the causes of cracking in buildings, Proc. Nato Advanced Study Institute on Optimisation and Decision Support Systems in Civil Engineering, Paper 19, 1989.
6.   PROPERTY SERVICES AGENCY, Defects in buildings, HMSO, London, 1989.
7.   ESI., PROLOG-2 Language reference manual, Expert Systems International, Oxford, 1986.
8.   TIZANI W.M.K. A knowledge based system for the diagnosis of cracking in buildings, Ph.D thesis, University of Bradford, 1990.
9.   BRE Digests, Building Research Establishment, Watford.
10.   BRE Defect action sheets, Building Research Establishment, Watford.
11.   MARTIN J.H. Inferring large dam behaviour from measurements and uncertain qualitative knowledge, Ph.D thesis, University of Bristol, 1990.

Advanced robots in the building industry – the present and the future

M. A. LAHOUD, Senior Scientist, BMT Ltd, and
S. SARANTOPOULOS, Research Director, Ergon S.A.

SYNOPSIS
This paper will review the present status of construction robots and analyze their possible application areas. The implications on the robot's topology will be considered as well as the software structure and the sub-systems necessary in order to implement the robots in the building industry. The philosophy and objectives of an exciting research programme in this important area will also be outlined.

INTRODUCTION

1.   Approximately 5.5 million workers are employed in the construction industry in America. In countries like Sweden and Japan, more than 16% of their Gross National Product is devoted to this industry. These figures serve to highlight its economic importance. However, the construction industry is a dangerous one, with more than seven times the number of fatalities per worker compared with the manufacturing sector. In spite of this, little or no advances have been made to automate the basic activities involved in building construction. Enormous scope therefore exists for the application of advanced robots in the areas which are hazardous to humans and can benefit construction efficiency and productivity. For example, construction productivity drops by approximately 25% when the temperature exceeds 30°C or falls below 0°C.

2.   At present Japan leads the world in the area of construction robots research with both Universities and Construction Companies active in Research and Development. An impressive example is the Shimizu Construction Company which maintains a Research Institute of over 200 staff. However, no such research commitment exists in any European University or Construction Company.

3.   The paper reviews the state of automated building construction methods and outlines an embryonic multi-national project to enable current technologies to be utilized in the development of a brick-wall construction system. The difficulties are outlined and directions into which fruitful effort can be invested, are described.

Application Areas and Potential

4.   The vital criterion for deciding whether to introduce robots into the construction industry, must of course be, the resultant economic benefit [ref. 1]. However, this section will first study in detail those application areas where robots may possibly be fruitfully used in the future, assuming the necessary technological and theoretical progress is made.

5.   Below is listed a speculative "wish-list" [ref. 2] of where robotics can possibly be applied in the broad field of construction and its related activities. It should be noted that some progress has already been made in a small number of the listed fields and these will be dealt with in more detail in a later section:

  (a)   concrete form and surface cleaning,
  (b)   building wall sand-blasting,
  (c)   tunnelling, drilling and pipe-laying,
  (d)   excavation and material handling,
  (e)   structural element placing,
  (f)   construction inspection and quality control,
  (g)   painting,
  (h)   surface finishing,
  (i)   construction tasks.

6.   It is on application (i) above that later sections of the paper will concentrate. The building construction activities can in turn be divided into sub-activities relating to the breakdown of the building into major components [ref. 3]:

  (a)   positioning   (erection of steel beams, scaffolding),
  (c)   connecting   (bolting, nailing, welding),
  (d)   attaching   (attaching hangers, partition boards),
  (e)   finishing   (trowelling, grinding, brushing),
  (f)   coating   (painting, plastering, spreading glue),
  (g)   concreting   (casting of columns, walls, beams),
  (h)   building   (block, brick, stone masonry),
  (i)   inlaying   (tiling, wood-plank flooring),
  (j)   covering   (vinyl, carpet flooring, wall-paper),
  (k)   jointing   (between precast elements, partition boards).

7.   Although all the above activities may be amenable to the application of robots, it is sub-activity (h) that will be high-lighted in later sections. However, it is likely that the application of robots will not occur immediately, but will follow an evolutionary, step-wise implementation which will probably consist of the following natural stages:

  (a)   increased automation with the use of programmable logic controllers, microprocessors [ref. 4] and advanced sensors (for example: excavation or tele-operation work),

(b) modification of the building technology and philosophy to simplify the tasks, and greater use of prefabrication components,

(c) greater use of the rapidly growing software developments in Artificial Intelligence (*AI*), Computer Aided Design (*CAD*) and Computer Aided Planning for the purposes of a closer integration of the design, costing and building stages of a construction project,

(d) development of heavy-duty, construction-environment-ruggedized robots designed for specific groups of construction tasks.

8. It is a fusion of the above four stages which will form the core of the pre-competitive research and development project whose objectives are outlined in this paper.

The Benefits

9. The working conditions within the construction industry point towards the need to apply automation to receive its attendant benefits, as has been demonstrated in the automobile and electronics industries for example. The motivations for wishing to employ robots are as follows [refs. 5, 6]:

(a) *improvement in working conditions and reduction of accidents*: The construction industry accounted for over 43% of accidental deaths in all industries, according to Japanese statistics for 1983. Furthermore, work conditions are poor with work being performed in conditions of extremely high or low temperatures, dust, poisonous gas, compressed air or often water. This has resulted in the incidence of occupational disease in the construction industry being twice that in all other industries.

(b) *shortage of skilled workers and ageing of the labour force*: The information technology age has brought about a change in the attitude and perception of young workers towards the types of jobs in the construction industry. Japanese statistics for 1983 show that over 67% of construction workers are over 40 years of age and the average age is approximately 44 years. This has resulted in a decrease in the number of skilled workers available with a consequent effect on the expected salaries. For example, in 1985 in Japan, there was a shortage of approximately 15% of most types of skilled construction workers (carpenters, steel-bar placers, plasterers, tilers, masons). However, in comparison with the manufacturing industry, the construction workers are paid less.

(c) *improvement in labour productivity*: The measure of labour productivity is the total financial value of production divided by the size of the labour force. In Japan, if one compares the labour productivity of the manufacturing sector with that of the construction industry, it can be seen that the construction industry's has remained essentially constant while the manufacturing sector's has shown a 100% increase for the ten years between 1975 and 1985.

(d) *increased competition*:
Customers are demanding greater quality with guaranteed time-scales; thus each contractor must attempt to utilize the available technology to their own best advantage.

(e) *demand for advanced construction techniques*:
With time and experience, architects and civil engineers become more and more ambitious with the design, the building materials, and the location of projects. This places constraints on the implementation and makes greater demands on the current technology which is expected to provide the enabling-technology for the expansion of the industry.

10.   The above summarizes the areas in which the application of robots would bring significant benefits to the labour force and the construction companies. However, despite these powerful social and economic pointers, there has not been rapid progress in this application area, in common with agriculture, mining, undersea or space environments, since [refs. 2 and 7]:

(a) the work is unstructured and the tasks are not clearly repetitive. The actions cannot be described as a repetition of simple human-performed tasks.

(b) mobility is usually required in the unstructured three-dimensional environment of the construction site.

(c) the force-handling capability of the construction robot is considerably larger than its manufacturing counterpart.

(c) more advanced sensors and data processing are required to distinguish the condition of surfaces and structures.

(d) there is little or no integration of the various stages of execution of a construction project. That is, the construction industry lacks the equivalent of the manufacturing industry's Computer Integrated Manufacture (*CIM*) philosophy.

(e) architects are not in the habit, and have not been educated to design for automation.

(f) in Europe and the USA there is virtually no investment in Research and Development by the construction industry.

To summarise, the following quote from the "father of robotics", Joseph F. Engelberger, is appropriate [ref. 2]:

> "Probably no industry could benefit as much from robotic technology as the construction industry. As robot capabilities burgeon grand opportunities will arise. At this writing the Japanese are virtually alone in seeing the potential."

European Developments

11.   Progress in this application area in Europe has been relatively small, with only three recent noteworthy projects. The European Strategic Programme for Research and Development in Information Technology (*ESPRIT II*) funded project whose acronym is LAMA [ref. 8] (project number 2280), has the objective to develop a large reach, high-load manipulator to move work-pieces or tools precisely in a programmable task execution mode in a manufacturing environment. Although not directly related to construction robots, its has direct application to the construction activity due to the potential high-load and far-reach capability of the manipulator studied.

12.   Another *ESPRIT II* project, ARMS [ref. 9] (project number 2637), has the objective to develop a robot manipulator system capable of performing a range of assembly tasks. Again, although in the manufacturing area, its work on handling objects with imprecise geometry and of a pliable nature, would also be of use to the construction robot.

13.   The painting robot [ref. 10] of the Centre Scientifique et Technique du Batiment (*CSTB*) in France has been one of the few European achievements in this area. The work was significant since it demonstrated mobility of a construction robot. However, this was an experimental machine and not a robot in service by European construction companies.

14.   The Finnish research reported in [ref. 11] describes the approach taken to the control-system design work for a heavy-duty manipulator.

Japanese Developments

15.   In Japan, there is no standard definition of construction robots and for the purposes of this section of the paper, the following definition will be used [refs. 5, 12]:

> "A machine that can replace a worker or workers, is called a construction robot."

16.   This is in contrast to the definition of the Robotics Institute of America which defines an industrial robot in the following manner [ref. 13]:

> "A robot is a reprogrammable multifunctional manipulator designed to move material, parts, tools, or specialized devices, through variable programmed motions for the performance of a variety of tasks."

17.   As an example of the commitment of the Japanese to the Research and Development in the construction robotics area, three large Research structures will be described:

(a)   *Waseda Construction Robot Project:*
       The System Science Institute of the University of Waseda has studied the application of construction robotics since 1977. With

researchers from 11 companies, the objective was to investigate methods to improve productivity by applying construction robots.

(b) *"Ministry of Construction" Research Project:*
This 5 year project started in 1982 had a budget of 500 million Yen (approximately 2.8 million ECU). Its objective was to advance construction technology.

(c) *Research and Development Project of Robots for Critical Environment:*
With a value of 2 billion Yen (approximately 110 million ECU), this is one of the largest projects run by the Ministry of International Trade and Industry. Although the main objective is to develop robots and robotic technologies for critical environments, the results will used in the construction industry.

18. Using the categorisation in paragraph 15, the number of Japanese applications is large and below is outlined a brief list and description of some of them [refs. 14, 15, 16]:

(a) *shotcreting robot:* uses a shotcreting gun mounted on a conventional earth excavator.

(b) *tunnelling robot:* uses rotating blades for earth excavation and concrete ejection and is controlled through feedback from earth pressure sensors.

(c) *excavating robot:* uses probes and sensors to detect utility pipes buried underground.

(d) *reinforcement mapping robot:* detects and maps the location of reinforcement steel embedded in concrete.

(e) *concrete distribution robot:* uses an articulated arm to direct a concrete pumping hose.

(f) *fireproofing robot:* a guided vehicle with an articulated arm and holding a spraying gun.

(g) *drilling robot:* a numerically controlled machine for drilling into rocks during tunnelling work.

(h) *tile inspection robot:* tests the adhesion of vertical tiles while moving vertically on a wall.

(i) *underground inspection robot:* a tele-operated vehicle for the inspection of hazardous environments.

THE ENVIRONMENT

Introduction

19. As mentioned earlier, the outline of the European-wide Research and Development project to be described, will specialize in the brick-wall construction application of robots. This section will demonstrate the scale of the problem as a result of the harshness of the environment and its essentially unstructured nature [ref. 17].

The Site

20.   The building of walls usually takes place in an open-air environment. Recently there has been some development of prefabricated structures for the protection of an entire building but these protectors suffer from limitations and are expensive. In addition, the following complicating conditions exist:

(a)   dust from cement, sand and cutting operations,
(b)   a ground surface cluttered with construction debris, excavation results, pools of standing water,
(c)   falling debris from higher levels,
(d)   the location of the raw materials such as the bricks or blocks may be a long way from the building activity,
(e)   a power distribution network will probably not be in place in the site at this stage of construction, and
(f)   a multi-storey building will require the movement of the building-robot vertically as well.

21.   The implications of the environment on the robot, its sensors, its mobility, and its control systems, are considered in greater detail in a later section.

Wall Types and Construction Techniques

22.   The natural raw stone was probably the first material to be used as an atomic building element (*abe*). However, in a modern context it is not considered a suitable *abe* as a result of its high specific weight and its difficulty of handling in an automated fashion. Thus, it is likely that stone will continue to be limited to special decorative applications in future buildings.

23.   Fortunately, modern industrial processes are able to mass-produce a great variety of *abe*s, the simple red-coloured brick being the most familiar. This has allowed new shapes of *abe*s to be produced, possibly with new materials to be used with modern bonding adhesives or methods. Modern energy-conservation requirements impose great demands on the insulation properties of the walls, with the consequence that additional requirements are placed both on the properties of the brick and the assembling and fitting processes. The double external wall with an internal insulating layer is an example of a modern *abe*.

24.   There is a large number of types of artificially produced bricks, all with special properties depending on the application and the bonding adhesive. A brief example list is given below:

(a)   porous bricks   (PMz 1.2/60),
(b)   bricks with longitudinal holes   (LLz 1.2/60),
(c)   bricks with horizontal holes   (HLz A 1.2/100),
(d)   cement bricks   (KHLz 350),
(e)   compact bricks   (Mz 100),

(f)	view bricks	(VMz 150),
(g)	cement bricks	(VMz 350).

25. Although bricks are standardised to DIN 105, various smaller or larger bricks may be produced for special purposes and special assembly processes. This possibly will be of use to the robotized building task since it is anticipated that the assembly procedures will need to be carefully reviewed to optimize the performance of the system. The further properties of the *abe* which will determine the characteristics required of the robot and the gripper are the *abe*s:

    (a)   specific weight,
    (b)   dimensions, and
    (c)   strength in compression.

26. The bonding adhesive between the *abe*s will directly influence the robotization philosophy since further handling equipment would need to be designed. At present the bonding adhesive is either lime mortar, lime-cement mortar, cement mortar or rarely no mortar for special *abe*s. Mortar is standardized according to DIN 1053 with types I, II, and III but advanced bonding adhesive is required for advanced material *abe*s such as ALFABLOCK or LECABLOCCO.

27. If a bonding adhesive is required for the automated system, the way in which the adhesive is applied to the *abe* needs to be carefully considered. The following methods are possible:

    (a)   the raw materials are input, they are mixed and applied as desired,
    (b)   the ready-mixed adhesive is input and the machine applies it where required on the *abe*,
    (c)   the bonding adhesive is packaged in some fashion and the packages are applied to the *abe* where required.

28. These aspects will be touched upon again in a later section.

PRESENT TECHNOLOGY

29. A brief overview will be given of the present enabling technology for the robot operated brick-wall construction system. Where possible, this will be related to the requirements of the system.

The Robot and its Control

30. The kinematic arrangements of modern robots (manipulators), are many and varied [ref. 18]. They are usually classified according to the number of links and the types of joints. The joints could be revolute, like a hinge, or prismatic which allows linear relative motion between two links. One configuration (whose joints are revolute, revolute and prismatic) which is suitable for assembly operations is the Selective Compliant Articulated Robot for Assembly (*SCARA*), robot. The actuator at the joints could be

electrically, hydraulically or pneumatically controlled depending on the application and the operating environment. The number of joints determines the degree of freedom (*DOF*s) of the manipulator. With fewer than 6 *DOF*s (three for positioning and three for orientation), the manipulator will not be able to reach every point in its workspace. To perform such typically human tasks as reaching behind obstacles, more than 6 *DOF*s are required. Such a manipulator is referred to as being kinematically redundant.

31.   Of equal importance to the kinematic design of the robot, is the design and configuration of its control systems. Considerable research and development effort has been devoted to designing robust controllers for the robot which is a highly non-linear dynamical system with considerable interactions between control loops. The simple point-to-point trajectory operation presents few problems to the control-system designer [ref. 19]. However, the force-control problem during the contact of the end-effector and the environment is still an essentially unsolved control problem although there has been considerable recent progress [refs. 20, 21].

Positioning and Mobility

32.   It is likely that the operative workspace of a robotic arm will not enclose the required workspace of an entire wall. Thus, its relocation will be necessary. As mentioned earlier, the absence of any smooth surface for positioning and orientation, points to the need for an independent system for gross robot transportation. Heavy-duty lifting equipment is available, but it is currently not able to be controlled in an automated fashion. Furthermore, a system of this nature would require global positioning information in order to maintain an adequate level of positional accuracy. A system based on a pair of tracks and a moving vehicle, will also be considered.

Peripheral Mechanisms

33.   The end-effector of the robot is of vital importance since the ability to manipulate the *abe* is required for its correct placing. A comprehensive treatment of robot end-effectors is given in [ref. 22]. To facilitate and ease the handling of the *abe,* it may be necessary to modify its physical design (for example: shape, presence of holes, surface finish) without compromising any of its mechanical properties.

34.   The unstructured nature of the building environment demands that the robot be adequately equipped with the appropriate sensors for:
    (a)   global position detection to account for gross movement of the robot,
    (b)   position and velocity detection on each joint for the position control of the end-effector,
    (c)   six *DOF* force and torque sensors for the possible force control during environment-constrained operations,
    (d)   vision system for mapping the position of *abe* supplies or the structure of the gross movement environment,

    (e)   texture detection system for choosing *abe* types.

35.   A further problem to consider is the facility to cater for the need for non-standard *abe* sizes at door and window frame edges. This may be accounted for as follows:

    (a)   leave a space where the non-standard size *abe* should fit and let it be filled by a human worker,
    (b)   provide computer controlled cutting machinery,
    (c)   produce a range of special sized *abe*s for the construction system to select as required.

FRAMEWORK OF AUTOMATED CONSTRUCTION OPERATION

36.   The previous sections have attempted to present an overview of the currently available hardware for the robot and its necessary peripheral components. This section will outline the hardware and software aimed at, as part of the current research and development effort.

The Hardware Constituent Components

37.   The design philosophy to be adopted will ensure that flexible modules are developed that will be able to be used together. If off-the-shelf hardware exists which will satisfy all the requirements, it will be specified rather than valuable development effort being wasted. An approximate decomposition of the system is as follows:

    (a)   a 6 *DOF* robot with appropriate joint actuators,
    (b)   an *abe* presentation module for the robot (possibly),
    (c)   an *abe* sizing module (possibly),
    (d)   local control sensors,
    (e)   global control sensors,
    (f)   local computer control hardware,
    (g)   global computer control hardware,
    (h)   customized end-effector,
    (i)   mobility platform or mechanism,
    (j)   power supplies,
    (k)   bonding adhesive applicator (depends on the results of the *abe* research).

38.   Special research attention will be paid to the need for the equipment to operate consistently and reliably in the harsh construction environment.

The Software Constituent Components

39.   The success of the brick-wall building robot depends on the sophistication of the software. It is envisaged that the software will fall into six categories:

    (a)   the software for the implementation of the low-level control algorithms of the robot joints and the end-effector,

(b)   the software for the trajectory position control for handling the *abe*s and the co-operation with the *abe* presentation module,

(c)   the software for handling the on-site user control information and alarm monitoring,

(d)   the software for accepting information from databases and *CAD* packages so that the building activity can be planned and optimised with the possible use of recent AI scheduling and planning developments,

(e)   an off-line comprehensive geometrical simulation facility for the visualisation and verification of proposed building schedules and system configurations.

(f)   an off-line control system design and simulation facility for the low-level robot joint and end-effector controllers.

PROPOSED-SYSTEM CONSTRAINTS AND FUTURE DIRECTIONS

40.   For the proposed system to be successful, it is necessary that new and, possibly revolutionary, concepts be developed for the building techniques and that there is a move away from the present, natural constraint of attempting to emulate the human being. The ability to receive data directly from the architect or civil engineer would greatly advance the technology and allow the manufacturing industry's *CIM* philosophies to be used in the construction industry.

CONCLUSIONS

41.   A general review has been given of the penetration of robotization in the construction industry. The building problem has been considered as a special case and its particular problems considered. The breakdown of the hardware and software into modules opens up the possibility of further applications. The concepts, in broad-brush terms, have been presented of a new initiative for the robotization of the building activity. The achievement of its objectives will produce tangible results for productivity within the construction industry and promote the use of further automation.

REFERENCES

1.   SKIBNIEWSKI M.J.: *"Robotics in Civil Engineering"*, published by Van Nostrand Reinhold, 1988, ISBN 0-905451-77-5.

2.   ENGELBERGER J.F.: *"Robotics in Service"*, published by Kogan Page Ltd., 1989, ISBN 1-85091-358-7.

3.   WARSZAWSKI A. AND SANGREY D.A.: *"Robotics in Building Construction"*, Journal of Construction Engineering and Management, Vol. 111, No. 3, September 1985, pp. 260-280.

4.   PAULSON B.C.: *"Automation and Robotics for Construction"*, Journal of Construction Engineering and Management, Vol. 111, No. 3, September 1985, pp. 190-207.

5.   SUZUKI S., YOSHIDA T. and UENO T.: *"Construction Robotics in Japan"*, in the Proceedings of the Third International Conference on Tall Buildings, Chicago, 1986, pp. 507-552.

6.   SAGAWA Y. and NAKAHARA Y.: *"Robots for the Japanese Construction Industry"*, IABASE Proceedings P-86/85, IABASE Periodica 2/1985, pp. 77-92.

7.   SANGREY D.A.: *"Introduction"*, Robotics in Construction, The proceedings of a Workshop Conference held at Carnegie-Mellon University, June 17-20, 1984, CMU-RI-WC-85-01, Civil Engineering Report R-85-148, pp. 1-2.

8.   ESPRIT: *"Synopses of Computer Integrated Manufacturing: Projects and Exploratory Actions"*, Directorate General XIII Telecommunications, Information and Innovation Commission of the European Communities, III/292/90, Volume 6 of a series of 8, September 1990, pp. CIM-114 to CIM-115.

9.   ESPRIT: as in [ref. 8], pp. CIM-156 to CIM-157.

10.   SALAGNAC J-L.: *"SOFFITO, an experimental mobile robot for Construction Work"*, Franco-Finnish colloquium, CSTB, VTT, Valbonne Sophia Antipolis, CSTB, 1988.

11.   KARKKAINEN P. and MANNINEN M.: *"Supervisory Control of Large-Scaled Manipulators in Severe Environments"*, Robotics in Construction, The Proceedings of a Workshop Conference held at Carnegie-Mellon University, June 17-20, 1984, CMU-RI-WC-85-01, Civil Engineering Report R-85-148, pp. 59-68.

12.   WARSZAWSKI A.: *"Robotics in Building Construction"*, Department of Civil Engineering and Robotics Institute, Carnegie-Mellon University, Pittsburgh, Pennsylvania 15213, July 1984, Report R-84-147.

13.   HUNT V.D.: *"Industrial Robotics Handbook"*, Industrial Press Inc., New York, 1983.

14.   YOSHIDA T., UENO T., NONAKA M. and YAMAZAKI S.: *"Development of Spray Robot for Fireproof Cover Work"*, Robotics in Construction, The Proceedings of a Workshop Conference held at Carnegie-Mellon University, June 17-20, 1984, CMU-RI-WC-85-01, Civil Engineering Report R-85-148, pp. 69-95.

15.   SHIMOMURA Y. and SONADA T.: *"Tunneling by Robot - Shield Driven Automatic Control System"*, Robotics in Construction, The Proceedings of a Workshop Conference held at Carnegie-Mellon University, June 17-20, 1984, CMU-RI-WC-85-01, Civil Engineering Report R-85-148, pp. 97-126.

16.   HASEGAWA Y. and TAMAKI K.: *"Work Modularization for Building use Robots Development"*, Robotics in Construction, The Proceedings of a Conference held at Carnegie-Mellon University, June 24-26, 1985, CMU-RI-WC-85-2, Civil Engineering Report R-85-152, pp. 179-188.

17.   SARANTOPOULOS S: *"Robot-Operated Brick-wall Construction System"*, Final report, BRITE/EURAM SME Feasibility award, Commission of the European Communities, January 1990.

18.   SPONG M.W. and VIDYASAGAR M.: *"Robot Dynamics and Control"*, John Wiley and Sons, 1989.

19.   LEAHY M.B. (Jr): *"Compensation of Industrial Manipulator Dynamics in the Presence of Variable Payloads"*, The International Journal of Robotics Research, Vol. 9, No. 4, August 1990, pp. 86-98.

20.   LAHOUD M.A., MUNCH H., SURDILOVIC D. and FRAILE M.: *"The Benefits to CIM of Robot Deburring: The Use of Modelleing and Control"*, Proceedings of the Sixth CIM-Europe Annual Conference, 15-17 May 1990, Lisbon, Portugal, ISBN 3-540-19616-1, pp. 53-64.

21.   FAESSLER H: *"Manipulators Constrained by Stiff Contact: Dynamics, Control, and Experiments"*, The International Journal of Robotics Research, Vol. 9, No. 4, August 1990, pp. 40-58.

22.   ROSHEIM M.E.: *"Robot Wrist Actuators"*, John Wiley and Sons, ISBN 0-471-61595-1, 1989.

CHIPS – highway management systems

J. G. BARTON, Senior Engineer, Roads Directorate, The Scottish Office

SYNOPSIS

This paper explains the CHIPS (Computerised Highway Information and Planning System) database, what it contains and the usage made of it by the Roads Directorate and others. It discusses the way in which the information is contained and updated in one central source and thereafter downloaded onto stand-alone Browsers. The paper also addresses the development of the Browsers and their role in providing readily accessible information in an easily understood form. The final part of the paper will discuss ongoing/future development of the system.

INTRODUCTION

1.   In 1973, what was then the Scottish Development Department, Road Engineers Division (now the Scottish Office Environment Department, Roads Directorate) started to develop a computerised database which would enable investment and maintenance decisions to be taken on an objective, consistent and defined basis throughout Scotland. Originally CHIPS used the hierarchical database management system (DBMS) known as System 2000 to control and structure the data. In 1987 CHIPS was converted to a relational database mounted on a DEC VAX/VMS using the DBMS system INGRES.

2.   Computers have come a long way since the first CHIPS system was developed. Similarly CHIPS is constantly being enhanced. Today, as well as the mainframe database, CHIPS includes a series of user defined stand-alone Browsers; microcomputer based graphical presentations of subsets of the main CHIPS database.

BACKGROUND

3.   The Scottish Office, Roads Directorate is responsible for all technical matters relating to the 3200km of Trunk Roads and Motorways in Scotland. The geographical coverage and extent of the Scottish Trunk Road network is shown in Figure 1. This network ranges in character from 3 lane motorway through to one single track road with passing places.

4.   The Directorate's annual budget for Trunk Roads and Motorways for the financial year 1990/91 is approximately £200m of which approximately £55m is related to structural, routine and winter maintenance. In common with other roads

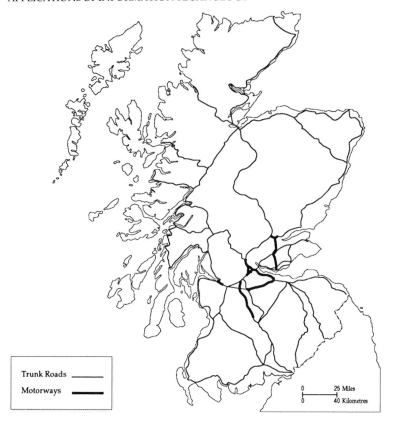

Trunk Roads ———

Motorways ▬▬▬

0   25 Miles

0   40 Kilometres

Figure 1 - The Scottish Trunk Road and Motorway Network —————

authorities, the Roads Directorate is responsible for the development, maintenance and safe operation of the roads under its control.

5.   In order to do this a detailed knowledge of the road system and what is happening is necessary. This knowledge includes data on the network itself, on traffic volumes and composition, on accident records and on the structural condition and maintenance requirements of the network. The information, which is not only required centrally, should be easily accessible and should be capable of being cross related.

6.   As a result the computerised Highway Information and Planning System better known as CHIPS emerged as the management information system. CHIPS is hosted on a DEC VAX/VMS computer and utilises the DBMS INGRES. It is a relational database with the road network acting as the common thread which relates one dataset to another. This makes the system extremely flexible and a very powerful tool for undertaking the type of analysis required by the Roads Directorate. It means that different datasets may be cross related. For example one could assess the incidence of skidding accidents at sites before and after they have been surface dressed. The relationship between the different datasets is shown in Figure 2.

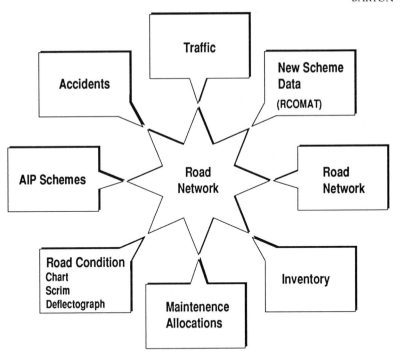

Figure 2 - Structure of Chips ————————————————————

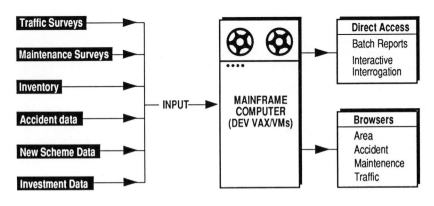

Figure 3 - Data Storage and Access ————————————————

297

7.   All of this information is contained within the main CHIPS database. In order to make the information more readily accessible, sub-sets of the database are downloaded onto microcomputer-based graphical presentations known as the Browsers. The relationship is shown in Figure 3; the basic philosophy is that of a central source which is maintained and updated and thereafter downloaded onto stand-alone Browsers.

CHIPS DATASETS

8.   In order to understand the application of CHIPS in the management of the Trunk Road and Motorway network, it is necessary to know what the system contains. The following is not exhaustive, it is merely sufficient to provide an appreciation of the range and scope of CHIPS.

Network

9.   The road network is the common thread running through all of the datasets. The CHIPS network is split into a series of LINKS and SECTIONS.

10.   LINKS are typically about 10km long and represent a length of road which carries a consistent volume of traffic. Normally LINKS tend to run between major junctions. LINKS are sub-divided into a number of SECTIONS (typically about 2km long). Each SECTION represents a length of road of similar character: each carriageway of a dual carriageway will have its own SECTION identifier. The SECTIONS can be further sub-divided using centreline chainages.

11.   The network is fundamental to the database and contains the basic attributes such as; the lengths of the roads, the speed limits, the road type (Class, single/dual carriageway), centre line co-ordinates and the radii and gradients. It provides basic technical information for, amongst others, the NESA (Network Evaluation from Surveys and Assignments) parameters of an existing length of road (hilliness, bendiness, traffic, accidents and maintenance regime).

Maintenance and Inventory

12.   The structural condition of the existing road network is assessed, broadly in 3 ways:

- CHART[1]
- SCRIM[2]
- DEFLECTOGRAPH

13.   The maintenance management system within CHIPS was developed to utilise the output from CHART and thus provide the Directorate with a set of measurable criteria defining the present condition of the road, and a means of allocating funds on a needs basis. The computer database also allows us to assess the

---

[1]CHART - COMPUTERISED HIGHWAY ASSESSMENTS OF RATINGS AND TREATMENT

[2]SCRIM - SIDEWAYS COEFFICIENT ROUTINE INVESTIGATORY MACHINE

effects of different maintenance and investment priorities and keep a check on deterioration rates.

14. The inclusion of SCRIM and Deflectograph data provides additional information on skidding resistance and residual life of the road, giving a fuller picture of its condition. In this way maintenance funds can be allocated on a consistent basis and comparisons can be made Region by Region or route by route.

15. The Scottish Routine Maintenance Management System (SRMMS) introduced in 1986 required inventory information to be collected as a part of that process. Whereas for structural maintenance, the inventory is of the network itself and its basic characteristics, for routine maintenance it is the items to be maintained; the road infrastructure and furniture.

16. Implementation of SRMMS is presently in hand with Regional authorities.

17. By relating the information from the routine maintenance management system with other sub-systems such as traffic, accidents or road materials it allows trends and relationships to be investigated in a much more efficient and effective manner. For example, minor carriageway repairs could be compared with heavy goods vehicle flows and pavement construction materials; accident rates could be compared with SCRIM values and again surfacing materials and date laid.

18. CHIPS and the associated Browsers allow all of the data that results from the inventory collection, the inspections, the costing procedures and the monitoring regimes to be stored systematically, accessed in an efficient manner and cross related where necessary.

Accidents and AIP[3] Schemes

19. Accident data is provided by the relevant Police Authority. Information about the prevailing conditions at the time of the accident (the "attendant circumstances") are collected on a consistent basis using the Department of Transport's "Stats 19" form. All of this information for Trunk Road accidents is contained in CHIPS. The structure of the accident data in CHIPS reflects that of the Stats 19 form with separate tables containing details of the accident, the vehicles involved and the casualties.

20. The accident data is used extensively: at one level it provides the basis for answers to questions raised by Members of Parliament, the press and the public; it is used to formulate policy and to assess schemes; and it is used by the Accident Investigation Unit to identify accident clusters which may, after investigation, lead to AIP schemes. Recently extensive use has been made of this data in providing guidance on route strategies such as the white lining and surface dressing programmes. A number of programs/retrieval routines have been developed to make this analysis easier. For example the moving cursor program will analyse a route or part of a route in a series of sections, highlighting where clusters of accidents occur. Parameters such as the threshold value (No of accidents), step length, and type of accident can be defined by the user.

---

[3]AIP - ACCIDENT INVESTIGATION AND PREVENTION

21.   Coming full circle, the location of AIP schemes and also other road improvement schemes, are contained in the database so that their performance can be assessed.

22.   It is also important that schemes financed from one budget do not conflict with those from another. In this case AIP schemes might be planned at the same location as maintenance schemes. CHIPS "feathers" the 2 sets of bids together and identifies where they overlap.

Other Data Sets

23.   Traffic information is available, broadly, for each CHIPS link. Each link is counted once every 6 years. As well as this, a large number of ad hoc counts and information from the automatic classifier sites are fed into the traffic database and, from there, into CHIPS.

24.   Details of the construction of major road improvement schemes is collected on Trunk Road construction sites using the microcomputer based RCOMAT (Road Construction Materials) database. This is fed into CHIPS and will be used to assess the performance of different materials and their sources as well as providing information on pavement construction for Deflectograph analysis and whole life costings.

25.   Much of the information in CHIPS can be output using a plotter, to any required scale. These geographic representations are very often used, for example, as network overlays.

26.   Although the information contained in CHIPS is shown as a series of tables, this is merely a convenient way of filing the data. In common with other relational databases, it is quite simple to link any 2 or more data sets via the road network. Indeed, this is how the database is often used in practice. Thus, wet road skidding accidents will be linked to SCRIM ratings, which in turn can be related to surface material and even the source and life history of that material; alternatively the Accident, Traffic and Link tables will be linked to derive accident rates per million vehicle kilometres.

THE BROWSERS

27.   Although there is a need to interrogate and retrieve information from the main database, this is not a task that many practising civil engineers find attractive. INGRES offers a reasonably user friendly query language but it still needs some effort to master the basics. Many people are still apprehensive of computers, particularly if it requires typing queries, and can relate much better to map based information.

28.   The Browsers get round this by the use of simple pull down options displayed on the screen. They all use Microsoft Windows and are menu driven, operated almost exclusively using a "mouse". The Browser is generally connected to a printer/plotter so that anything displayed on the screen can be produced in hard copy format.

29.   The Browser screen is divided into a number of discrete areas, each serving a specific purpose. Microsoft Windows provides a number of facilities which make it possible to combine all of these areas on one screen, although they sometimes overlap. Figure 4 shows these screen areas.

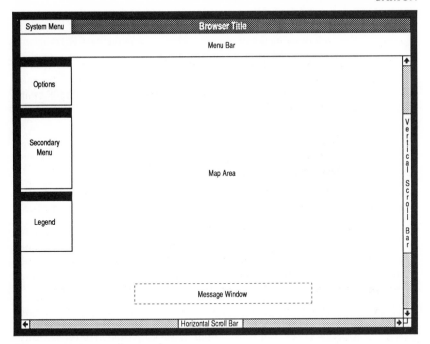

Figure 4 - Browser Screen Area ————————————

30.   <u>Map area</u> The map area is the largest area on the screen and is the one on which the map or other graphical data is presented. The graphical data may be temporarily superimposed by text in the form of user-requested tables or message windows but is reinstated automatically on removal of the text window. Map data is always drawn to the correct aspect ratio.

31.   <u>System menu</u> There is a small system menu in the top left hand corner of the screen. The options in it drop down when the cursor button is depressed over it. The options provide information about the software versions and enable the Browser to be exited.

32.   <u>Menu bar</u> The menu bar contains a number of application menus, which may be arranged in one or more rows. The last menu is always HELP which has no options in it. The other menus are menu titles which are not application functions themselves.

33.   Selection of a menu title with the mouse causes the menu options to drop down over the map area. Selection of an option is done by dragging the mouse down the menu until it is over the option required and then releasing the mouse button. Releasing the mouse button also causes the menu to disappear.

34.   There are a number of menus on the main menu bar which will be present in all CHIPS Browsers because they provide both general display manipulation functions and CHIPS network drawing and annotation functions. Some of the more important are:

* Window Options - these control the scale and content of the map area.

* Network drawing options - responsible for drawing the CHIPS network and background data (eg Regional boundaries, Links, Sections, centrelines, non-trunk network).

* Network labelling options - used to annotate the CHIPS Link and Section network (Link and Section Numbers and Lengths, Route numbers, Section types, primary route destinations).

* Find/Miscellaneous options - enables the user to identify, on the map, portions of the CHIPS network (eg Find Link, OSGR (Ordnance Survey Grip Reference) or Route).

35. Secondary menu The secondary menu is used for the display of any menu options required to refine a selection made from the menu in the main menu bar.

36. Options The options area is currently unused.

37. Legend The legend area is used to display the current map scale, the OSGR of the last probed point and the currently selected Link and Section, if any.

38. Scroll bars The display, be it graphics or text, can be scrolled either horizontally or vertically using the mouse. This allows data not on screen to be viewed.

39. Message boxes When user input in the form of text, or occasionally a picked or probed point, is required, a prompt giving details is displayed in the message window which temporarily superimposes the map area. Information and error messages are also displayed in this way.

40. Figures 5 and 6 show all and part of the trunk road network in Scotland as displayed on the Browsers. The boxes on the left hand side of the screen provide information on the scale of the map and, where appropriate, the Link/Section and OSGRs. It is a simple matter to zoom in or out of the screen using the mouse.

41. Figure 7 shows how a section of road can be labeled with the link and section numbers. The various lines show the increasing detail which may be applied to the map; links are drawn as straight lines which are then subdivided into sections thereby defining the road more precisely. Finally the actual centreline of the road can be drawn onto the map. These varying degrees of accuracy are useful for different functions.

42. The Browsers are built to a common format so that once an engineer is familiar with the operation of one Browser he can with the minimum of effort, operate others. Obviously they vary in the information contained, how they are used and who are the prime users. All run on IBM PC-ATs, PS2s or compatible personal computers with a minimum of 512kb of memory. The basic philosophy is that of a central source of data that is constantly maintained and thereafter various subsets of this data are downloaded onto stand-alone microcomputer based graphical systems.

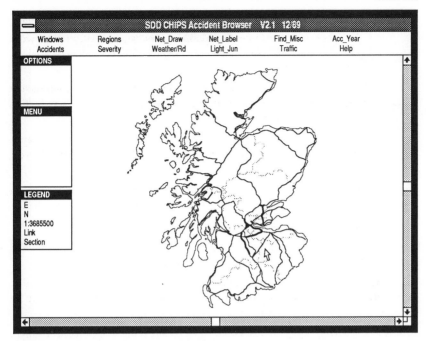

Figure 5 - Browser Display - All Scotland

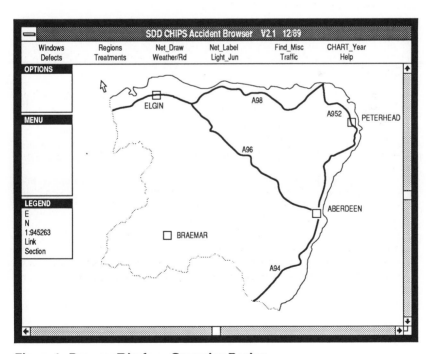

Figure 6 - Browser Display - Grampian Region

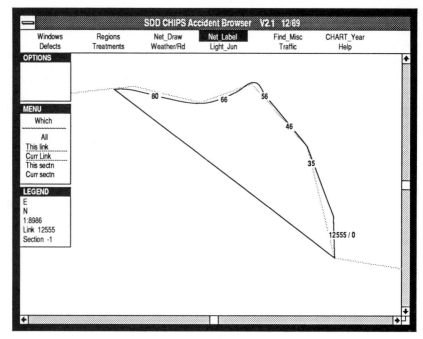

Figure 7 - Browser Display - Link and Section Numbers

AREA BROWSER

43.   This is perhaps the most widely used of all Browsers. It may be appropriate, therefore to explain in some detail its facilities and usage and thereafter merely highlight the main attributes of other Browsers.

44.   The Area Browser contains information on; the condition of the road, maintenance schemes, inventory, accidents and traffic. It is used primarily by the Territorial (Area) Engineers to inform them of the condition and performance of that section of Trunk Road for which each has responsibility. It contains all of the general Browser features together with a number of specific functions. The main ones are:-

45.   CHART defect options. Any or all of the CHART defect options (Wheel Track Rutting, Edge Defects etc) may be investigated and displayed, either graphically or in the form of charts or tables. Significance levels can be set for each defect under consideration so that only sections of road with ratings above this value are highlighted. Defects can be looked at over a number of years to assess, for example, rates of deterioration.

46.   CHART treatment options. Within CHART, the various defect ratings are combined to provide treatment ratings (Surface Dressing, Resurfacing, Overlay, Major Strengthening). As with the defects, any or all of the treatment options can be investigated and highlighted (graphically, charts, tables). Again significance levels can be set and the ratings can be viewed over a number of years.

47.   SCRIM and Deflectograph options. These work along the same lines as the defect and treatment options and give an indication of the skidding resistance and residual life of the road.

48.   Maintenance scheme options. These enable the user to annotate the map with proposed and completed maintenance scheme information and to display it in tabular form. Some of the more important options are; the locations (represented by rectangular boxes drawn along the lengths to which they apply), the names of the schemes, the scheme work codes and the option which enables maintenance scheme data for all the currently selected CHART years to be displayed in tabular form.

49.   Traffic options. This allows the user to annotate the map with traffic flow data information. Traffic flows can be labelled as a series of open rectangular boxes parallel to the links to which they refer (of widths proportional to traffic flows), as a numeric Annual Average Daily Flow (AADF) and/or as the percentage HGVs.

50.   Accident options. This option enables the user to select accident severity categories and to display the data graphically. Each accident year selected will be represented by its own colour code. Alternatively a summary of accidents occurring over a specified period (usually 3 years) can be selected.

51.   Inventory options. Any of the inventory information collected under SRMMS and stored in CHIPS can be downloaded to the Browser. Thus, the locations of central reserve safety fences (including emergency crossing points), traffic signs, lighting columns etc can be displayed graphically.

52.   The comprehensive range of information contained in the Area Browser allows the Territorial Engineer to have a good overview of what is happening on the Trunk Roads in his area. More importantly the graphical display and ease of access actually encourages the user to "browse" through the network.

53.   As with all Browsers, the link to a printer/plotter allows hard copies of any information displayed on screen to be obtained. Thus the engineer is able to obtain, in map form, the location of defects, maintenance schemes, accidents and traffic flows; perhaps prior to a visit to the site.

ACCIDENT BROWSER

54.   The Accident Browser contains details of all trunk road accidents from 1986 onwards. It is used predominantly by the Directorate's Accident Investigation Unit and by their counterparts in the Local Authority Regions. It is also used as a part of the checking procedures carried out on all Trunk Road Accidents.

55.   As well as the location, severity and years of the accident, there are certain key features held in 3 separate tables. Traffic data is combined with the accidents to produce accident rates per million vehicle kilometres.

56.   This type of facility is clearly useful in a wide range of accident related matters. It is used to provide background data for, amongst others, answers to press and public, for planning applications and for improvement schemes. The ability to view accidents on the trunk road network, select the section of road to be analysed and then produce a hard copy quickly is fundamental to the Browser's usefulness.

TRAFFIC BROWSER

57.   The earliest traffic browser was developed using the Aladin relational database management system and contained band width flow data, HGV flows tied back to classified counts and Annual Average Daily Flows (AADFs). Traffic information is also held on both Area and Accident Browsers as basic AADFs and HGVs (number and percentage).

58.   Currently a separate computerised Scottish Traffic Database is being developed on a MicroVAX. This will collate traffic count data from a number of sources, including the automatic classified counts. The Traffic Browser is seen as a display vehicle and access medium for this data.

MAINTENANCE BROWSER

59.   The Maintenance Browser is similar in design to the Area Browser. The main difference is that where the Area Browser contains data for a particular Region, the Maintenance Browser contains all-Scotland data. This allows, the Headquarters Engineer to assess what is happening at an all-Scotland level. In turn, this makes the tasks of comparing allocations on a route by route or Region by Region basis very much more simple. In addition it allows the Network Manager to look at the relationship between maintenance schemes in adjacent Regions thereby ensuring that disruption to the public is kept to acceptable levels.

FUTURE WORK

60.   The pace of development of computers and computer systems has, over recent years, been quite remarkable. Any predictions on how systems will develop long term are therefore problematic. However, there are a number of enhancements to the CHIPS system on the near horizon.

61.   In terms of data collection, the High Speed Road monitor and other automatic collection devices will replace the remaining manual systems, leading to a more rapid and consistent approach to data collection. It is envisaged that all of this data will be loaded directly into CHIPS.

62.   The enhancements to the system itself centre on the development of the Browsers. Two things in particular are worthy of mention.

63.   First the provision of background Ordnance Survey maps upon which the CHIPS network would be graphically imposed. This will enable those using the Browsers to more readily identify where they are on the road network thereby making the Browsers even more user friendly.

64.   The second enhancement is the provision of a video/photo library which would be accessed via the Browser and stored on laser disc. Thus the engineer would be able to "see" the road in combination with assessing its condition from collected data.

CONCLUSION

65.   The management of something so diverse as the Scottish Trunk Road and Motorway Network needs a very large database. CHIPS provides a comprehensive, coherent approach to such a computerised database thereby allowing this information to be readily accessed. The parallel operating systems of the mainframe computer and the microcomputer based Browsers allows the balance between ease of access and depth of interrogation to be addressed flexibly.

66.   The system is used by staff within the Roads Directorate and in the Agent Authorities. In particular the Browsers are used as a management tool by Engineers responsible for individual areas of the network. Increasingly, network management and the need to take an overview is becoming more and more important. The new legislation regarding Public Utilities will require the Network Manager to be able at anytime to check the extent of road works on a particular section of road. The Browser is ideally placed to take on this role. New developments such as the use of laser discs to store a photographic record of the network will further enhance the system.

67.   Of course there will always be a need for the "human element", ensuring that the Directorate's responsibilities are carried out effectively. However, the emergence of a user friendly, robust system has enabled this responsibility to be undertaken in a focused and consistent manner, compliant with current requirements of accountability.

REFERENCES

1.   ROBINSON F and INNES J (1982). Computerised Highway Information and Planning System. Seminar on Information Technology, Institution of Municipal Engineers, Edinburgh.

2.   MACKENZIE N B and INNES J (1985). Maintenance Management Systems - The Practice in Scotland. National Workshop, Institute of Highways and Transportation, Leamington Spa.

3.   WINGATE P J F and PETERS C H (1975). The CHART System for Assessing the Structural Maintenance Needs of Highways. Department of Transport TRRL Supplementary Report 153 UC.

4.   HOSKING J R and WOODFORD G C (1976). Measurement of Skidding Resistance - Part 1, Guide to the use of SCRIM. Department of Transport TRRL Report LR 737.

5.   DRUITT S (1986). A Microcomputer Based Graphics Interface to a Highway Inventory Database System. PTRC Summer Annual Meeting, University of Sussex.

6.   MACKENZIE N B and MCCALLUM D (1986). A Locationally Referenced Highway Management Information System: The CHIPS Database in Scotland. PTRC Summer Annual Meeting, University of Sussex.

ACKNOWLEDGEMENTS

The author wishes to thank the Director of Roads, The Scottish Office Environment Department for permission to publish this paper. He also acknowledges the software development work carried out on behalf of the Roads Directorate by SIAS Ltd.

The views expressed in this paper are those of the author and not necessarily those of The Scottish Office.

Experience of contrasting approaches in the design and development of highway systems

R. ROBINSON, Assistant Director, N. C. LAMB, Hermis
System Manager, R. BLAKELOCK, Hismis Systems Manager and
J. D. BELL, Netter System Manager, Rendel Palmer & Tritton Ltd

SYNOPSIS. Factors are discussed which should be taken into account or considered when identifying the most suitable structure of computer systems in particular situations. These are based on recent experience of developing systems for use in the highways sub-sector. The use of structured systems development methods is also discussed, and it is recommended that a flexible approach should be adopted to choosing a structured analysis, design and implementation method.

INTRODUCTION

1. A more systematic approach to the management of infrastructure, whereby expenditure must be justified in terms of need and related to the fulfilment of policy objectives, is becoming an integral part of many managers' work in the 1990s. Whether the manager is responsible for waterways, highways, railways or utilities networks, many of the issues which must be addressed and resolved are the same. The perceived core of any management system designed to support a systematic approach to management increasingly is becoming a computer system and data. The ways in which these two ingredients can be put together are numerous and the 'best' way forward can alter rapidly with computer hardware developments which often occur faster than system implementation.

2. This paper addresses the factors which should be taken into account and considerations which should be made in identifying the most suitable system structure and the options available for such structures based on recent experience developing the following systems:

a) HERMIS - an integrated highway information and management system
b) HiSMIS - a bridge management information system
c) NETTER - a highway network investment model.

In addition, experience of developing logical designs for both pavement and bridge management systems, using the Structured Systems Analysis and Design Methodology (SSADM), will also be discussed.

THE SYSTEMS

3. The three systems have been developed for use in the highways sub-sector and reflect a range of client needs in terms of type of problem, user requirements, data volumes and computing environment.

The HERMIS system

4. This system was developed by Hertfordshire County Council using computing and engineering support from Rendel Palmer & Tritton to provide an overall management and information package, intended ultimately to encompass routine and pavement maintenance, traffic, accident, public utilities, bridge inspection and maintenance, and all other facets of the duties of a highway authority. The essential concept of HERMIS is that any highway-related data required by more than one application are stored in a central databank which can be accessed by these various applications dealing with different components of the highway management process.

5. The system is designed to handle large volumes of data in an efficient manner. In Hertfordshire, over 2 million highway inventory items are stored together with network, inspection and other data, requiring 600 Mbytes of storage. There is also a requirement for remote multi-user access, with the system currently being used in Hertfordshire both by Head Office, and by district and divisional staff in 14 remote offices. Each of these offices has been equipped with microcomputer workstations and printers for the local manipulation of data, and with modems for access to the central database.

6. It was recognised from the outset that the system being developed had a potential for commercial exploitation. Development has therefore reflected this with user-defined parameters being used instead of hard coding, wherever possible, to provide the flexibility for customisation to a wide range of user needs. In addition, specific system development standards were formulated and used to ensure that a consistent, robust and supportable system evolved.

7. HERMIS has been developed using the full functionality of the INGRES database management system. The choice of database was made following a detailed investigation of competitive products in terms of their functionality and of the development tools that they provided. It was chosen despite the fact that it would not operate on any of the hardware at that time available in Hertfordshire ˙ CC Highways Department, meaning the introduction of a new hardware platform and operating system. The procedural programming language is FORTRAN 77 which interfaces with the fourth generation INGRES environment. The system now operates on DEC VAX minicomputers running under VMS, and on SUN computers running under UNIX.

The HiSMIS system

8. HiSMIS was developed as a speculative venture by Rendel Palmer & Tritton, although part funding for the work was obtained from projects for the London Borough of Southwark and for the Government of Sri Lanka. The original idea for the system followed a commission from the Transport and Road Research Laboratory to write a Road Note on the inspection of bridges in developing countries. A paper-based standard inspection reporting system was developed as part of the Road Note. It was recognised that the use of a standard inspection reporting method such as this would be enhanced by the ability to store the inspection records on a computerised database, with the ability to manipulate, interrogate and report on the data so stored. Although the concept of HiSMIS started with bridge inventory and inspection data, the system, as finally developed, is capable of storing and manipulating maintenance, financial and historical data, providing a comprehensive management tool for bridges or other highway structures.

9. The data needs of a bridge system are much less than those of highway inventory and, as such, it is practical to store the data associated with all but the largest bridge stocks on a microcomputer. Discussions with possible users also indicated a preference for micro-based systems. This was therefore chosen as the initial development environment, but with the intention of developing the system further to run on minicomputers and workstations and to interface to, or integrate with, HERMIS. The system operates on any IBM-compatible PC with at least 500 Kbytes of RAM available. Approximately 8-12 Mbytes of disk storage is needed for an average bridge stock, although much larger volumes can be handled.

10. HiSMIS uses as its base the standard database software package dBase IV, marketed by the Ashton Tate Corporation. A major factor in the decision to base HiSMIS on dBase was that this has effectively become the industry standard for database applications on microcomputers. The choice of Version IV was made to provide upward compatibility to UNIX-based machines in the future. Version IV has also allowed HiSMIS to be equipped with a powerful report and query generator, enabling the system to be adapted easily to users' existing operational systems. Like HERMIS, HiSMIS has utilised user-defined parameters instead of hard coding, wherever possible, to provide flexibility for customisation.

11. As for HERMIS, system development standards were used for HiSMIS to ensure that the commercial product had internal integrity, was robust and supportable.

The NETTER system

12. NETTER is a tool to assist with policy analysis in the highways sub-sector and, in particular, to enable investment choices to be made which take into account the implications of whole life costs. The original version was developed for use in Malaysia to assist with the formulation of axle load policy in connection with a programme of future road and bridge upgrading works. Since then, the system has been developed further on a speculative basis by Rendel Palmer & Tritton to address a wide range of highway investment areas.

13. Being a policy analysis tool, NETTER is essentially a single user application and, unlike both HERMIS and HiSMIS, NETTER is processing-intensive rather than data-intensive. As such, it does not utilise a relational database but, instead, reads its definition data from a series of flat files and manipulates these data using direct access files. These files then form the input to a range of post-run analysis programs, each written to perform a specific analytical job or to produce a specific report. The need for rapid processing and the availability of access to a client computer led to an original choice of development environment as FORTRAN running on a minicomputer. With the more recent advent of faster processors on micros, the system has recently been converted to run using FORTRAN 77 in this environment and to run on UNIX-based systems.

14. Further facilities have recently been added to the system to make use of dBase IV to help in the process of assembling the input data required and to provide simple reporting facilities on that data which were not previously available without specific programming work.

15. In-house development standards that are used on all FORTRAN programs have been applied to NETTER to provide robust, reliable and supportable software. Recent developments have increased the quality of the user documentation as is appropriate to a commercial system.

DESIGN AND DEVELOPMENT ISSUES

16. Experience with these and other systems has suggested that system design and development issues need to be considered under the following key areas

a) user requirements
b) data handling and efficiency
c) supportability
d) user environment.

USER REQUIREMENTS

17. Design and development of systems must meet fully the needs of user requirements, which implies that either

a) systems must be developed to meet a specific customer, or group of customers', needs, or

b) systems must be very flexible and utilise user definable parameters so that they can be customised to meet individual user requirements.

18. Both HERMIS and HiSMIS systems are built around relational databases and, in both, database tables have been used to store parameters, or meta data, which are set up at the time of system installation to meet user requirements. Both HERMIS and HiSMIS are very flexible in this respect. In particular, HERMIS can be utilised in a wide variety of network-based inventory management applications in, or outside, the highways sub-sector. As such, procurement of a flexible system such as this is not a straightforward off-the-shelf purchase: considerable attention must be given by the user as to how the system should be set up for use, and the set-up process itself can be relatively complex and time consuming. A limited number of days of free consultancy is supplied with HERMIS, some of which purchasers normally utilise to assist with the setting up of the system, although the process can be undertaken by users themselves by following the steps in the installation guide. A further advantage of this parameter-based approach is that changes can be made to the way a system operates at stages in the future, although changes to some of the fundamental parameters could require careful adjustment of existing data if the system had been in operation for several years.

19. NETTER is an example of a system that can be used more or less off-the-shelf without the need for complying with detailed installation procedures. The system is used on an annual cycle for strategic decision-making, rather than for day-to-day access. There is no requirement for ad hoc reporting, since all reports are fixed, and a database management system is not appropriate. When buying the system, the user knows that they are purchasing modelled relationships and algorithms that have a wide international acceptance. The requirement for customisation is limited, and local usage is reflected in the input data, with the specification of unit prices and other local data.

20. The provision of flexibility in software so that a wide variety of user needs can be met requires that system development time will be prolonged, and this must ultimately be reflected in purchase price. Other implications are that the software requirements to provide a high degree of flexibility may well result in a higher degree of machine dependence than with less flexible software that is more portable. For example, NETTER will run on any hardware supporting FORTRAN 77, whereas HERMIS currently requires a platform supporting the full INGRES development environment.

DATA HANDLING AND EFFICIENCY

21. Where large data volumes are to be manipulated and managed by software, it is crucial that system design reflects the need for data efficiency. If not, system response times will increase at a disproportionate rate as the volume of the data increases, with the result that users will soon be disillusioned about the utility of the system. Unfortunately, many systems available for use within the highways sub-sector never get tested with really large data volumes until they have been operational for a reasonable period and the data stored has built up over ·time. By the time the poor performance of the system has been appreciated fully, there may have been a large investment in the system and its data, and a reluctance by those who recommended its purchase to admit to the problem. Users again become dissatisfied.

22. It is therefore crucial that system and hardware choices are tailored to realistic estimates of data volumes and database access requirements, if efficient and cost-effective day-to-day operation is to be obtained. The example systems being discussed are each tailored to different orders of magnitude of data, and their design and target hardware platforms has reflected these differences.

23. As noted earlier, NETTER is processing-intensive, rather than data- intensive. Its design, therefore, makes no use of a relational database, but utilises flat files for input, and internal direct access files to provide an appropriate speed of access within the main FORTRAN program.

24. In contrast, HiSMIS is expected to store to and process databases containing no more than about 40 Mbytes of information. Given the anticipated single user environment, it was considered appropriate to base the system on a microcomputer and to write the software around the dBase IV relational database. This environment is sufficient to provide adequate response times with the volumes of data being considered, and the choice of dBase IV provides the potential for future operation of the system under UNIX in a multi-user environment, running on workstations or minicomputers.

25. The HERMIS system has been developed specifically to handle very large volumes of data. The 600 Mbyte application in Hertfordshire is typical of the requirements of target users. This usage has dictated the target hardware and environment of minicomputers and workstations, and the choice of a 4GL database: INGRES. This environment also meets the need for multi-user access from remote sites with its requirements for multi-level security of access to both data and software. This level of sophistication would not be readily available within a totally 3GL environment, and the alternative of producing original high level language software to meet the requirements would be prohibitively expensive.

26. Where access to large volumes of data is involved, experience particularly with development of the HERMIS system has demonstrated forcibly that use of the database language in a textbook manner is unlikely to give the levels of data efficiency that are required. Special techniques have been developed to reduce the number of database accesses and to undertake other processes, each of which has had dramatic effects at reducing program run-times, sometimes from hours to a matter of a few seconds. Careful design of the database is also necessary in terms of indexing and the structure of tables if the system is to be tuned to give maximum efficiency. A further area worth considering is to recognise that not all reports from the database need to be produced interactively and that considerable gains in efficiency can be obtained by allowing less urgent reports requiring larger numbers of database accesses to run under 'batch', either concurrently with interactive users, or preferably deferred until over-night. The latter choice has the added benefit of

making full use of the available processing capacity of the hardware. In the case of the HERMIS implementation under the UNIX operating system, this requirement has necessitated the writing of a special batch-stream manager.

27. Users' acceptance of systems is often conditioned by response times of data accesses and it is crucial that proper attention is given to the data management aspects of software design.

SUPPORTABILITY

28. Any commercial system must be supportable. This requires the use of systems design, programming standards and an appropriate quality of software documentation. In addition, the organisation marketing the software must have in place a support structure in terms of staff to administer the software support, hardware which can be used to investigate problems, systems for managing the database of users, and 'help-lines' backed up with technical support personnel.

29. Despite the differences in the three example systems being discussed here, in terms of their scope, size and complexity, each requires a similar level of support back-up.

USER ENVIRONMENT

30. The three systems under discussion operate in different computer environments as are appropriate to the type of problems being solved and the data volumes involved. The appropriate user environment should be selected using these same considerations. When choosing a system, basic questions should be asked about

a) what is the issue or problem that the system is to address?

b) who will need to use the system, and where will they be located?

c) what will be the data requirements in terms of
   - collection
   - storage
   - interrogation and reporting?

d) how are the user's requirements likely to develop over time?

e) what will be the costs and benefits of the introduction of this particular system?

31. It is normal in user environments that personnel costs and data costs dominate totally the system implementation and operating costs. Despite this, choice of hardware is often the first decision that is made by organisations when embarking upon a system implementation. As a result of this, other decisions are often severely limited because of the hardware constraints, and gross inefficiencies result in the use of personnel and the management of data. It is crucial, when implementing systems, that a total view is taken of costs and benefits, and that choice of hardware should be made to support the chosen system and not _vice versa_.

STRUCTURED SYSTEM DESIGN

32. Formal methods exist for designing systems in a structured way to ensure that user requirements are met. The Department of Transport now insist on the use of the Structured Systems Analysis and Design Methodology (SSADM) which is administered by the National Computing Centre. The method was originally developed by Learmonth and Burchett Management Systems with and for the Central Computer and Telecommunications Agency (CCTA) in 1981 and Version 4 of the method has been the release this year. It is an example of a structured method of system design. Two projects have been carried out by Rendel Palmer & Tritton for the Department of Transport in the highways sub-sector using this methodology: for the feasibility study of a pavement management system and of a bridge management system.

33. The purpose of SSADM is to ensure that a sound logical design is completed and shown to satisfy business needs, before any attempt is made to produce a physical implementation. Experience by others has shown that the untimely confusion of logical and physical issues can be a major contributory factor to the production of flawed systems. SSADM is conducted in six stages

1. Analysis of system operation and current problems
2. Specification of requirements
3. Selection of technical options
4. Data design
5. Process design
6. Physical design.

34. Although SSADM can be carried out using a one pass analysis, where each of the above stages is executed, two pass analysis is preferred where these six stages are preceded by a feasibility study consisting of two further stages
01.   Problem definition
02.   Project identification.

35. Both the pavement and bridge management studies carried out for the Department of Transport consisted of SSADM feasibility studies, and the work on pavement management systems is now proceeding to the development of a full logical design. As a result of experience with this work, the following comments can be made about the use of SSADM for the types of systems discussed in this paper.

36. There are clearly many potential advantages in the use of a structured approach in terms of the quality of products produced, the system documentation, and the ability to meet management requirements. Additionally, the cross-checking that is an inherent part of a structured method such as SSADM, and the availability of computerised support tools to help with the production of documentation and with the storage and manipulation of the information discovered about the system under study, combine to help the elimination of errors in analysis that potentially can arise using other unstructured methods.

37. Drawbacks include the expense of working to these standards, the resulting huge volumes of paper that are produced, and the difficulty of understanding some of the SSADM documentation by system end-users. SSADM appears to be well suited to developing computerised versions of existing manual systems. In these cases, . there are existing system users who can specify the functionality required of the computerised system. However, where SSADM is used to analyse and design new and innovative systems, there are no existing users who can specify the total functionality required. The specification of the system is likely to require modification after prototypes become available and the system is used in a test environment. This will require changes to the existing documentation to be made in addition to the changes in the prototype software.

38. Within the Department of Transport, SSADM has been used principally to document systems that are to be passed to commercial vendors for subsequent development and release to the marketplace. The Department then makes use of compliance test packages to ensure that the commercial systems meet formalised system requirements before they can be adopted for applications on that part of the national road network for which the Department is responsible. Certain facilities within SSADM are very appropriate for the production of logical designs for this purpose. However, experience at Rendel Palmer & Tritton for the production of operational systems suggests that, for these applications, the full rigour of SSADM is not necessarily cost-effective.

39. Development of the three systems described here has all been carried out by joint teams of engineers and systems analysts. In addition, all of the systems personnel in managerial positions on the projects are, in fact, engineers who have specialised in computer applications, and so understand the engineering principles involved. As such, it has proved more expedient to replace the formal SSADM user interviews by an engineering specification which is developed interactively by the project team together with users. With such an approach, a relevant level of logical design documentation is produced in going from the engineering specification to the physical design. This is then used as the basis of coding.

40. In the case of the HERMIS and HiSMIS systems, many of the applications incorporated existed previously as paper-based systems. Although SSADM would have been appropriate in these cases, a less formalised but nevertheless effective analysis and system design method was utilised. Many user interviews were carried out, but these took the form of devising and agreeing engineering specifications. These were turned into systems specifications by an engineer who specialises in computing.

41. On the other hand, the NETTER system is largely innovative and is processing-intensive. SSADM was not considered appropriate. In its stead, an overall system structure was specified showing the interaction of various sub-routines. Each of the sub-routines was then specified in detail, coded and tested independently. The overall data structure was carefully monitored, but was left flexible until all sub- routines were linked and the required output from the model has been finalised. The system documentation was therefore largely derived on completion of each part of the system rather than being developed before coding of the program.

DISCUSSION

42. This paper has considered the development of three computer systems for the highway sub-sector in order to contrast the different approaches that have been taken to their development. The different approaches reflect different user requirements, the needs for efficiency in data handling, requirements for system support and issues concerning the user environment.

43. It was recognised that determining user needs must be the first step when choosing a system implementation. This requires that systems must either be developed to meet specific customers' needs, or must be flexible and capable of customisation in order to meet a wide variety of user requirements.

44. The ability of systems to handle data efficiently is a crucial issue where large volumes of data are involved. Users soon become dissatisfied with systems where response times are slow. Whilst it was recognised that both the choice of hardware and software will influence the speed of data handling, experience has shown that the use of a database language in a textbook manner is unlikely to give acceptable levels of efficiency where very large volumes of data are involved. Special techniques may be required to reduce the number of database accesses and to undertake other processes in order to reduce response times to an acceptable level.

45. It was noted that, in normal user environments, personnel costs and data costs dominate totally the system implementation and operation cost. It is therefore crucial that, when implementing systems, a total view is taken of costs and benefits, and that choice of hardware should be made to support the chosen software and not vice versa.

46. Experience of using SSADM for producing logical designs has demonstrated the advantages of such methods in terms of the quality of the products produced, the standardisation of system documentation, and the ability to meet management requirements. However, there are drawbacks in terms of the expense of working to these standards, the resulting huge volumes of paper that are produced, and the difficulty of understanding the SSADM documentation by system end-users. A further problem appears to be that SSADM is not best suited to designing new and innovative systems, and that for processing-intensive systems an alternative approach may be beneficial. It is recommended that, when a new project to develop software is initiated, a review is made of available structured system analysis, design and implementation methods, and that a method appropriate to the requirements of the system be adopted. Notwithstanding this, system documentation is ultimately vital to ensure supportability.

47. We conclude that a flexible approach to systems analysis, design and implementation is preferred, with the method chosen to reflect the particular operational requirements and development environment.

Design and use of databases in professional marketing

B. D. GREENHALGH, Director of Professional Development,
School of the Built Environment, Liverpool Polytechnic

SYNOPSIS. All organisations operating within a
commercial environment keep records of their
clients and customers; actual, potential and
latent. By the nature of the construction
industry, records are also invariably kept on
firms from other disciplines within the
professional team. With the advent of low cost
computer hardware and powerful database packages,
it is possible to increase the efficiency of these
records and relate them together in order to
improve management information. Case studies are
given to illustrate how these relationships can
work in practice.

INTRODUCTION

Everyone responsible for business generation
within a company keeps records. These records may
be in the head of the responsible
partner/director, with the obvious difficulties if
the person leaves; they may be in the form of a
list of present or previous clients, contacts made
or calls received; they may be in the form of a
record card index giving all of the above
information, but still relying on a small number
of people with an understanding of the
relationship between the records and the situation
between each contact. These are all databases.
Information Technology and computerised databases
cannot replace the personal contact which is often
required for professional marketing, but what it
can provide is a more efficient management tool
which can be instantly accessible at various
locations, is up to date, and can cope with
different people inputting information which may
save duplication of marketing effort. The major
advantage, however, is that a computerised
database will allow much greater management of the
information to:

a)   filter the records so that you only look at,
      for example, firms of Architects in
      Blackburn.

b)   form relationships, i.e. How many Consulting
      Engineers **and** Quantity Surveyors have
      experience of water and sewerage
      infrastructure work in Devon and Cornwall.

Computerised databases can be very cheap to
install; a fairly standard desktop PC with a hard
disk can use any of the off-the-shelf package such
as dbase 4.1, Dataease, Retrieve or Paradox and
the software cost will be in the region of £400-
£500. However, the costs rise substantially in
adapting the package to suit your requirements,
inputting the initial data and maintaining the
database to ensure it is up to date.

It is the purpose of the remainder of this paper
to consider the issues involved in both the design
and use of computerised databases, to ensure that
the technology works for the company, not vice
versa.

DESIGN OF DATABASES
Your promotions database will, if used to its full

advantage, become the engine that drives the total
marketing activity of the company. It can help you
target clients within the most active area of your
business and match other professional consultants.
It can help you discover new opportunities, guide
existing marketing and report on the success (or
failure) of past activity. It will do this
because the database should be no less than the
accumulation of all that you know about your
market, and potential clients.

There are two ways in which a computerised
database may
 be used:

a)   Reactively
b)   Proactively

The commonest way in which a database is used is
reactively, where a project opportunity has arisen
and there is a need to find other professional
consultants of the right experience and calibre.
The database is used to generate the requisite
list or report because it contains the information
required, is fast and can carry out complex data
manipulation.

However, as companies gain more experience of both structured marketing and the role of databases within that function, managers will become much more prepared to use databases as tools for generating new business.

As examples of the proactive use of computerised databases, it is possible to ask:

a)   Who expressed an interest in our services, when and in what geographical area?
b)   Who followed up the enquiry?
c)   Were they clients, consultants, contractors?

It is also possible to ask 'what-if' questions:

a)   The now-privatised regional water companies have budgeted to increase their capital spending programme by 5%
b)   Could we service a civil engineering infrastructure programme in West Yorkshire?
c)   Are any of our competitors better placed?

It is important to realise therefore, that a database may be called on to satisfy two quite distinct needs within the marketing of professional services; it may be used to make your company attractive to potential clients and other professional consultants, or secondly it can be used to target sectors of the market that you feel are good business propositions.

So far we have only discussed computerised databases as a faster marketing information system, in that it helps you to understand what is happening within the professional services market and within your customer base, and also to identify opportunities and establish effective methods of approach.

The database can have another important logistical function in that it acts as a communications driver producing mailing labels, individually addressed letters etc. to dramatically reduce the costs of targeted marketing.

HANDLING INFORMATION
All databases whether computerised or manual, are only as good as the information they contain. Let us now look at the causes and costs of poor information.

There are several sources of problems of poor information within a database:

a) **Information leakage** is a natural process which goes on all the time. Whenever a company moves, or grows, an individual changes job, or leaves; leakage has taken place. This means that you can never stand still, databases must be updated constantly for them to be effective.

b) **Dirt** is the misinformation that finds its way into every database. The two main sources of misinformation are human and computer.

    i) **Human error** can occur because of mis-spelling, incorrect information being given to the operator, unaware of the effect their entry will have on the relational nature of a database. For example, if two managers make contact with the same company and one enters the name as 'Acme Developments of Essex Ltd' while the other enters 'ADE Ltd.' then the computer will regard these as two different companies with obvious problems when interrogating for relationships.

    ii) **Computer error** is rarely a true 'error' in that it is a mistake made by the computer; rather, as systems develop in complexity it is possible to programme the computer to infer relationships such as matching, de-duplication and gender inference. It is the latter which is the obvious source of computer error; for example, Tony Benn's son is called Hilary, which gender would you programme the computer to infer from that! Many Welsh names are also equally applicable to both sexes.

There are a range of costs associated with holding out-of-date or inaccurate information; these can be:

a) **Missed opportunities** where you fail to identify a project, client or other consultant.

b) **Poor targeting** where the wrong people are approached thus wasting their time and yours.

c) **Unnecessary research** of a geographical or business area.

d) **Duplication** as mentioned previously.

Most information entered onto a Database
originates from paper based sources. Entering
that data into the software is known as
'Datacapture' which can be achieved either in
large batches, i.e. creating the initial database
from contacts lists of Partners or Directors, or
updating individual pieces of information
following a telephone conversation with a client.

Capturing information is the most important but
the least glamorous of all the database management
tasks, as incorrect data can create considerable
problems in the long term. Additionally, since
the major feature of the database is its
relational capacity, all information is built upon
the basic building blocks of the contact name,
firm and address. If this core data is incorrect
then the foundation of the whole database
structure is undermined.

ACCESSING THE DATA
Access to the data, especially for editing
purposes should be carefully restricted, in order
to avoid the major sources of error and problems
with datacapture outlined

above. The main practice should concentrate on
eliminating error, both human and computer
generated, and there are a number of steps which
can help to reduce the scope for error:

a)   **Standard updating procedures** should be
      written down in plain English (not computer
      jargon) and circulated to those with
      authority to edit and update the database.
      These would include rules for value ranges
      for fields and style of entry (e.g. open or
      closed punctuation).
            It is managerial rather than technical
            problems which lead to database failure,
            so sufficient time and resources must be
            given to the maintenance and updating of
            the database.
b)   **Training** given to authorised users. It is
      important that only authorised users update
      the database if only to avoid duplication of
      entries and consistency of style.
c)   **Security levels** can be built into the system,
      not only to prevent unauthorised access, but
      also to prevent the deletion of records by
      operator error. Different users may also
      have restricted access to different options,

but this needs to be carefully worked out
when more than one person is in contact with
a prospective client.

d)   **Maintaining an audit trail** is a method of
finding out when and why a particular record
was amended. This will permit mis-
corrections to be rectified and provides the
opportunity to log possible causes of error.

INFORMATION REQUIRED
As has been mentioned, one of the inherent
problems with a Database is that it can become out
of date very quickly, although individual pieces
of information will have a different shelf-life.
They fall into the following categories:

a)   **Static (rarely or never change)**
          Name of company
          Type of company (Client, Architect, QS,
          M&E etc.)
          Previous clients of your or other firms
          No. of enquiries about your services

b)   **Semi-static (sometimes change)**
          Address of client company
          Telephone/Fax of client company
          Geographical area of interest

c)   **Volatile (always changing)**
          Contact names
          Contact history (date of original
          enquiry, status following initial
          approach)
          Details of offers made
          New firms being entered onto the system

Within most marketing databases, data will
generally be static or semi-static, and once the
records are created there will be little need for
changes but a constant need for updating. What
must be remembered is that all individual pieces
of information have to be assessed in this way as
this will have an impact on the way that data is
displayed on screen, archived, stored and
analysed.
Wherever possible, tables should be used to store
data that is common, this allocates a single
character to denote a particular item. For
example:

For titles
0   Unknown
1   Managing Director
2   Senior Partner
3   Commercial Director
     etc.

This ensures a common spelling for regularly used
pieces of data, cuts down on input time and allows
the user to select and analyse the data more
easily.

Sophisticated software packages and ad-hoc
databases may have an ability to detect duplicated
pieces of information within the database, called
'deduplication'. This can be done manually with
very small databases but for anything over a few
hundred records becomes very laborious.
All Database Management Systems should contain
some deduplication facility; which may be effected
as new records are entered onto the system, when
the computer will automatically search for similar
sounding names. When processing large volumes of
data, this is often carried out in batch mode. An
obvious use for this in marketing is to compare
enquiries received against contacts made.
The software works within a tolerance level, so
that fields that are slightly different can be
compared. i.e. Road and Rd. would be recognised
as the same but care must be taken with comparing
Adrian Smith against A. Smith as there may well be
an Andrew somewhere.
The software also derives a 'matchkey' based on
critical elements of the record such as postcode,
since to compare every field would considerably
slow down the processing speed.
Once the software has recognised a duplication, it
will follow a preset programmed response by
filling in any gaps in the original record from
the duplicate record and asking the user whether
the duplicate record should be kept. However,
when setting up the database, duplication can
often be advantageous and provision should be made
for it in certain circumstances. i.e.

a)   Where multiple decision makers within the
      same firm operate at the same address
b)   Where multiple decision makers within the
      same firm operate at different or multiple
      addresses
c)   One decision maker per firm per address

ANALYSIS AND MODELLING
Data analysis is an essential part of using a
marketing database. The principles are the same

as those employed in Market Research and Response Analysis.

A Database can produce standard prespecified reports, regarding the number of enquiries received, the number of contacts made, and depending on the sophistication, a competitor analysis in various geographical regions. It should allow you to analyse any combination of data elements, in terms of 'What-if? questions, without incurring expensive software charges. Statistical Analysis packages can also be used to work on samples of data, provided they are captured in numeric-only fields. For example, by analysing your present client base by geography and industry sector will allow you to compare your base against future predictions of the industry and regions. This is known as penetration analysis.

CONCLUSIONS

Computerised Database packages can be of very great benefit for professional

marketing. The packages themselves are relatively inexpensive, but the time taken to capture the data is very expensive. Therefore there are certain rules which should be followed when using databases as an aid to marketing:

a) Ensure the commitment to the database is total, from the Managing Director downward.

b) Ensure you are totally clear about your exact requirements, if you are unsure bring in a consultant with experience of this type of audit.

c) There will need to be dedicated staff for database management tasks, with adequate training and authority.

d) Managers must not suffer from a fear of technology. If used properly, the database will support the business and identify opportunities.

e) The database must be a corporate tool, not owned by an individual director or department.

f) Be creative in data manipulation, and build in this flexibility at the beginning. Use it to learn what is happening in the market, and to identify patterns and trends.

CASE STUDY 1 - SITE SPECIFIC DATABASE APPLICATION

This case study is typical of a situation which presents itself with remarkable regularity in design offices.

We start with the knowledge that the workload of an office will be composed of projects which 'just came in through the door' and many others will have been generated by members of the Practice themselves. The process is a familiar one and usually involves the vision and hard work of one of the partners. It may be that he identifies a site with potential for development of some kind or he identifies an end user with a requirement which is, as yet, unfulfilled. In each case much work is involved in putting the opportunity together and creating a full team which includes professional advisers, end-users, developers and funding institutions.

The labour intensive nature of the preliminary work means that fast routes need to be found for team assembly and project development.

As firms become more nationally involved, it is not always possible to keep track of the many hundreds of people in related professions that we meet. The well organised database can be an invaluable tool in helping us out of this problem.

This case relates to a waterfront development site in a small port in southern England. The site was occupied by a major mineral extraction and processing company but was surrounded by residential and commercial development. There was no particular reason for the mineral company to cease operation on the site, and they were unaware that their site value had increased to such an extent that it may be viable for them to move elsewhere, releasing the land for development.

An engineer based in the north of England heard about the site through the mineral company, who are clients of his. He looked at the site and devised a method by which the extraction process could be accommodated on an out-of-town site which his firm also had an involvement. The technical details of how to

accommodate the plant were well within the engineer's expertise, and involved the same architect as for the out-of-town site. The missing ingredient at this point was the **local knowledge** required to put together a feasibility study and appraisal of the development costs and profit.

The firm had a well managed database and were able to access information on both a geographical and professional classification. It was thus possible to access names of surveyors and estate agents in the county of West Sussex. The search resulted in five individuals being identified from three firms based within 20 miles of the site. On telephone enquiry, one of the individuals agreed to take part in the further development of the scheme through to the involvement of a developer also known to the surveying firm in question. The scheme was successfully secured for the practice and will commence on site during 1991.

Footnote:
The individual in the surveying firm was someone who had met the engineering company three years previously, although the original contact had subsequently left the engineering firm, so without the database there would have been no knowledge of that particular contact. Relying purely on memory is insufficient in a dynamic marketplace.

CASE STUDY 2 - IDENTIFICATION OF AREAS FOR EXPANSION

A firm based in Liverpool is finding that their traditional local market is becoming overcrowded, and they cannot identify enough local and traditional work for them to continue profitably at their current staffing levels. They have three options:

a)   To cut staffing levels
b)   To diversify their service offer to cover new disciplines
c)   To expand their area of operation outside the local boundaries they have been used to

Taking advice from their marketing consultants, they decided to go for option three.

Initially, the firm felt that their own database, which had been built up over the last ten years, would be sufficient for them to generate enough enquiries in the area bounded by Preston, Manchester and Chester for them to be able to

generate the necessary leads and convert them into
business. It very quickly became clear however
that the types of contacts they had were with
companies in competition with themselves, or* with
companies with little relevance to their new
potential client base in the expanded region.

The practice provided its most efficient service
to companies with more than one building in their
portolio and who organised their building and
maintenance from a central office. Most potential
clients would fall into the following categories:

  * Building Societies
  * Banks
  * Multiple shops and Supermarkets
  * Service companies operating from various
    premises
  * Major manufacturing, pharmaceutical and
    chemical companies

with more than one premises in the operational
region

The firm decided to buy a list from a broker based
on the above categories. The list was provided in
floppy disk format and allowed a mass mailing
based on a questionnaire to be returned to the
firm by the facilities manager or premises
manager.

The response rate to this questionnaire was 12%
(above average for a cold mail shot) and the
activity resulted in several leads being
identified.

The exercise was felt to be useful in that many of
the respondents provided information on who
presently provided services for them, even though
they expressed no interest in changing their
arrangements. Market intelligence of this nature
is invaluable to firms in building up their own
services to match and better their competitors -
the essence of marketing.

Footnote:
The costs of buying or renting lists is not
prohibitive and saves very many man-hours provided
that the list is:

a)   up to date
b)   relevant
c)   clean
d)   provided in suitable format for loading
      straight into the database and for production
      of address labels

REFERENCES
WILSON A. Practice Development for Professional
Firms; McGraw-Hill (1984)
OZIMEK J. Structuring a Property Database for
targeting; Proceedings from 'Databases - the
essential tool when marketing property, Henry
Stewart conference studies, 11 September 1990
WALLINGER J. Database management techniques; ibid.
McCOLL PROPERTY MARKETING - Internal database

Quality competetiveness: using experimental training technology

Professor J. A. POWELL, Head of Department of Design
Studies, and P. NEWLAND, Senior Research Fellow, Portsmouth
Polytechnic

SYNOPSIS. The time of traditional training is past;
the value of experiential education – where learners
know the moment and how to act – is the future. In
this paper we discuss and demonstrate learning
approaches, supported by advanced interactive media,
which aim to give emotive and involving experience
rather than imitative training.

ACQUISITION OF INVISIBLE KNOWLEDGE
1. The real problem is usually to know what the
real problem is (ref.1). Our underlying aim was to
understand how the quality of British (Engineering)
Design competitiveness could be enhanced by the new
training technologies. The verb 'train' here may be
misleading, since we have in mind neither the one
way teacher-to-learner 'chalk and talk' pedagogy nor
the 'imitation' of traditional training. Rather, we
have been investigating the role of interactive
media in the creation of appropriate experiential
learning environments for use in the area of
continuing professional education. We have found
such self motivating interactive learning
technologies promote confidence in the acquisition
of useful skills and decision making knowledge.
Indeed, we intend to demonstrate that the quality of
professional decision-making and competitiveness can
be enhanced by such technologies.

Flaws with Imitation – an analogy for understanding
2. A good demonstration makes explicit the
decisions made in the course of the activity. Thus a
good demonstration shows the student what not to do
as well as what to do. A skilled performance makes
these same decisions invisible (ref.2). This insight
from Olson and Bruner hints at two crucial factors
we have found to be missing when inappropriate
understanding results from traditional pedagogic
training and 'rote' learning, as opposed to emotive

experiential learning.

3.   Much skilled professional performance, especially complex decision-making, has components of actor, stage and script and is essentially a set piece. As with acting, we believe introducing any form of training to naive professional learners which simply instigates mere imitation of set pieces has two fatal flaws with respect to the knowledge learned:

    i. no account can be taken of either change on the stage (context) or in the script (content)

    ii. no account can be taken of learners (actors) cultural/psychological nature (timing).

4.   If we maintain the theatrical analogy of learning contexts just a little longer hopefully to aid understanding. Imagine a naive actor (learner), who has simply 'rote' learned a script, being faced with one of those magical revolving stages whose sets she had not seen before. A ninety degree rotation of the stage would produce a totally new set, a novel situation with which our naive (learner) actor would at least feel uneasy.   If the script no longer matched the setting what would they do, since their 'rote' learning would have left them without, either the confidence to create a new script for the novel set, or the experience to ad lib around this anomaly until the previous set returns.   Imitation of the skilled performance leaves our (learner) actor bereft of truly **useful** tacit knowledge of how to act in the sort of 'wicked' contexts (ref.1) that so often frequent, not only the stage, but especially the real world.

5.   Furthermore, we suggest that as with our naive actor, without proper timing, the professional will be unable to assimilate the skilled performance. For, learning through imitation negates the development of adaptive ability necessary for real world decision-making of the professional and spurns the possibility for creative self-discovered knowledge.

6.   Looking for a means to overcome these two flaws has served as the generator for the present investigations - this is we believe the real training problem for professionals. In particular we seek approaches for creating educational environments which will motivate useful and emotive experiential learning for busy building professionals.

7.   *As an aside the above situation would also defeat the classical expert system - if one would exist to promote learning - whose rules are only formed from known contexts: self-closure is inherent*

*in such rules and openness to novelty has been
abandoned.*

Approaches to learning

8. Accepting this, our first goal was to tackle
the problem of individual preference for the
assimilation of knowledge. Various studies
including our own (refs.3-5) have looked at the
approaches different individuals, including
architects, engineers and surveyors, take in order
to acquire knowledge (about design and construction)
in order to act viably in their practice world. Our
research strategy was particularly guided by the
seminal theoretical work of Pepper (ref.3) who
argues with adroitness that there can exist only
four approaches for individuals attempting to
understand the world they inhabit - only four
strategies that permit them to operate in some
viable way, thereby allowing a continuous flow of
useful sensory input about the world to be
structured in their minds, preparing them for
necessary and parsimonious action. Pepper believes
these world views are generated by a process of
structural corroboration, where individuals attain
a refined knowledge of reality by continuously
testing any new notion against their existing model
of the world.   Further, *to keep their professional
sanity*, he indicates that individuals have a strong
predisposition to reduce uncertainty and doubt by
strictly adhering to those beliefs which support one
world view - their world view - rather than others.
New understanding only seems to replace the
inappropriate old when a diversity of **personal
observations and experience** truly provides a
consistent alternative for them.

9. The particular *strategic action pattern* taken
onboard by different individuals has been found to
closely relate to the way they approach learning.
The field of learning has been extensively
investigated by Kolb (ref.6) who summarised the
various approaches open to an individual by a
learning cycle, shown in Fig.1. Kolb's model
portrays an ideal situation where the learner has
immediate experience of the world, steps back to
reflect on this feeling in context, thinks up an
abstract model to explain the phenomenon, which is
then tested by further active exploration. These
doing actions cause the learner to re-sense the
world and so begins a new learning cycle.

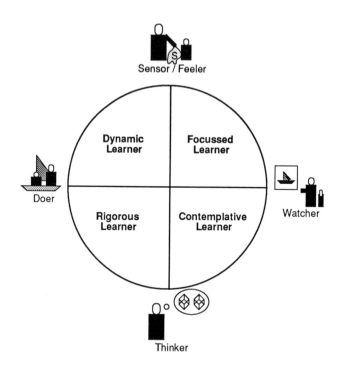

Fig. 1 The Learning Cycle (after Kolb)

10. It might be thought that well balanced individuals would be those who follow this idealised learning circle. For this should give them a well balanced view of the world. However, Thompson's work (ref.4) indicates that such a fully rounded view may be impossible and even counter productive to real world living, learning and especially complex problem decision-making. His view is based on the observation that in the real world people are not simply individuals learning by themselves, rather they are social animals in continual negotiation with each other as they learn. He, and we, have found that learning is clearly as much a socialisation process as a means of acquiring factual knowledge. Socialisation imposes severe constraints on learning, leading different people to learn in different or **preferred** ways. This itself eventually drives particularly professionals to adopt one of the four different and often incommensurable world views which we portray in summary below and in detail elsewhere (ref.5).

11.   In order to cope with pressures of time and
money, decision-makers will tend to *stick* to their
preferred learning approach and corresponding action
style while practising their profession. This gives
them a secure basis from which to make decisions and
they rarely change their approach to learning new
ideas – it is not only too much effort, it also
drains their confidence. In summary, it appears
that all individuals have a predisposition to learn,
then think about the world as they see it and
finally act in it, using one of four *strategic
action patterns*, each is different, independent and
recognisable. Powell (ref.7) has called the types
of learner-actors who portray these underlying
traits Dynamics, Focussed, Rigorous and
Contemplatives. Let us briefly discuss each of
these in turn.

i. <u>Dynamics</u> have an approach to learning which is
    centred on *doing and sensing*. They are
    entrepreneurial and innovative, acting for the
    moment, sensing its potential and doing
    something about it immediately. It is the
    dramatic active events in the world which give
    them motivation and allow them to register
    understanding. To learn they must be personally
    involved and if this necessity is satisfied then
    they are eager for challenges and novelty. By
    being assertive and individual in their actions
    they can swiftly switch tack, being
    entrepreneurial and initiating centres of profit
    at one moment and, at the next, rapidly creating
    innovative designs. They seek acclaim for their
    work. Their risk-taking attitude makes them good
    copy for glossies and the professional,
    financial and management pages of national
    newspapers.

ii. <u>The Focussed</u> concentrate their attention on
    decisive action. They operate in the world with
    a down-to-earth approach which is above all
    practical. Their need to do can often lead them
    into being campaigners and expounders of
    alternative technologies and conservation
    policies. Their *small is beautiful* philosophy
    may make them reticent to try untested
    approaches. Instead these people stay with the
    safe, known approach.

iii. <u>The Rigorous</u> understand the world by creating
     abstract models of it. These models give the
     rigorous predictive power over the environment.
     Through assumed knowledge of the underlying
     patterns from nature these professionals have
     secured rules that guide them in all their

decision making. They stand as the guardians of professional standards and aim to produce regularly competent solutions.

iv. Contemplatives with their emphasis on reflection, may feel no great urgency in real world decision making. Their reluctance emanates from a desire to create the all encompassing solution. To this end they will thoroughly analyse all the data which is at hand and then try to retrieve more in an effort to ensure every angle has been covered.

Appropriate tone and interaction

12. The preceding fourfold of *strategic action patterns* have guided our design and production of information or learning systems which enable the acquisition of useful professional knowledge about different aspects of building design. The important means by which our systems are different from others but thus become acceptable to busy building professionals relates primarily to the special ways in which they handle the *interaction* with the learner and especially through the *tone* of the information portrayed to the learner. We place particular emphasis here on getting the *tone* of knowledge in the system right as a means of achieving resonance between any individual and the imagery, learning, interpersonal interaction preference, philosophical basis and social assumptions they naturally seek. However, of equal importance is the development of an acceptable acquisition mechanism for the information in the system. For example the visual portrayal of a topic could be either: by a set of still photographs with text annotation; or via a film with an audio commentary; or through self-paced questions and answers; or as audio/visual sequences etc. The mix and style of media presentations provided by any system like film, audio and text will facilitate different self-informing strategies (refs. 8-9). The following descriptions indicate the general characteristics of media presentation, tone and interaction relevant for each strategic action patterns.

13. Dynamic. The tone of information needed for a Dynamic individual centres around the notion of 'information transfusion'. In terms of portraying a particular topic, a sense of transfusion is only invoked when a topic is made tangible. Therefore, for these individuals, any topic of information transfer should draw heavily on personal experiences or shared experience events leaving them to weave a

description of the topic into their own viewpoint. Dynamics portray their knowledge through their actions, and to be of a matching tone, an information source needs to be similarly active. It appears to us that retelling anecdotes to others is one such active expression by Dynamics and helps them personalise, retain and find meaning in information. Another acceptable alternative for Dynamics is listening to autobiographical experience from other similar individuals. Taking a topic and describing it by having individuals talk of their personal experience with the topic would encourage the Dynamics to give this information source attention. However, such communications need to be short, for if their interest is not caught then such Dynamic individuals will soon want to present their own personal experience of the topic in question instead of taking on board the alternative views of others. Appropriate interactions with information sources would be ones that attempts to facilitate such self-discovery and allow these professional learners to engage in a series of raw and challenging experiences. Interaction, for them, needs to be novel with respect to both style and access. We have found one useful mode of interaction for Dynamics is setting up a framework of challenges. Such challenges can give a near *real life* quality to involvement with an information source thereby demanding spur-of-the-moment acquisition of knowledge.

14. <u>The Focussed.</u> Those who choose to inform themselves by a Focussed strategy seek information that has a 'tone of transposition'. For this individual there should be provision for practical knowledge both at a general and specific level. For knowledge to be acceptable to these individuals it should be capable of grabbing their attention and being naturally incorporated or transposed into their own normal professional processes. The Focussed engage with the environment in order to understand why processes are as they are and their's is essentially a *small is beautiful* philosophy which demands information with a clear cut, down-to-earth quality. Focussed individuals are encouraged by and take an interest in information which is voicing beliefs of adaption and equilibrium of man with nature. The necessary tone of information required to support such beliefs is only possible with directness and presentation by similar believers. In essence Focussed individuals want to be assured there are others of like mind who support their views. We suggest the best presentation for this

learner is an audio/visual documentary style, where a presenter, who comes across as both friend and supporter, gives faithful, step-by-step and coherent guidance on any topic. The main emphasis in such documentary productions would be parsimonious case studies of relevant problems and their sound solutions. These individuals would appreciate an interaction which makes it possible to readily interrupt the documentary style case studies when detailed questions are raised. Such interrupts would give the Focussed opportunity to: review the material presented; enquire about the general usefulness of the topics covered for their present concerns; select particular points in the material for which greater detail could be requested. In essence the aim of such an interaction is to allow these individuals to navigate their own path through a tone of information which is in *good faith* with their beliefs and seeks to provide well-founded guidance on practical issues which is endorsed by respected others.

15. <u>The Rigorous</u> attain viability through the principle of 'transcribing' codes into practise. Individuals who find this strategy appropriate are those who seek information which reinforces the validity of the rules they already use to guide their action. Such rules are recognised as emanating from authorities. In a similar fashion information which is seen to have been generated by these authorities will also be given credence as well. Therefore, they would be assured by information whose tone implies it is a code or standard practice. Procedural information would also be welcomed for its strength in providing straightforward, economical solutions. An appropriate interaction for the Rigorous is with a stable, historically accumulated knowledge base, on a given topic of precedents which would emphasise the training algorithm of pretest – teach – post-test. In our view Rigorous individuals appreciate being stage managed through an introduction which gives a topic authoritative approval, then delivers a logical set of procedures and finally gives an opportunity to quantify their expertise. In essence Rigorous individuals require formalised knowledge which can be retrieved from a well structured hierarchy of authoritative findings.

16. <u>Contemplatives.</u> Our Research shows that those who choose to adopt a Contemplative strategy are interested in a broad spectrum of information. For them a comprehensive montage is necessary to adequately support their desire to accumulate a mass

of knowledge which is sufficient to allow them to transcend a unifying principle. These individuals are given confidence through having access to a wide range of primary information sources. Though they are willing to listen to others' opinions, and summaries of primary sources, they much prefer delving into the unedited data and drawing their own conclusions. Unlike the Focussed approach, commentaries which in anyway preempt the Contemplative arriving at their own conclusions would be a low priority option. Contemplatives would prefer to self-pace themselves through annotated high quality visual stills and be given access to comprehensive references and global views of a topic's causes and effects. In essence these individuals are seeking the means to undertake an integrative analysis of a topic and a welcomed information source would need to divulge uncensored data and incorporate guidelines to unify the known facts.

Technological facilitators

17. Embracing the above scenarios has lead us to investigate information technology which could facilitate educational environments which allow response on a bespoke basis to at least four different types of user. We have already developed one such information system which presents information on energy conscious design from four perspectives and aims at engaging individuals of any strategic action pattern preference (ref. 5). This is accomplished by use of interactive videodisc a medium which allows a pictorial base of film and stills to be instantly sequenced and re-sequenced by the learner. The context from which such visual imagery is presented can be easily manipulated, extended by multi-track audio, integrated with text and combined with an overlay of computer generated graphics.

18. Recently we have been able to refine our learning/information system using Apple Macintosh series II computers extended by the addition of transputers and real-time video digitising boards. These hardware improvements have enabled us to make more responsive educational environments to support specific strategic action patterns.

19. The following detailed descriptions concern educational environments we have developed using this refined system. In particular, they have been developed mainly to present information to Dynamic individuals; they will be demonstrated at the conference which initiated this paper.

DEMONSTRABLE ENVIRONMENTS

20. Although the experiential environments described here are not directly aimed at civil engineers, they do relate to areas of considerable importance in finished structures, namely the command and control of a major (fire) problem and quality in design. The demonstrations also portray the possibilities of state of the art interactive technology. As such the techniques involved in their creation are easily adaptable to any profession which requires attainment of adaptive competency in its members.

Case Study I - ICCARUS (Intelligent Command and Control - Acquisition and Review Using Simulation)

21. The need. At present in Britain there are five thousand fire station officers. Each could find themselves having to take charge of a large fire incident (defined as one requiring the attendance of 5 or more pumps). In addition within the ranks of the fire brigade there are five hundred potential fire officers per year who require training before promotion and 200-300 per year who require refresher courses. The West Midland's Fire Brigade alone estimate that they spend approximately £1 million per annum on training and there are 62 such brigades in the UK. The efficient management of large fire incidents entails considerable cost benefits. The Fire Research Station estimate of the cost, for each minute that each fire rages, is about £10,000. Thus a reduction of each large fire by as little as 1 minute would produce a saving to the UK of almost ten million pounds per annum.

22. The problem. Effective command and control by an Officer-in-Charge of a large fire involves overall co-ordination of a wide range and high complexity of human and other resources. To do this the officer has to maintain a large scale real time information communication network. Acquiring management skills to do this effectively and efficiently is vital for potential fire officers - to prepare them for command - and for existing officers - to keep them alert to situations they might only deal with very occasionally. However, a primary problem in the effectiveness of Fire Officers' training lies in the realism of the training task when compared with *real* life incidents. Present training consists of a *blackboard and chalk* discussion in which a training officer describes a fire incident, followed by a question and answer session. Rarely is it possible to create a practice session involving real men and

hardware and, even when such role playing exercises are mounted, the situation is contrived and cannot easily be given the sort of realism and variety that would truly tax the skills of strategic command and control.

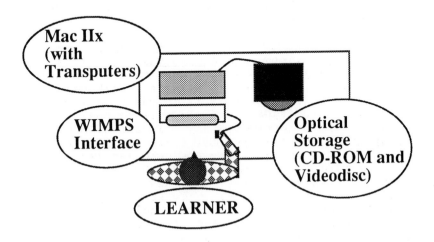

Fig.2 ICCARUS simulation set-up

23.   The solution.   ICCARUS is designed as a multimedia environment in which *realistic* emotive experience is gained of attending, commanding and controlling a major fire incident.   The implementation of AI techniques, supported by a Mac IIx, transputers, various optical technology and the use of a sophisticated WIMPS interface (see Fig. 2) allows the participating officer, as in *real life*, to become an information nexus: able to request and allocate resources within an audio/textual/visual environment, creating a real-time, event-based qualitative simulation, capable of realistically modelling the behaviour of both the fire and the decision making capabilities of the agents under the officer's control.   In the main the final simulator is a self learning tool for those individuals of a dynamic persuasion. However, there is an intelligent tutoring package back-up to the system which

343

accommodates the more Rigorous preference of fire training officers who can review and analyse the trainee's performance.

24. <u>The effectiveness.</u> So far we have only undertaken a preliminary evaluation of ICCARUS being used by 15 Fire Officers from different parts of Britain. This has shown the *restricted, but genuine* nature of the simulated environment we have created is an emotive experience which recaptures the stress and actuality of true to life command and control situations. Officers using ICCARUS have commented that the iconic interface, indeterminate audio/visual interrupts and semi-intelligent actors give a *suspension of disbelief* not experienced in previous simulations. Such officers also point out that their *private* one-to-one involvement with the system allows them to investigate the outcomes of 'wrong actions', which they find difficult to initiate in traditional role-playing sessions where their colleagues and peers are present. The knowledge of how mistakes can occur is therefore gained without loss of face and reduces the necessity for this experience to be obtained through real life occurrences.

Case Study II - QUALITY; My definition

25. <u>The problem.</u> In order to gain an understanding of different peoples strategies for attaining quality design, it is important for those managing a design project to have a clear, reciprocal awareness of what each active participant involved in the design process means by quality. At present quality is a noun looking for appropriate adjectives. In the round table design discussions normally associated with most early phases of designing each participant of a design team, and even the client, can bring their own particular and idiosyncratic view of quality to bear. In many cases they will not be sure themselves what they mean by quality. The project manager should somehow experience that *quality* too easily becomes a catch all noun to represent many facets and contradictions that can be left undefined.

26. <u>The solution.</u> Through the use of a MacIIx equipped with a video digitising board and CD-ROM/ videodisc storage sources is a one screen mouse controlled environment is created giving the learner access to a montage of information on designed artefacts portraying very different aspects of quality. A changing array of menus gives access to the views, thoughts and expressions on quality from architects, engineers, and product and fashion

designers using nine key artefacts as a suit of common parlance. Filmic vignettes of impressions of quality and a database of Design Council award products our also open to interaction. The agreements or otherwise of the participator are constantly stored and participants find themselves negotiating their own perception of quality which is summarised for them when they leave the package. The environment can also act as database of raw information appropriate for a more Contemplative individual.

27. <u>The effectiveness.</u> Students within our own Faculty, industrialists, managers and designers have found their use of the package illuminating and rewarding. All find they are familiar with at least one of the key artefacts and the range of comments accessible for each artefact is often surprising and an inducement to constructive discussion with colleagues when they have finished using the system. They leave with a clearer understanding of their own perception of quality and many comment that the experience encourages them to seek out the opinions of others on this concept. We have also seen that participants become more aware of the nature of language and the creation of definitions as a social construct. The design process itself then benefits from this heightened understanding that negotiation of as many viewpoints as possible to achieve an agreed design objective(s) is a fundamental basis for quality design.

CONCLUSION
We believe an edge in competitiveness is achievable if individuals can forge their understanding in experience rather than having it formatted as training. Use of our systems seems to aid decision making skills and understanding in building professionals: their capacity for immediately knowing the right actions to take when faced with novel situations is undoubtedly improved. The demonstration at the conference will show that interactive videodisc technology is approaching a quality where support for experiential processes is possible.

REFERENCES
1. RITTEL H.W.J. and WEBBER M.M. Dilemmas in a general theory of planning. Policy Sciences, vol. 4, 155-169.
2. OLSON D.R. and BRUNER J.S. Learning through experience and learning through media. in Media and

Symbols: the forms of expression, communication, and education. The 73rd year book of the National Society for the Study of Education (ed) Olson D.R. The University of Chicago Press, Chicago, 1974.
3. PEPPER S.C World hypotheses. University of California Press, Berkeley, California, 1942.
4. THOMPSON M. Beyond self interest, a cultural analysis of risk, 1981, WP-81-17 IIASA.
5. NEWLAND P.M., POWELL J.A. and CREED C. Understanding architectural designers' selective information handling, Design Studies 1987, vol. 8, no. 1.
6. KOLB D.A. The learning style inventory technical manual. MacBer, Boston, USA, 1976.
7. POWELL J.A. Is design a trivial pursuit, Design Studies, 1987, vol. 8, no. 4.
8. JONASSEN D.H. Learning strategies:- a new education technology. Programmed Learning and Educational Technology, 1985, vol. 22, no. 1, 26-34.
9. SALOMON G. The use of visual media in the service of enriching mental thought processes. Instructional Science, vol. 9 327-339.